W. GEORGE CROUCH, Ph.D. Princeton University, is Professor of English and Chairman of the Department at the University of Pittsburgh. Professor Crouch has been special lecturer for the Westinghouse Electric Corporation, Aluminum Company of America, and the Bell Telephone System.

ROBERT L. ZETLER, Ph.D. University of Pittsburgh, is Professor of English, and Director of the Division of Language and Literature at the University of South Florida. He formerly taught at the Carnegie Institute of Technology and in the Westinghouse Graduate Training Program, and was Chairman of the English Department at Chatham College.

A GUIDE TO
TECHNICAL WRITING

W. George Crouch

University of Pittsburgh

Robert L. Zetler

University of South Florida

THIRD EDITION

THE RONALD PRESS COMPANY • NEW YORK

G0654

2-VR

Library of Congress Catalog Card Number: 64–13939
PRINTED IN THE UNITED STATES OF AMERICA

Preface

This book is a guide to the principles and mechanics of good technical writing. We have sought to demonstrate the principles of composition in actual situations that require the competent use of English. But we have tried to avoid infringing upon areas which are more properly handled in other courses. This book is concerned with English—how to use it accurately in writing clear and effective letters, reports, and articles.

The preparation of the Third Edition of *A Guide to Technical Writing* has benefited from the valuable suggestions offered by many instructors who have used the book in their courses. In keeping with these suggestions, we have provided new materials to meet the requirements for examples of writing from the various technical fields and we have touched upon new areas of interest to technical people, particularly the devices for illustrating articles and reports. Throughout the book we have kept in mind the role of the scientist, the engineer and the technical man.

The intent behind our method of presentation is to be flexible rather than rigid. We have presented the chapter on language essentials and the Index to English Usage in such a manner that the student should recognize their content as a means to clear, fluent writing and not as a collection of arbitrary rules. The same principle applies to the chapter on speech. The style of the book is kept informal and at times even conversational. A few colloquial expressions, the omission of relative pronouns where ease is so obtained, and simplicity of diction are present by design. We recognize that every report must be tailored to the particular circumstances from which it rises, but we believe that a few first-class sample reports will afford students valuable models and will stimulate them to put their own originality and imagination to work on their special problems.

We want particularly to thank the heads of departments and the teachers of technical writing in many colleges, universities, and technical schools who have been so kind as to give us the benefit of their experience with the earlier editions. We also wish to extend our sincere thanks to the corporations that have allowed us to use material of various sorts. A specific statement of indebtedness accompanies each reproduction of material from corporate sources.

For help with the manuscript and for suggestions regarding its improvement we are indebted to Dean Harold Lancour, Miss Lorena A. Garloch, Librarian, and her staff, Dean G. Raymond Fitterer, Professor James Coull, Dean Albert B. Martin, all University of Pittsburgh; Mr. Elliott Hardaway, Mrs. Ethel Houle, Professor James A. Parrish, Dean Russell M. Cooper, Dean Sidney J. French, Dean Edwin P. Martin, all the University of South Florida; and Professor Herman A. Estrin, Newark College of Engineering.

W. George Crouch
Robert L. Zetler

Pittsburgh, Pennsylvania
Tampa, Florida
February, 1964

Contents

A GUIDE TO

TECHNICAL WRITING

1

The Technical Man's Writing Problems

The accomplishments of scientists and engineers in the twentieth century have been so dramatic, especially in the latter part of the century, that science, engineering, and their allied technical fields have taken on unprecedented glamor. The scientist and the creative engineer have become romantic figures. But the notion that technical men live in the ivory towers of research laboratories, coming out into the actual world just for lunch and dinner, would apply only to a few. Indeed, most of them are a part of the working world, whether they are engaged in space research or in the development of a new type of jet engine.

The writing of reports, letters, and occasional articles is part of the routine of their jobs. At times, they are also called on to speak effectively and persuasively, particularly when they discuss a project in committee meetings or justify to members of a government agency the need for a research grant. They must know how to get along with their fellow human beings and how to communicate with them.

To show some of a technical man's activities which involve the exact transmission of ideas in writing and in speaking, let us examine a typical day in the life of a technically trained person. Let us put him into an industrial corporation; let us make him an engineer with supervisory responsibilities. Our fictional engineer is Mr. Harry Schwartz, head of the Product Development Department of Smithton Petroleum Co.

Problems of the Day

When Mr. Schwartz arrived at his office, he began the day's work by reading his mail. The letters presented several representative problems. One of the sales engineers had written to find out what the

Company planned in its projected modernization program; a customer wanted to know what was being done in petrochemicals; an interdepartmental memorandum asked Schwartz to meet with a group to discuss problems of marketing. These communications, among others, had to be given prompt replies.

Answer to the Modernization Problem

In answering the sales engineer's question, Schwartz realized that he would have to give specific and complete information that would help the engineer to answer customers' questions about the Company's plans. The original letter and Schwartz's reply are reproduced below:

SMITHTON PETROLEUM COMPANY

Houston Office   May 17, 19--

Mr. Harry Schwartz, Head
Product Development Department
Smithton Petroleum Company
Berger Building
Oklahoma City 20, Oklahoma

Dear Mr. Schwartz:

   Several of our good customers have asked me what the Company is planning in the immediate future to modernize our refining processes. Because I was unable to attend the recent meeting dealing with projected developments, I should appreciate being brought up to date.

   The information will be of great help to me when I call on customers in this and other areas.

                              Sincerely yours,

                              Arthur F. Leeson

                              Arthur F. Leeson
                              Sales Engineer

In reply, Schwartz wrote the following letter:

SMITHTON PETROLEUM COMPANY
Oklahoma City 20, Oklahoma

May 19, 19--

Mr. Arthur F. Leeson
Sales Engineer
Smithton Petroleum Company
1894 Winslow Boulevard
Houston 18, Texas

Dear Mr. Leeson:

I was sorry that you were unable to attend our recent meeting dealing with modernization of our refining processes, but I shall be glad to give you a brief summary of what was discussed. The enclosed report contains detailed facts and figures regarding our plans.

To have the most modern refining facilities, we have authorized a new coking unit at Hokley. At the same site, we are going to build a new lubricating oil plant; and at the Elizabeth, New Jersey refinery a ten-million-dollar construction program is under way to modernize completely the whole installation.

A development program for computer control of process units is also under way at the Elizabeth refinery. Such control will ultimately improve operating efficiency by holding yields closer to optimum levels.

As you will notice in the report, many other recent improvements to the refining function are projected, all aimed to better our products, to increase efficiency, and to bring about lower costs.

If you have any questions about the report please let me know. All good wishes to you.

Very truly yours,

Harry Schwartz

Harry Schwartz, Head
Product Development
Department

HS:bt
Enclosure

Answer to Customer's Inquiry

In replying to the customer who was inquiring about petrochemicals, Schwartz had to have several conferences with people who knew petrochemicals in greater detail than he did. After he had gained the information he wanted, including a brochure to send the customer, he decided to make a few notes in outline form to guide him in his dictation, for the letter would involve a number of developments. His notes were made in a series of phrases that would recall to his mind what he wanted to say.

```
Acknowledge inquiry
Baton Rouge plant
Elizabeth plant
Los Angeles plant
Beckley plant
Ascon Chemical Company
Brochure
```

Dictating from these notes on the basis of information he had gathered, Schwartz wrote the following letter:

SMITHTON PETROLEUM COMPANY
Oklahoma City 20, Oklahoma

May 19, 19--

Mr. Elvis Clendenning
Oakdale Drilling Company
498 Richman Road
Tulsa 4, Oklahoma

Dear Mr. Clendenning:

I appreciate your interest in what the Smithton Petroleum Company is doing in the petrochemical field. To give you a brief survey of recent developments I am pleased to cite the highlights of our activity.

In 1961 we placed in operation at Baton Rouge the world's largest benzene plant. This petrochemical is used by manufacturers of synthetic rubber, plastics, detergents, pharmaceuticals, and many other products.

A new oxo alcohol and heptene plant was completed at the Elizabeth refinery early this year. The oxo alcohol unit produces very pure alcohols which are used in the production of

Elvis Clendenning   -2-   May 19, 19--

such everyday items as garden hose, toys, and detergents. Our
next step at Elizabeth will be the construction of a multi-
million-dollar benzene-cumene complex, with a benzene
section of moderate size and with what will be a large cumene
unit.

Construction will soon begin on a new ethylene plant at
Los Angeles, some thirty miles east of the city. This will
more than double our present ethylene capacity to over 800
million pounds per year. We plan to utilize this location
not only for the Company's first domestic petrochemical venture
to be located outside a refinery, but also for the development of a significant petrochemical complex.

Easton-Metro Chemicals, Inc., 50% owned by our company,
will further strengthen its leadership position in the field
of synthetic rubber by the completion this year of a new
poly-butadiene synthetic rubber plant at Beckley. This plant
will have an annual capacity of 20,000 tons.

In keeping abreast of the space age, the Ascon Chemical
Company, 50% owned by our company, specializes in research
and development of high energy fuels for missile and rocket
propulsion. In 1962, Ascon was selected by the Department
of Defense to supply a substantial quantity of pentaborane
needed by the Air Force for missile development.

The enclosed brochure, "Petrochemicals for the Space
Age," will acquaint you with the kind of research we
are now doing and are projecting.

                              Sincerely yours,

                              Harry Schwartz

                              Harry Schwartz, Head
                              Product Development
                              Department

HS:bt
Enclosure

Conference Work

The remainder of the morning would be taken up with the problems of marketing, to be discussed with members of other departments
and with some of the "top brass." In preparation for this conference,
Schwartz had to spend the half hour beforehand in thinking about the

strategy he would employ. He knew that he would meet opposition to some of his ideas, for he wanted to suggest realigning the former eight sales divisions so that there would be sixteen divisions accountable to four new regional offices. Boundaries, according to this plan, would no longer be set by state and county borders, but by market needs and distribution areas.

Taking a 3-by-5-inch card, Schwartz made a few notes designed to guide his thinking. They looked like this:

1. Agree with Evans and Brown that present eight sales divisions inefficient.
2. Put forward realignment.
3. Show need for Regional Vice-Presidents.
4. Delegate authority to each sales area.
5. Modernize service station facilities.
6. Install new imprinters at all stations.
7. Intensify advertising of Smithton products.

The real problem, Schwartz knew, was to convince the men attending the conference that the realignment should be effected. Several men were opposed to the plan; therefore it was important for him to know beforehand who would support his views. Evans and Brown had already talked over the new plan with him. To stress their agreement would strengthen his position. He would also try to find areas of agreement with the opposition so that the men against the plan would not think he was totally in disagreement with them. If he demonstrated willingness to understand their points of view, they would be more likely to listen to his ideas.

As he considered the points he had set down, Schwartz tried to think of the advantages to the Company. These would weigh heavily with everyone. The new organizational structure would meet market needs and distribution areas—key factors in any marketing operation. Furthermore, the new structure would delegate a maximum of authority to areas where sales would be made, thus encouraging a sense of responsibility and accountability at various job levels. A persuasive factor would be that salesmen could sell unhampered by administrative and operational duties. Their jobs would be to concentrate on customer needs, see that they were met, and get as much new business as possible. The modernization of service station facilities and the installation of imprinters would help to bring in new customers. If all of these factors were accompanied by an intensification of the Company's advertising, Schwartz was convinced that an increase in profits would result.

With his strategy clearly in mind, Schwartz thought over all the possible arguments that could be raised against his plan. Greenleaf might raise the point that the organizational structure would be too complicated. Schwartz could meet this argument by showing that under the present organization each of the eight sales divisions was accountable to a Regional Vice-President. Under his plan, even though the sales divisions would be doubled, only four Regional Vice-Presidents would be needed to supervise the sales divisions. Hillsdale, Schwartz realized, would cite a drop in sales during the past year and therefore the likelihood that the reorganization should wait until business picked up. Schwartz could counter by citing how his plan would increase sales by putting emphasis on the production of each salesman in the field.

Since a previous meeting had stressed the need for faster service to customers at the Company's stations, Schwartz decided to detail the advantages of the imprinters in speeding service. Moreover, the new imprinters would speed the recording of credit sales and reduce the chance of error on customer statements.

The work of thinking through ahead of time the possible arguments that would be advanced by the men at the conference paid off. When Schwartz actually took part in that conference, he knew how to meet his opposition. He had his plan in mind, presented it clearly, and answered objections easily. The opposition had plenty of ammunition, too, but Schwartz was able to get the main features of his plan adopted.

Interoffice Communications

Back in his office after lunch, Schwartz saw a letter on his desk marked for his immediate attention. It was an interoffice communication from the Vice-President in Charge of Public Relations. The message indicated that not enough was being done to impress on stockholders and the public what the company was doing in countries other than the United States (see page 10).

Revision of Brochures

Schwartz read over the copy, checked all facts on the basis of his knowledge of the Company's overseas operations, and returned it to Public Relations. Sure of the accuracy of all facts, Public Relations then revised the original copy. The changes, indicative of the kind of

Internal Correspondence

SMITHTON PETROLEUM COMPANY

To: Harry Schwartz, Product Development Department

From: Jotham Edwards, Public Relations

Date: May 18, 19--

Subject: BROCHURE ON OVERSEAS OPERATIONS

In view of our failure to acquaint both stockholders and
public with our overseas operations, I have written a draft
of a brochure entitled "International Dimensions of Smithton
Petroleum Co."

Since you have been in close touch with our overseas operations, I should appreciate your checking the facts cited.

---

revision which careful writers have to make, are reproduced below as
they appeared in part of the copy.

International Dimensions of the Smithton Petroleum Co.

Until ~~the time of~~ World War II, the operations of the Smithton Petroleum Co. ~~is
operations~~ were ~~largely~~ confined to the continental limits of the United States. Since
World War II, the Company has been gradually expanding these operations ~~them~~
by marketing its products overseas and acquiring ~~trying to acquire~~ properties in foreign countries. ~~It will be the purpose of~~ This
brochure ~~to~~ sets forth what has been done recently to ~~truly~~ give
international dimensions to the Company so that our stockholders and the public will ~~can~~ be informed about these developments

International Dimensions of the Smithton Petroleum Co.--Page 2

The Afghanistan Area

~~It should be noted that~~ T̲he Afghanistan area has been the
first area for expansion. In ~~the~~ Afghanistan ~~area~~ we have been
~~recently~~ marketing in Kandahar and Farah, and ~~only~~ last December eight ~~up-to-date~~ modern Smithton stations were opened in Herat,
thus marking our entry into this region's ~~rapidly expanding~~ growing
market. ~~It should also be noted that~~ T̲he ~~great~~ success of those
stations during the first nine months ~~points to the fact that~~ indicates that
the expected growth and acceptance of Smithton in Afghanistan will
be achieved. Fifteen stations are now in operation, nine more
are being constructed, and sites have been acquired for additional stations.

Another marketing venture beneficial to the Company is a long-term contract with Union Company, ~~which~~ This contract provides an ~~exciting~~ outlet
for Union C fuel manufactured at our Wazirabad refinery.
This terminal is strategically located ~~for supplying~~ to supply demands of our shipping ~~in the Afghanistan area~~ our products.

Other Areas of Growth

As ~~an important~~ part of our ~~international~~ world-wide marketing expansion,
there are other areas ~~in which~~ where Smithton is active. ~~In~~ At Hong Kong
a ship bunkering terminal is being constructed, ~~which is~~ scheduled for completion in 1963, which will be owned by Smithton.
In Manila an office has been established ~~for~~ with the ~~twofold~~ dual purpose of furnishing ~~up-to-date~~ technical advice to customers in
the Far East and ~~to study~~ studying market prospects in that area.

International Dimensions of the Smithton Petroleum Co.--Page 3

The ~~greatest~~ _highest_ rate of growth ~~that~~ _which_ we are presently experiencing is in the European market, where products are ~~marketed~~ _distributed_ through wholly owned subsidiaries. In the United Kingdom, Smithton is ~~undertaking~~ _engaged in_ an expanded program. The initial phase of this program is a fuel oil terminal ~~which is~~ now under construction at Maryport in the northwest section of England./ ~~This is~~ an area where about twenty-five percent of the English fuel oil sales ~~take place~~ _are made_. Elsewhere in Europe, we are continuing a normal growth program which ~~is designed~~ _will_ to improve our position as one of the major companies in this vast market.

Smithton as a leading marketer continues to expand throughout all ten provinces _in Canada_. The addition of retail outlets in promising areas has been supported by new terminals and many other facilities which have been designed to more efficiently handle _more efficiently_ the distribution of products and improve customer service.

In ~~total, then,~~ _summary_ our marketing organization has been able to achieve solid growth through ~~the highest~~ efficiency in operations and sound management. ~~It is hoped that~~ _We_ will continue to place our many quality products in any ~~part~~ _corner_ of the world where they ~~will~~ _can_ be distributed on a profitable basis.

Schwartz realized that the problem of Public Relations was to make the style as concise as possible. To accomplish this end, the editor had to take out needless words and phrases, change phrasing whenever a change would improve the original wording, write in any omitted words or phrases, notice the order and correctness of sentences, and check with company personnel important factual information. In addition, he had to check grammar, punctuation, and spelling.

Telephone Conversations

During his checking of facts for the brochure, Schwartz had been interrupted by a telephone call that required him to give information about the marine operations of Smithton. The caller represented a firm that was planning to expand its own marine operations, and he asked Schwartz for data about what Smithton had been doing.

Knowing how many owned, leased, and long-term chartered tankers the Company had in operation was part of Schwartz's job. He had the data at hand. But in talking with this other firm's representative, he had to organize his ideas on the spur of the moment and be sure of his facts. In citing what Smithton was projecting, he worked from a rapid mental survey of developments: the retirement of a number of small ships; the acquisition of larger, new vessels; the effecting of economies by the use of the larger vessels; problems of docking; and the need to modernize the Company's tanker fleet as rapidly as possible. The organization of his ideas came almost automatically, for he had kept in touch with what his company had been doing in its marine operations.

Schwartz realized the importance of maintaining good relations with other companies; therefore he was as helpful as possible to the caller. On the other hand, he was careful to withhold any confidential information or any data that his company would regard as secret.

His replies to questions had to be specific. He knew that he had to be as diplomatic as possible as well as polite. And he was aware that if he could offer the caller any printed material which the Company had and which could be released he would win good will for Smithton.

In all of Schwartz's telephone conversations he had to be sure of his facts and use language exactly. He had to be a diplomat, too, in talking to callers. What he said would create either a favorable or an unfavorable impression of the Company.

The Maintenance of Good Relations with Employees

Before going home for the day, Schwartz had a meeting with the members of his department. The problem that occupied him and the group was how to meet the competition of other oil companies by reducing expenses wherever possible. Schwartz aimed to show by an analysis of performance reports submitted by the personnel in his department that a degree of automation, if introduced into departmental operations, would effect considerable savings.

The subject was difficult, for some of the employees were afraid that their jobs might be eliminated, or that they would be transferred to other work. Whether the conference would result in something constructive would depend largely on the ability of Schwartz to be persuasive enough to allay the fears already generated.

In tackling the problem, Schwartz had to open by demonstrating the need for the projected economies. While introducing the subject of automation, he had to handle it in such a way that he could offset any fear that automation would result in reduced personnel. And during the discussion, he had to be sure that the views of the men would be expressed freely because of his deft management of the meeting.

A large part of Schwartz's day was taken up by personal contacts with his men. These contacts made him aware that technical knowledge alone is insufficient for anyone in a supervisory position. Knowledge of human psychology is equally important. The supervisor, he recognized, has to know how to handle people, for he has to persuade, rather than order them, to follow certain courses of action. Schwartz knew that, the more he studied human beings and their motives for action, the more likely he would be to do his job successfully. This knowledge of human psychology was needed just as much in his writing as in his conferences.

Part of this knowledge deals with the willingness of supervisors to take suggestions from their men and consider the applicability of the suggestions to problems. Schwartz gained several suggestions from his meeting: the possibility of a more careful control of the expense budget; more frequent reporting of operations; the speeding up of shipments to service stations. These suggestions were offered in the spirit of cooperation, and Schwartz complimented several of the men on their thorough appraisal of the problem.

He knew that a word of praise given for meritorious work helps to keep an organization harmonious. He was convinced, too, that frequent informal conferences with individuals about their work and frank judgments about the effectiveness of each individual showed his men that he had a personal interest in their welfare. The whole area of human relations was as much a part of his daily work as his detailed knowledge of the petroleum industry.

The Writing of Articles

Earlier that day, Schwartz had talked with the vice-president to whom he reported about the writing of an article on what the Company had been doing in its exploration for oil, both in the United States and abroad. He had been urged to write it, and was glad that the idea had been well received. He knew that if he wanted to enhance his reputation he would be expected to publish something every now and then.

That evening he mulled over the idea. As a start, he thought about a title. Since the article was to be slanted to catch the interest of the investing public and of the company's stockholders, he decided that he should have a title which would have human interest. Finally, he decided to use "Exploring for Liquid Gold."

Finding that title was fairly easy, but actually beginning the article presented problems. What should be his approach to his readers? After that, what should be the logical development of the idea? And once this development had been decided, how could he create and maintain interest? What aspects of oil exploration would prove most exciting to people who knew the oil business only superficially? How much detail should he cite to illustrate the points he wanted to make? These and many other questions passed through his mind.

To resolve them, he knew that he would have to think through the problem and attempt to outline what he planned to do. He spent over an hour in trying to set down the order of his ideas. After several unsatisfactory attempts, he made the following outline:

```
    I. Excitement of man's search for oil--a twentieth-cen-
       tury romance
   II. Application of this idea to what the Smithton Petro-
       leum Company had been doing.
  III. The breadth of the search.
       A. Evaluation of undeveloped acreage in the United
          States.
       B. Wildcat drilling in Northern Alberta.
       C. Activity in Venezuela.
       D. Bolivian discoveries.
       E. Explorations in Libya and Nigeria.
   IV. Future explorations in promising areas.
```

This outline would serve to guide the actual writing of the article. Each part would have to be expanded by facts, statistics, examples of company operations, or other devices to maintain reader interest. The general development of the idea, however, had been dictated by

Schwartz's knowledge of company operations in his own country and abroad. The development of the article on a geographical basis appeared satisfactory.

Before leaving the outline, Schwartz decided to try writing the opening paragraph. The next day, or whenever he could find the time, he would finish the first draft of the entire article. The introduction was written as follows:

> The search for the proverbial needle in the haystack was never so exciting as man's search for oil beneath the surface of the earth. This search, painstakingly undertaken by geologists, has led men into explorations that rival in human interest the latest developments in nuclear chemistry. The story of these explorations is a twentieth-century romance--a romance in which the Smithton Petroleum Company has had a large part.

Schwartz knew that he faced an exceedingly difficult task before he would complete the article. Writing is hard work at any time. He thought of the corrections he had seen on the brochure prepared by the Public Relations Department. He recalled how difficult it was for him to write letters that required the utmost in tactful customer relations. He knew that ideas and phrasing would have to be considered in the light of the purpose of his article. Even with the most thorough changes, what he would write would probably never satisfy him completely. Nor should it. Intelligent dissatisfaction, even with one's best efforts, acts as an impetus for doing even better when the next attempt to write is made. But he had made a start—the hardest part of writing anything. In hours when he could find the time or in subsequent evenings, he would finish the article.

Summary

You may say that the events set down do not show an average day of a technical man—that most of his work is mathematical or scientific. Perhaps you feel that his day is made up wholly of struggles with new ideas and new devices, or that he spends all his time in the laboratory testing the viscosity of several grades of oils or examining specimens of sand. Or perhaps you believe that a great part of his time is spent in wrestling with the values that may be given to the square root of minus one. Certainly he has to do such things occasionally. On the job, however, the technical man finds that most of his day is taken up with human contacts. He is first an individual and after that a specialist, and in this period of huge industrial organizations, human contacts are made through letters or telephone calls as well as by person-to-person talks.

Schwartz's day is fairly representative of what a man in his position has to do. He is constantly having to answer questions put to him by his fellow workers, the people in his department, or the men in the field. The question asked by the sales engineer drew on Schwartz's knowledge of the business of his company and his remembrance of what had gone on at the meeting. The letter in reply had to be gracious, diplomatic, and informative. Schwartz was experienced enough to realize that the report containing detailed information would give the engineer more about the problem than a short letter would; yet he summarized in his letter the highlights of the meeting to acquaint the engineer with the over-all view and to have this summary act as an introduction to the report.

To answer the customer's inquiry about petrochemicals, Schwartz went to the trouble of talking with several men in his company before he wrote his reply. But he knew that those interviews, which resulted in his getting the desired information, were necessary if the customer were to be satisfied. He was careful to make his letter appreciative of the customer's interest in his company's business; he was equally painstaking to set down specific facts about what Smithton was engaged in doing in the field of petrochemicals. The brochure he enclosed was a thoughtful act, for that brochure would allow the customer to read about the subject in detail.

Oral communications are quite as important as written. Conferences, whether they include large groups or small, have to be prepared for carefully. In conferences, the technical man has to deal with people directly. Schwartz was wise to estimate the kind of group he would be meeting, the people who would be likely to support his points of view, and the individuals who would make up the opposition. Mapping strategy is the mark of a wise participant.

The kind of interoffice letter sent Schwartz by the Public Relations Department is a sample of a large number of such letters exchanged every day between the departments of a company. This sort of correspondence has to be concise, complete and exact in information, and clear.

The revision of brochures demonstrates how exact writing has to be. Large companies, especially, send out a number of brochures to stockholders, customers, and the public. These have to be correctly and clearly written as well as exact in technical detail.

Besides such work as that outlined, technical people have to transact much business over the telephone. The most successful individuals are those who are as polite, thoughtful, and willing to help over the telephone as they would be if they were interviewing customers in an office. The same qualities are necessary in relations with employees, for the wrong attitude toward an employee can endanger the harmony of any organization.

But the writing of articles, you may say, might never be your lot, even though you will probably answer inquiries and do all the other jobs Schwartz did. Admittedly, some men never contribute to their companies or to their field by writing articles. The men who do, however, are the men who become known, whose advice is frequently sought, and who get deep satisfaction out of knowing that they have enlarged their knowledge about the subject in hand. These are often the men who are considered most when promotions are discussed by top executives. And these are the men who, in all their business communications, strive for exact expression of ideas.

Discussion Questions

1. What kinds of writing is a technical man likely to be called on to do?
2. What are some of the most important points to be considered in answering a letter of inquiry?
3. In what ways does a brief outline of a letter help the dictator?
4. If you had to lead a conference discussion, what sort of preparation should you make beforehand?
5. How can you estimate probable opposition to some of your ideas?
6. How does the form of internal correspondence differ from that of outgoing letters to customers?
7. What does the revision of any piece of writing entail?
8. To what extent can you be helpful to customers when you talk to them by telephone?
9. How can good relations with employees be fostered?
10. Examine the revisions of the article given on pp. 10–12. Determine the type of revisions made and the reasons for the changes.

2

The Business Letter

For many types of domestic transactions the American businessman uses the telephone or the telegraph. In a few seconds he can complete a telephone call to any part of the country. Within a short time, he can have a necessary part for a machine or an order for several carloads of air conditioning equipment on the way to his plant. He finds that a telegram is a fast means of transmitting vital information and that a night letter is quicker than ordinary mail. But agreements reached by telephone or telegraph are usually confirmed by letter, as are matters of policy, contractual arrangements, quotations on equipment, explanations of the advantages of one type of machine over another, or a variety of other business. Letters are still an important means of communication in spite of the development of other and speedier methods.

The volume of letters originating in an office will vary with the type of business. As an individual's responsibilities in a firm increase and his importance to it grows, his need to dictate letters will also increase in frequency. He will have to know how to plan a letter and how to express his ideas in clear and effective English prose in the shortest time possible. He will even need to know the accepted conventions for the forms of letters because he will have to check the correctness of his stenographer's or his secretary's work. Accordingly, he should have up-to-date knowledge so that he will be able to check intelligently. A survey of the various conventions and forms discussed in this chapter should help a dictator to perform his work efficiently.

The Basic Parts of a Business Letter

There are seven basic parts of a business letter:
1. The heading and date line
2. The inside address
3. The salutation
4. The body

5. The complimentary close
6. The signature
7. The stenographic reference

The following letter, written to the manager of the Crescent Refining Company about an oil which had the wrong viscosity for turret lathes, illustrates the use of these parts.

Heading   GROTON MACHINE CORPORATION
                         Groton, Massachusetts

Date Line   March 2, 19--

              Mr. C. E. Crow, Sales Manager
Inside   Crescent Refining Company
Address   Grandolph Building
              Boston 34, Massachusetts

Salutation   Turret Lathe Lubrication
and   Dear Mr. Crow: Our Order #15321--Your Order S-62
Subject

                  On February 24, we sent you our order for 15
              barrels of oil, SAE #10, to be used on the turrent lathes
              in our shops.

                  Instead of sending us SAE #10, you shipped 15
Body of   barrels of SAE #20. Since the viscosity of this oil
Letter   is too great for the type of machinery for which it is
              needed, we shall be unable to use it.

                  We shall appreciate as quick an adjustment as you
              can make, since our production will be slowed un-
              less we have the proper oil by Monday, March 23.

                  We feel sure that you will give us your utmost
              cooperation in this matter.

Complimentary   Very truly yours,
Close
Written   A. R. Handley
Signature
Signature   A. R. Handley
                                          Purchasing Agent

Steno-
graphic   ARH:cf
Reference

THE HEADING AND THE DATE LINE

When a company letterhead is used, it constitutes the heading for a letter. The date line appears two lines below the last line of the letterhead and ends at the right-hand margin. When a writer uses plain white paper, as in personal correspondence, he types his address (but not his name) in the upper right-hand part of the sheet. This address should include his street and number, his city, his postal zone, if he has one, and his state. The date appears on the line below. Such a heading would look like this:

141 West Sixth Street
Columbus 5, Ohio
January 10, 19--

THE INSIDE ADDRESS

The inside address specifies the correct name of the individual or firm to whom the letter is addressed. It should give an individual's initials and his title, if he has one, and his exact address. At least two lines should be left between the date line and the first line of the inside address. This spacing may be increased if the letter is short. The name of a firm should be written exactly as that firm writes it on its official stationery. If an individual has no special title, "Mr.," "Mrs.," or "Miss" should precede the name.

THE SALUTATION

The salutation is a polite but conventional greeting to the reader. It begins at the left margin and is followed by a colon. Although varying degrees of formality used to be observed in salutations, practice now sanctions "Dear Mr. Brown:" or "Dear Mrs. Jenkins:" as suitable forms of address for individuals who have no special titles. "My dear Mr. Brown:" or "My dear Mrs. Jenkins:" would be considered as slightly more formal than the preceding forms.

"Dear Sir:" and "Dear Madam:" should be reserved for form letters. Letters to individuals should use the names of those individuals in the salutations. "Sir:" or "Madam:" can be used to address such dignitaries as the President of the United States, governors of states or mayors of cities, and churchmen or military men of importance. Practice sanctions such forms of address as "Dear Mr. President," "Dear Governor Layton," or "Dear Mayor Jones."

THE BODY

The body of the letter, which begins two lines below the salutation, sets forth the message to be communicated to the reader. If this message consists of more than one paragraph or more than ten lines of typescript, each paragraph should be single spaced, with double spacing between paragraphs. Letters of ten lines or less should be double spaced, with an indentation of at least five horizontal spaces for each paragraph.

THE COMPLIMENTARY CLOSE

Like the salutation, the complimentary close has been greatly simplified. It symbolizes a gracious leave-taking. "Sincerely yours," or "Yours truly," are considered fitting for almost any letter. Variants are "Very sincerely yours," "Yours very sincerely," "Very truly yours," and "Yours very truly." "Cordially yours," would be used chiefly in letters to individuals whom you know well or in very informal communications. The complimentary close is typed two lines below the last line of the final paragraph and is placed slightly to the right of the center of the page.

THE SIGNATURE

Since the average man's signature can be read only by him, the written signature, which is placed about two lines under the complimentary close and below the capital letter of the first word in the close, should always be followed by the typewritten name. This typewritten name should also be started directly underneath the first letter of the initial word of the complimentary close. The dictator's title or his department designation goes under the typewritten signature. This begins under the first letter of the typewritten name, as in the example below:

Very truly yours,

F. H. Monteith

F. H. Monteith
Vice-President

Some companies specify that the company name shall be typed two lines below the complimentary close, with the dictator's name signed in ink and his typewritten signature beneath the written signature, as is shown below:

```
                    Very truly yours,

                    KEYSTONE FREIGHT COMPANY

                    F. H. Monteith
                    F. H. Monteith
                    Vice-President
```

THE STENOGRAPHIC REFERENCE

The stenographic reference is placed one or two lines below the last line of the signature and starts at the left-hand margin. The dictator's initials come first, in capital letters. These initials are followed by the secretary's first and last initials, usually in lower case. A colon, a slanting line, or a hyphen separates the dictator's initials from those of the typist. The stenographic reference could assume any one of the following forms:

```
ALR:sn
ALR/sn
ALR-sn
```

Many firms are omitting the stenographic reference on the original of letters and are placing it only on the carbon copies. The reasoning underlying this practice is that the reference has meaning only to the firm sending the letter. It has almost no meaning for the recipient and is not used by him.

OTHER NOTATIONS

Other notations often used by business writers are attention lines, subject lines, reference lines, as well as personal, enclosure, and carbon copy notations.

THE ATTENTION LINE

Attention lines are necessary when the writer wishes a letter addressed to a company to reach the desk of a particular individual who, in his opinion, can expedite the business. The letter is addressed to the firm, for the person to whose attention the letter is directed might happen to be out of the city or to be ill. Under these circumstances the letter would be opened by any qualified employee. Attention lines may be placed in any one of the following ways:

```
Chalfont Iron Works
Graystone Building
829 Fifth Avenue
New York 10, N.Y.

Attention: Mr. E. A. Solmes
           Division Engineer

Gentlemen:
```

or

```
The Weston Corporation
1693 Creighton Boulevard
Los Angeles 34, California

              Attention of Mr. H. V. Jones, Sales Engineer

Gentlemen:
```

If a writer uses an attention line, he must also place it on the envelope. Its position is shown in Fig. 1.

```
T. A. Richards                              Stamp
Iron City Company
362 Orchard Avenue
St. Louis 6, Missouri



              Chalfont Iron Works
              Graystone Building
              829 Fifth Avenue
              New York 10, N. Y.



    Attention: Mr. E. A. Solmes
               Division Engineer
```

Fig. 1. Position of attention line on envelope.

THE SUBJECT LINE

In recent years the custom of emphasizing the subject of the letter in a special subject line has come about because it eliminates the need to explain in the first paragraph what the writer intends to discuss. A well-chosen subject line focuses the mind of the reader on the over-all purpose of the message. The subject line may be placed in any one of the following positions: five or more spaces after the salutation and on the same line; two lines above the salutation and centered on the page; two lines below the salutation and centered on the page, as in these illustrations:

```
Mr. Alfred T. Naughton
Assistant Vice President
Causeway Products Company
5862 Ridgeway Avenue
Omaha 18, Nebraska

Dear Mr. Naughton:      Subject: Installation of Generators
                        Our Order #24P546--Your Order #1538

or

Mr. Alfred T. Naughton
Assistant Vice President
Causeway Products Company
5862 Ridgeway Avenue
Omaha 18, Nebraska

            Subject: Installation of Generators
            Our Order #24P546--Your Order #1538

Dear Mr. Naughton:

or

Mr. Alfred T. Naughton
Assistant Vice President
Causeway Products Company
5862 Ridgeway Avenue
Omaha 18, Nebraska

Dear Mr. Naughton:

            Subject: Installation of Generators
            Our Order #24P546--Your Order #1538
```

The word "Subject" is preferable to "In re" or "Re." Many dictators ask their secretaries to omit "Subject" and place the actual statement of the subject of the letter in the appropriate position on the page. If open punctuation is used, no mark of punctuation follows the subject line. If close punctuation is used, a period ends the statement of the subject. But close punctuation is rarely used.[1] The subject is understood chiefly as a mechanical device to bring it to the attention of the reader.

THE REFERENCE LINE

Often, a reference line giving a filing number or asking that a certain person be addressed in the reply to the letter is a convenience for the reader. If a subject line is used, the reference line appears two or more lines below the date line, as:

```
                                        September 10, 19--

                                        In reply please
                                        refer to A. F. Need
```

THE "PERSONAL" NOTATION

If the contents of a letter are personal and the writer wants his letter read only by a single individual, he may place the word "Personal" three or four lines above the inside address.

```
Personal

Mr. Richard Benetti
Personnel Manager
Keystone Oil Company
80 Arroyo Plaza
Dallas 8, Texas
```

The word "Personal" may be underscored to attract attention. It should also be written in the lower left corner of the envelope. Underscoring is especially desirable here. The envelope illustrated (Fig. 2) carries out these principles. The return address of the sender, whether printed or typed, is placed in the upper left-hand corner. Avoid using "Personal" merely because of a wish to catch the attention of an executive when any employee in the firm can answer your letter. Such a device is irritating. It may even lose business for you.

[1] See pages 29–30 for a discussion of open and close punctuation.

T. Hinds, Sales Department
Caflisch-Hanes Corporation
Edenville, California

Stamp

Mr. Arthur P. James
Executive Vice-President
Diesel Oil Company
155 Eighth Avenue
Tulsa 17, Oklahoma

Personal

Fig. 2. "Personal" envelope notation.

THE ENCLOSURE NOTATION

Sometimes a writer needs to enclose something, such as a pamphlet, a check, or a card, in his letter. If so, he should refer to the enclosure in the body of the letter. He should also place an enclosure mark below the stenographic reference. This serves to prevent the over-looking of the enclosure. A single enclosure is indicated by "Enclosure," "Enc," or "Enc." If more than one enclosure is to be noted, Arabic numerals would indicate the exact number. The various forms for enclosures are illustrated below.

```
HVN:ev          HVN/ev       HVN-ev       HVN:ev
Enclosure       Enc          Enc.         Enc.--3
```

Checks, money orders, and other important enclosures are usually noted specifically in the enclosure line.

```
HVN:ev                HVN:ev               HVN:ev
Enc--Check #1586      Enc.--Money Order    Enc--Policy #9870
```

Sometimes an enclosure is to be returned. This is noted in parentheses following the enclosure mark.

```
HVN:ev
Enc.--(to be returned)
```

CARBON COPY NOTATIONS

To tell the addressee that a carbon copy is being mailed to another person, place the notation "CC" or "cc" below any other notations which may follow the stenographic reference and write out the name of the person to whom the carbon copy is being sent.

```
EBN:ap
Enc.--3
CC Mr. A. B. Jones
```

```
EBN:ap
cc Mr. A. B. Jones
```

THE POSTSCRIPT

A postscript is not used unless the writer is dictating a sales letter which, from the sales point of view, will be enhanced by the mention of some special message in this position. As a general rule, postscripts signify afterthoughts and are considered to be evidence of careless planning.

Second Sheets

A double-page letter should have a heading for the second sheet. Although most businessmen prefer to write one-page letters, sometimes they have to discuss complex matters which, if the recipient is to be given complete information, require two pages or more. At other times so many necessary technical details have to be included that the dictator is forced to use a second sheet. The completeness and exactness of the message is always more important than the length of the letter. The effective writer, however, tries to express his ideas in one page if he can do this without sacrificing essential information.

The heading for each sheet after the first is needed because additional sheets sometimes become detached from first sheets; therefore a brief identification of the second page and any succeeding pages saves time and prevents confusion. A heading may follow any of several accepted forms:

```
Mr. E. A. Bruce              -2-              July 10, 19--
Mr. E. A. Bruce, page 2, July 10, 19--
Mr. E. A. Bruce
7/10/--
Page 2
Mr. E. A. Bruce              -2-
7/10/--
```

Any one of these headings would be appropriate in correspondence. The dictator usually instructs his secretary about his preferences. She will generally begin the heading at least one and one-half inches from the top edge of the paper and will start it at the left-hand margin. She will leave four to five lines between the heading and the first line of the continuation of the body. A minimum of three lines of type should be carried over from the preceding page to justify a new sheet.

Margins

The appearance of a letter can be affected adversely if margins are uneven, for the message should have the appearance of being framed by the margins. The space left at the bottom of the page should be roughly equal to that left between the top edge of the paper and the top edge of the letterhead. In a long letter, margins should be at least an inch at each side. They should be larger for a relatively short letter. This detail of layout is left to the secretary, although the dictator is the final judge of whether the letter presents a balanced appearance.

Open and Close Punctuation

Within the body of a letter, punctuation [2] follows the standards set by a recognized style sheet or by a reputable handbook on style.[3] One of two styles may be chosen for punctuating the heading and date line, the inside address, the salutation, the complimentary close, the signature, and the envelope. These two styles are the open and the close style.

Almost all secretaries use the open style unless they are instructed otherwise. This style omits punctuation marks to close any line in the heading and date line, the inside address, the salutation, the complimentary close, the signature, and the envelope. Each line in these parts is left open at the end. If a line ends with an abbreviation, such as the abbreviation for company, a period signifies the abbreviation. The colon is often used after the salutation and the comma after the complimentary close, even though the style is open. The dictator

[2] See pages 403–414 for a discussion of punctuation.
[3] See S. J. Wanous and L. W. Erickson, *The Secretary's Book*, The Ronald Press Co., 1952.

should tell his secretary if he wishes these marks used in the parts indicated. The following illustrations are both in open punctuation.

                                        1862 Pride Street
                                        Chicago 21, Illinois
                                        April 10, 19--

Mr. Henry F. Bakewell, President
Goodfellow Industries, Inc.
592 Park Central Building
Des Moines 8, Iowa

Dear Mr. Bakewell   Subject: Copper Wire: Order #65432

                           Very truly yours

                           ANACONDA WIRE & CABLE CO.

                           T.F. Butterworth
                           Sales Manager

                                        1862 Pride Street
                                        Chicago 21, Illinois
                                        April 10, 19--

Mr. Henry F. Bakewell, President
Goodfellow Industrial, Inc.
592 Park Central Building
Des Moines 8, Iowa

Dear Mr. Bakewell: Subject: Copper Wire: Order #65432

                           Very truly yours,

                           ANACONDA WIRE & CABLE CO.

                           T. F. Butterworth
                           Sales Manager

In these illustrations, open punctuation does not affect the inside of lines. They are punctuated in the conventional way. The comma is needed between the zone number and the state, as well as in the date line between "April 10" and "19--." In the inside address the comma is necessary between the name of the addressee and his title, between the name of the company and "Inc.," and between the city and the state. The abbreviation "Co." in the signature has a period after it. The second illustration uses a colon after the salutation and a comma after the complimentary close.

On the envelope, the address is an accurate copy of the inside address in the letter. Stenographers and secretaries type their envelopes from inside addresses.

Close punctuation is uneconomical in the use of punctuation marks. In a heading, a comma follows the street address and a period closes the line which gives the city and state. A period is placed at the end of the date line. In the inside address commas follow each line and a period ends the last line. The salutation must be followed by a colon; a comma must follow the complimentary close. In the typed signature, a comma follows each line except the last, where a period is used. If the preceding illustration of open punctuation were changed to close punctuation, it would appear as follows:

```
                                    1862 Pride Street,
                                    Chicago 21, Illinois.
                                    April 10, 19--.


Mr. Henry F. Bakewell, President,
Goodfellow Industries, Inc.,
592 Park Central Building,
Des Moines 8, Iowa.

Dear Mr. Bakewell:          Subject: Copper Wire: #65432.

                            Very truly yours,

                            ANACONDA WIRE & CABLE CO.

                            T. F. Butterworth,
                            Sales Manager.
```

Because of the extra number of punctuation marks, close punctuation lacks the neat look of the open style.

Paragraphing

Each topic in a letter should be the occasion for a new paragraph. As far as possible, the writer should keep his paragraphs short. Short paragraphs are easier to read than long ones; moreover, the short paragraph attracts attention to the point under discussion. One-sentence paragraphs are common in the business letter, particularly if the writer wants to stress a point that is complete in itself. If the unit of thought demands extended discussion, try to break the thought into two or more short paragraphs. The length of any paragraph is governed by the amount of discussion needed. In this respect, the writer's judgment will be the determining factor.[4]

Folding the Letter

Although the folding of a letter and its placement in the envelope may seem unimportant, these matters never appear superfluous to an addressee who receives an improperly folded letter. He is likely to regard the writer as sloppy. Attention to folding is as important as a clean typescript.

To insert a standard sheet of paper ($8\frac{1}{2}$ by 11 inches) in the smaller size of business envelope ($3\frac{5}{8}$ by $6\frac{1}{2}$ inches) turn the bottom edge of the paper to within a quarter of an inch of the top edge and exactly parallel to it (Fig. 3a). Crease the fold. With the sheet now folded almost in half, turn over the right edge one-third the distance to the left edge and crease. Now turn the left edge to within a quarter of an inch of the right edge and crease again. Insert the folded letter so that the quarter-inch of space which has not been covered by the last fold is at the top of the sealed side of the envelope.

When the long envelope is used (usually $4\frac{1}{8}$ by $9\frac{1}{2}$ inches), fold the bottom edge of the paper approximately one-third the measurement (not quite four inches) of the sheet, see that the edges of the paper are parallel, and crease (Fig. 3b). Take the top edge of the sheet and fold to within one-quarter of an inch of the bottom fold. Crease again. Insert the folded letter so that the quarter-inch of space which has not been covered by the last fold is at the top of the address side of the envelope.

Letter Styles

The two most popular letter styles for business are the balanced block and the semiblock. The full block style, quite popular some years ago, is now used by relatively few firms.

BALANCED BLOCK STYLE

In this style the inside address, the salutation, and the paragraphs begin at the left margin, but the complimentary close and the signature begin in the center, or slightly to the right of center of the page

---

[4] For further consideration of the structure of the paragraph, see pages 270–287.

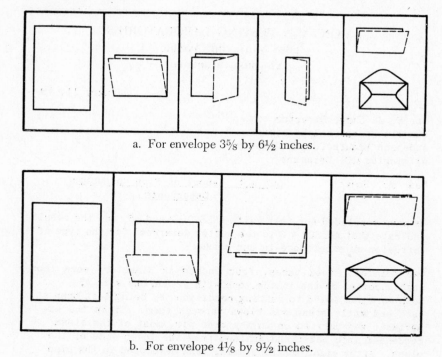

a. For envelope 3⅝ by 6½ inches.

b. For envelope 4⅛ by 9½ inches.

Fig. 3. Folding letters for insertion in envelope.

in order to balance with the position of the inside address. The date line is placed at the top right-hand side of the letter.

Many business houses prefer this style to the full block form. Stenographers and secretaries find that the lack of indentation for paragraphs saves them time, because they do not have to set their marginal stops to accommodate this form.

The letter to Mr. Shaw of the Anderson Manufacturing Company, if put in balanced block form, would appear as given on page 34.

SEMIBLOCK STYLE

This form is a variant of the balanced block style and is often favored in present business practice. It has the inside address and the salutation at the left margin, but each paragraph is indented. The complimentary close and the signature appear in block form and begin in the center, or slightly to the right of the center of the page. Paragraph indentations are usually five spaces, although they may be increased according to the taste of the writer. Some dictators like the

MONTANA TESTING LABORATORIES
2058 Murrayhill Avenue
Kingston, Montana

January 11, 19--

Mr. E. J. Shaw, Director
Plastic Research Laboratory
Anderson Manufacturing Company
Wilmington 10, Delaware

Dear Mr. Shaw: Subject: Report on Pipe Corrosion
                                  Deterrents

We have concluded our tests with ANESCO #2 and #5, and the results
indicate that ANESCO # 2 is the better deterrent for the type of
corrosion we experience in our works.

Two seamless steel tubes, four inches in diameter, were thoroughly coated on the inside, one with #2 and one with #5.
Both were subjected to rusting conditions by being left open at
each end while steam was blown through them. Since the experiment was carried on in the open air, most of the steam
condensed into water and drained from the lower ends of the
pipes. After eight months a small leak developed in the pipe
which was coated with #5.

The pipes were then turned through 180° and the test was repeated. Again the pipe coated with #5 developed a leak. Because of the corrosion which had already occurred, the second
leak was found at the end of five months.

The other pipe, which so far had shown no leak, was then cut
open. Measurements taken of the depth of corrosion showed it
nowhere to exceed five to six millimeters.

Our test means that ANESCO #2 is the preferable medium for the
prevention of corrosion as far as conditions here are concerned.

Very truly yours,

R. N. Gould

R. N. Gould
Chief Chemist

RNG:tv

Balanced Block Style

indentation to begin under the colon which follows the salutation. This is not practicable if the name of the addressee is very long. In such instances, the indentations become too noticeable.

One of the best features of this type of letter is the neat appearance it makes on the page. There is a symmetry to the whole that is lacking in the full block style and that is not present to such a degree in the balanced block.

The letter to Mr. Shaw, if put in semiblock form, would appear as shown on page 36.

FULL BLOCK STYLE

An example of a letter typed in full block style is reproduced on page 37. Although the full block form is the most convenient for any secretary since it necessitates no indentations of any kind, it has disadvantages. The full block style demands that the heading and the date, the inside address, the salutation, the paragraphs, the complimentary close, and the signature be started at the left margin. Consequently, the whole letter has an unbalanced appearance. The reason for this is that there is no balancing of the complimentary close and signature with the inside address. The full block style is rarely used.

Consistency in Form and Style

A first-class letter should contain all the necessary parts given in the preceding pages and should be consistent in the style chosen—balanced block, semiblock, or full block. What happens when this consistency is absent is apparent from the letter reproduced on page 38.

It is difficult to tell whether the dictator meant to write a letter in the balanced block or the semiblock style. The letter follows no acceptable form and contains obvious errors. The name of the month is abbreviated in the date line—something to be avoided unless an abbreviation is necessary to conserve space and make the date line appear in proper proportion to the rest of the letter. In addressing a company, the accepted salutation is "Gentlemen" rather than "Dear Sirs." The second line of the inside address should begin at the left margin.

The attention line [5] should either begin at the left margin or be centered on the page. Since the first line of the inside address contains a company name, this name should govern the kind of salutation used —"Gentlemen:" in this instance—rather than the name of the individual

[5] See pages 23–24 for a discussion of attention lines.

MONTANA TESTING LABORATORIES
2058 Murrayhill Avenue
Kingston, Montana

January 11, 19--

Mr. E. J. Shaw, Director
Plastic Research Laboratory
Anderson Manufacturing Company
Wilmington 10, Delaware

Dear Mr. Shaw: Subject: Report on Pipe Corrosion
Deterrents

We have concluded our tests with ANESCO #2 and #5, and the results indicate that ANESCO #2 is the better deterrent for the type of corrosion we experience in our works.

Two seamless steel tubes, four inches in diameter, were thoroughly coated on the inside, one with #2 and one with #5. Both were subjected to rusting conditions by being left open at each end while steam was blown through them. Since the experiment was carried on in the open air, most of the steam condensed into water and drained from the lower end of the pipes. After eight months, a small leak developed in the pipe which was coated with #5.

The pipes were then turned through 180° and the test repeated. Again the pipe coated with #5 developed a leak. Because of the corrosion which had already occurred, the second leak was found at the end of five months.

The other pipe, which so far had shown no leak, was then cut open. Measurements taken of the depth of corrosion showed it nowhere to exceed five to six millimeters.

Our test means that ANESCO #2 is the preferable medium for the prevention of corrosion as far as conditions here are concerned.

Yours very truly,

R. N. Gould

R. N. Gould
Chief Chemist

RNG:tv

Semiblock Style

MONTANA TESTING LABORATORIES
2058 Murrayhill Avenue
Kingston, Montana

January 11, 19--

Mr. E. J. Shaw, Director
Plastic Research Laboratory
Anderson Manufacturing Corporation
Wilmington 10, Delaware

Dear Mr. Shaw: <u>Subject: Report on Pipe Corrosion</u>
                                    <u>Deterrents</u>

We have concluded our tests with ANESCO #2 and #5, and the results indicate that ANESCO #2 is the better deterrent for the
type of corrosion we experience in our works.

Two seamless steel tubes, four inches in diameter, were thoroughly coated on the inside, one with #2 and one with #5. Both
were subjected to rusting conditions by being left open at each
end while steam was blown through them. Since the experiment
was carried on in the open air, most of the steam condensed
into water and drained from the lower end of the pipes. After
eight months, a small leak developed in the pipe which was
coated with #5.

The pipes were then turned through 180° and the test repeated.
Again the pipe coated with #5 developed a leak. Because of the
corrosion which had already occurred, the second leak was
found at the end of five months.

The other pipe, which so far had shown no leak, was then cut open.
Measurements taken of the depth of corrosion showed it nowhere to exceed five or six millimeters.

Our test means that ANESCO #2 is the preferable medium for the
prevention of corrosion as far as conditions here are concerned.

Very truly yours,

R. N. Gould

R. N. Gould
Chief Chemist

RNG:tv

Full Block Style

EXETER ELECTRONICS
Exeter, Ohio

Jan. 10, 19--

The Coping Company
Coping Building
Pittsburgh 19, Penna.

Attention of Mr. A. F. Gamp, Purchasing Agent
         Subject: Your Inquiry regarding FILTRON

Dear sirs:

We are pleased to get your inquiry concerning the filtron, the
air filter which has been perfected by Exeter Electronics for
use in the office and the home.

     Since you have not given us enough details about the kind of
installation you want, we should like more information. What
are the actual dimensions of each of your offices? The cubic
feet space each office will determine the effectiveness of
service we can gie you.

When we have aforesaid information we can quote you prices on
equipment and will in a position to have our engineers work
on your prolem.

Yours very truly,

            F. P. Myers

            F. P. Myers
            Sales Engineering

FPM:pr

---

given in the attention line. "Dear Sirs" is obviously not the proper
salutation to be given a company.

     Paragraphs are neither consistently blocked nor indented. Good
practice demands that the secretary follow a uniform method. The
subject line [6] should be centered, either two lines below the salutation
(acceptable when an attention line is also used) or two lines above
it, or be placed on the same line as the salutation. At least five spaces
should be kept between the colon of the salutation and the first letter

     [6] See pages 25–26 for a discussion of subject lines.

of the subject line. The complimentary close beginning at the left-hand margin is isolated from the signature, which is balanced with the inside address.

A trade name like *Filtron* should be typed in full capitals, even in the body of the letter, to make it stand out on the page. The misspellings and the omissions in this letter indicate a careless secretary. They would create a bad impression of the dictator's firm.

Planning and Dictating Letters

The planning of a letter and its dictation are the most difficult aspects of business correspondence. Some writers learn their technique the hard way, by the trial-and-error method. They read over a letter quickly, catch the main points that require an answer, and begin without any specific plan in mind. Because the results of their dictation indicate lack of logical order of ideas and therefore a loss in clarity or emphasis, such dictators have to rewrite—a costly process in time and money.

LETTER ANALYSIS

To be efficient, a writer should read over every letter carefully to find out what his correspondent wants. He should underline the points to be answered, paying special attention to any questions asked. It is good technique to list the main points for the paragraphs of the answer in the margin of the letter received. If the dictator is originating a letter, he can jot down his ideas on a note pad. Before calling in his secretary or reaching for his dictating machine, he should have checked the logical order of the points in his outline. Because he has planned what he wants to say and what the arrangement of his material will be, he will find that the actual phrasing of his points will be relatively easy.[7]

LETTER OUTLINES

The effective dictator is sure of one thing. Any letter which is complex in substance should be written from a carefully arranged outline. If a letter is very important, many businessmen dictate a first draft; then they revise this draft. For routine letters, such as quotation letters or the answers to simple inquiries, they work from a mental outline of the points.

[7] See pages 45–52 for a discussion of phrasing the letter.

LETTER PATTERN

The pattern for good letters, no matter how varied their content, is basically the same:

1. Statement of purpose
2. Analysis of purpose
3. A conclusion aimed to restress the purpose or to create good will

LETTER EFFECTIVENESS

The following letter deals with a problem that confronts businessmen frequently: how to deal with a situation diplomatically. The problem is to explain to the president of the Institute of the Aerospace Sciences why the writer will be unable to present his paper on "The Delta Wing" at the San Francisco meeting of the Society.

Because it is an honor to be asked to give a paper before any national organization, the writer has expressed in the opening paragraph his appreciation of being invited to do this. He stresses how much he would like to accept the invitation and tells specifically why he has to refuse.

Realizing that Mr. Hepburn is likely to have difficulty in getting another speaker, the writer offers a substitute and the promise to send copies of his paper if the substitute is accepted. This offer should please Mr. Hepburn; moreover, the writer's courtesy might lead to his being asked to present another paper at some future time.

The last two paragraphs contain additional courtesies extended to the recipient. The offer of a preprint of the new article, if it is published, should create a good impression on Mr. Hepburn. The personal regards help to humanize the letter and cement good will. The complimentary close "Cordially yours" adds to this effect. It would not have been used if Mr. Hannon had had only a slight acquaintance with Mr. Hepburn.

Throughout, the letter is diplomatic and considerate in phrasing. The ideas are logically arranged and are expressed in simple language that gives the message a conversational tone. The entire letter indicates careful planning.

Dictating Technique

Letters may be dictated either to a secretary or to a dictating machine. In both instances, the dictator should try to speak in a natural, even tone. He should enunciate clearly. He should spell out

BOSTON AIRCRAFT CORPORATION
19 Hershey Square
Boston 10, Mass.

April 1, 19--

Mr. J. P. Hepburn, President
Institute of the Aerospace Sciences
148 Constitution Avenue, N.E.
Washington 12, D.C.

Dear Mr. Hepburn:

I appreciate your asking me to deliver my paper, "The Delta Wing," at the annual meeting of the Institute to be held in San Francisco this coming June 10. Under ordinary circumstances, I would put aside other duties to do this. A deadline I must meet on a government contract, however, will make it impossible for me to be in San Francisco to read my paper.

My associate, Mr. A. S. Timmins, plans to attend the Convention. If you would care to have him deliver my paper, I would be pleased to have him act as my proxy. I will send by express 300 copies of the paper for distribution to the members if you are willing to accept the substitution.

I have recently finished an article entitled "A New Type of Jet Engine." If it is accepted for publication by <u>Aircraft Engineering,</u> I shall be glad to send you a preprint.

Please accept my best regards. I know that under your guidance the San Francisco meeting will be successful.

Cordially yours,

C. L. Hannon

C. L. Hannon
Engineering Research

CLH:as

---

unfamiliar names for the secretary and should give their initials. He should also spell out difficult and unusual words, especially technical terms, for he cannot expect a secretary to have as much technical information as he has gathered through training and experience. Names of streets and towns may need to be spelled out. The dictator should also give punctuation for any sentences where inaccurate punctuation could lead to distortion of his ideas. The words "period" after the end of a sentence and "paragraph" at the end of a dictated paragraph will help the secretary to be accurate in her transcription.

In using a dictating machine, the dictator should observe the preceding principles, with a few additions. He should make sure that he speaks into the mouthpiece; he should indicate all corrections on the memorandum slip so that his secretary will listen to the correction instead of typing the wrong words. He should also indicate on the slip the end of each letter so that the secretary will know how to adjust for margins and how to center the letter.

An efficient dictator aims to speak in a measured but fluent manner. He avoids *er*'s and *ah*'s and sentences that sound like "I—*er*—*er*—appreciate being asked—*ah*—*er*—to deliver—*ah*—*er*—my paper to—*er*— . . ." Such dictation style is exasperating. Other dictation habits that drive stenographers and secretaries to nervous breakdowns are the dictator's pacing back and forth, his speaking out the window to the man whom he can see in the office across the street, his shouting some phrases and whispering others, his irrelevant remarks to himself or to his secretary, or his tendency to wander in his thinking from the main subject of his letter.

DICTATION FROM AN OUTLINE

Most dictators, even the most experienced, dictate from either a mental or a written outline of the points a letter will contain. It is good practice to read carefully all letters that have come to your desk and to underline important statements and questions that need answering. Decide how you will arrange the points logically in your answer and put them in numerical order in the margin of the letter. Usually a single word or phrase is enough to remind you of each point. This marginal outline is the blueprint for your reply. It will keep you from groping for what you want to say. If you are initiating letters, you can put your outline of points on a memorandum pad.

NEED FOR PRACTICE

If you are a beginner at dictation, practice on a rented dictating machine for a week or two is helpful. Take home a few letters from the office each night. Dictate answers; then play back your dictation and examine it critically. Begin by using letters that will require short replies. After you have gained facility in answering this kind of correspondence, go on to letters that are more complicated and that exact your most careful thinking. A few weeks of practice should give you confidence.

Proofreading the Letter

Good letters require as much accuracy as equations; therefore the conscientious dictator never signs a letter without proofreading it. He reads for tone, logical organization of ideas, completeness of information, and mechanical correctness. If the letter contains errors, he asks his secretary to retype it. A letter that has typewritten strike-overs, misspelled words, omissions, or poor phrasing or planning should never leave an office. The reputation of a firm rests partly upon its letters to its customers, just as the reputation of a technical man is enhanced by his care about details. He must be a stickler for absolute correctness.

The *You* vs. the *I* Point of View

An effective letter writer keeps his reader and that reader's needs constantly in mind. He writes from the reader's point of view rather than his own. In the letter to Mr. Hepburn on page 41 the writer adopts the *you* point of view. His aim is to please Mr. Hepburn; in fact, he makes this a point of primary importance. "I appreciate *your* asking me to deliver my paper"; "if *you* would care to have him deliver my paper"; "if *you* are willing to accept the substitution"; "I shall be glad to send *you* a preprint"—all are phrases which show that the writer is keeping Mr. Hepburn's interests uppermost in his thinking. Successful letter writers, whether they are handling business correspondence or personal letters, adopt this attitude.

The opposite, or *I*, point of view has to occur frequently in letters, but the danger is that it will be overused. The letter to Mr. Hepburn uses *I;* yet this point of view is subordinate to the *you* attitude. Although the use of *I* in business letters is better than the self-effacing *the writer* or *the author,* practice of the *you* attitude will help the beginning dictator to eliminate too many *I*'s.

Courtesy and Tact

The *you* attitude is courteous. It shows a regard for the rights and interests of others. This element of courtesy should be part of every letter sent out from a business office, not only because it brings more business than a curt letter but also because it advances cordial human relations.

Tact is another quality of a successful letter writer. This quality is present in the letter to Mr. Hepburn. The writer has to disappoint Mr. Hepburn, yet he avoids ruffling his feelings. His offer to send a substitute to read the paper and his promise to send Mr. Hepburn a preprint of his new article help to offset the disappointment. The writer is a diplomat.

Conciseness

The letter to Mr. Hepburn is concise too. The writer could have thought of certain windy phrases, such as, "It is indeed an honor and a privilege to have been asked to present before the Institute of the Aerospace Sciences my paper on 'The Delta Wing.'" More judicious thinking would make him substitute "I appreciate your asking me to deliver my paper, 'The Delta Wing,' at the annual meeting of the Institute." This is simpler than the first sentence, less pompous and more direct. The full name of the Institute has been mentioned in the inside address. After that, there is proper authority for reference to it merely as "the Institute" in the body of the letter.

The concise writer will eliminate deadwood from his writing, such deadwood as needless adjectives and adverbs, superfluous words and phrases, and worn-out business expressions. He will give his writing vitality by making nouns and verbs carry the burden of his thought without unnecessary qualifications of the main ideas.

Conciseness can be carried to extremes. Always, its value should be weighed against completeness of information. Only a foolish writer would try to compress his message into one page of typescript at the expense of omitting vital facts and statistics. Every letter must be complete as well as concise.

Tone: The Good Will Element

The letter to Mr. Hepburn also has the quality called "tone," treated in a later part of this chapter. Good will and diplomacy of phrasing are the elements in a letter which bring in business, make friends for a company, and assure any firm of more orders for the future. When you send your best regards to a businessman, when you offer him a service which he hasn't asked for, when you go out of your way to please him, then you are creating goodwill for the company and are demonstrating your diplomacy. You are meeting the reader of your letter more than halfway.

Qualities of the Effective Letter Writer

To be a good letter writer, you need to know the layout of a letter: its parts; the accepted forms, such as the balanced block, the semi-block, and the block; and the purely mechanical details. You also have to know how to plan a letter clearly and logically. Most of all, you have to be able to phrase your letters exactly and diplomatically, to foresee the needs of your reader, to write from that reader's point of view, and to create good will for your firm. If you examine letters written by top executives, you will find that they embody these qualities. All the technical training that the schools can give is of little use to you unless you can express your ideas in forceful written language.

Language of the Business Letter

One definition of "diction" is "choice of words to express ideas." No matter how carefully a writer plans his letter or how carefully he outlines its points and sets up its form, if the words which will suitably express his ideas are lacking—or even worse, if the words only approximate the thought—he might better give up the whole attempt.

PRECISENESS

Every thought should have precise expression. Edgar Allan Poe said that he had never had an idea which he could not express accurately in words. Although Einstein found that he had to give his conception of space in mathematical terms, he succeeded in expressing what he wanted. The word, nevertheless, is your symbol for communicating what you want to say, and it is possible to be as precise with this symbol as with the computation of a pH constant. What you say must give your exact meaning without distortion.

SIMPLICITY

The best kind of expression is simple expression, which uses the shorter and more common words. The most effective words are the shortest, providing they express your thought. The following letter is much too pompous.

EBRO MOTOR COMPANY
Ebro, Ohio

October 14, 19--

Mr. Kenneth B. Dembler
Union Steel Castings Co.
Coraopolis, Pennsylvania

Dear Mr. Dembler: <u>Contractual Obligations toward</u>
                                  <u>Union Steel Castings</u>

   Pursuant to our extended conversation of the fourth instant,
I am gratified to be able to convey to you our firm's assurance
that they will be able to implement their contractual obligations to your company relative to crane motors.

   The monetary considerations are presently under advisement.

Very sincerely yours,

R. A. Graham

R. A. Graham
Legal Department

RAG:pr

The trouble with this letter is obvious. The words convey the meaning—if you know what the words mean. Mr. Dembler could have gone to the dictionary and found out what his correspondent intended to say. But if you drive the addressee to *Webster's*, you will irritate him.

OVERWORKED EXPRESSIONS

The use of clichés—overworked, trite, outworn words—makes any letter, no matter how interesting and valuable its subject matter, a tiresome affair. Compare the following letters. Both of them say the same thing, but one says it so much better than the other that there is no doubt which is the more effective.

There is scarcely an original phrase in this entire letter. The words are certainly common ones, but they are so common that they are worn out.

The new form of the letter is entirely different. The clichés have

MELLON RESEARCH INSTITUTE
Pasadena 6, California

September 9, 19--

Mr. Andrew B. Philpott, Secretary
Manufacturers' Institute
233 West Sixth Street
New York 10, N.Y.

Dear Mr. Philpott: Subject: Membership in Institute

Yours of the 2nd instant received and beg to state that
I am interested in your proposition of becoming a member of
the Institute. History tells us that the successful man needs
more than honest toil to keep body and soul together. He needs
the help of divers and sundry of his fellows. It is the irony
of fate that even the ablest of us is unable to make progress
in his field if he goes it alone. Even in the broad daylight
of competition, the best of engineers can do no more than eke out
a precarious existence if he depends solely on his own efforts.
Consequently, please accept my accompanying application for
membership.

Very sincerely yours,

S. P. Elliott

S. P. Elliott
Research Fellow

SPE:nr
Encl.

been eliminated; the sloppy tone of the first draft is gone. The letter
is concise.

The first draft of the letter to Mr. Philpott has more errors than
any letter, regardless of length, can successfuly withstand. These
mistakes are not in the mechanical form (you'll see that the date line,
the inside address, the salutation, the complimentary close, the signature, and the stenographic reference are all correct); they are errors
in judgment. Admitting that "yours of the 2nd instant received and
beg to state" is a threadbare phrase to find in a letter, it still isn't so
bad as "the irony of fate" or "eke out a precarious existence." These
may possibly have been bright, meaningful groups of words when they
were originally coined, but now they are merely boring. The technical

MELLON RESEARCH INSTITUTE
Pasadena 6, California

September 9, 19--

Mr. Andrew B. Philpott, Secretary
Manufacturers' Institute
233 West Sixth Street
New York 10, N.Y.

Dear Mr. Philpott: Subject: Membership in Institute

    I was pleased to have your letter of September 2, in which
you offered me membership in the Manufacturers' Institute.

    I am glad to enclose my application.

                            Very sincerely yours,

                            S. P. Elliott

                            S. P. Elliott
                            Design Engineering

SPE:nr
Encl.

---

man, because so much of his education lies in strictly scientific fields, is not very likely to notice phrases of this sort because his attention has been centered on the actual object rather than on its word-image. Look through this list of old phrases that no longer have any vitality. It's probable that you'll find some that you are too fond of yourself.

In Speech	In Business
dead as a door-nail	favor of an early reply
heavy as lead	yours received and contents noted
quick as a flash	glad of this opportunity to serve you
brown as a berry	take pleasure in informing
a laborer in the vineyard	under separate cover
silence reigned supreme	I am gratified to know
all the world's a stage	indeed an honor
well, by and large	pursuant to your order
thirteen to the dozen	implement our agreement
path of least resistance	contact your representative
fit as a fiddle	assuring you of our interest

In Speech	In Business
fair, fat, and forty	beg to advise
tall, dark, and handsome	and oblige yours truly
drunk as a lord	in due course
boiled as an owl	please be advised
down to the sea in ships	forward the same
nine times out of ten	enclosed please find
consensus of opinion	thanking you in advance
as a matter of fact	yours of recent date received
solid as a rock	wish to assure you

These phrases are all conventional; Grandfather used them as much as they are used today. In speech these clichés are not likely to be so noticeable as they are in writing. When a letter is drafted, it is assumed that the writer has not only enough time to think over what he wants to say, but also enough time to use original expressions.

Euphemisms

Other words which generally ought to be avoided are euphemisms. The euphemistic style of writing is one which looks for words which seem more genteel than the straightforward expression. Perhaps this tendency can be illustrated by the Victorian phrase, "Horses sweat, men perspire, and young ladies get all glowy."

Euphemisms have three outstanding faults. In the first place, they take more time to dictate and to type than do the plain, ordinary words for which they stand. Why stir up the phrase, "Dr. John E. Morgan, purveyor of science to the masses, became deceased last night," when what you really mean is that "Dr. John E. Morgan, a popularizer of science, died last night"?

A second fault of the euphemism is that it always requires an extra mental effort on the part of the reader. He must more or less translate your phrase into his own vocabulary before he completely understands the idea you want to transmit.

The most important failing of the euphemism is that it stands in the way of direct communication. It is a pale, nerveless thing; it does not give the realistic image of the more direct and outspoken word for which it stands. It lacks reality.

OVERTONES OF PHRASING

Any piece of writing has what may be called "tone." Tone comes as a result of the phrasing; it is a general effect that the reader of the letter feels rather than understands intellectually. Often this effect is secured by individual words, and sometimes it is directly opposite to the one the writer wishes to produce. Consider the following letter from W. T. Grant of the Central Steel Castings Company. Grant was answering an inquiry about two large flywheels which had been ordered and which had not arrived on the scheduled date. The fault lay with the railroad and not with Central Steel Castings, but Mr. Grant's letter had a tone that made the addressee conclude that he would never again specify this company as a supplier of material.

CENTRAL STEEL CASTINGS
Barkley, Ohio

April 12, 19--

Mr. A. R. Harkness, Works Manager
Molyneux Iron Works
Murdoch, Tennessee

Dear Sir: Flywheels—Our Order #2B4593

It is very unfortunate that the two flywheels which we are supplying to the Molyneux Iron Works have not, as you allege, arrived at your Murdoch Works. These were shipped from Barkley on April 4 by the Chesapeake and Valley Railroad. We contend that we have taken every care to insure the prompt arrival of the apparatus, and suggest that you write the Chesapeake and Valley for further information.

Very truly yours,

W. T. Grant

W. T. Grant, Superintendent
Shipping Department

WTG/fr

If the tone of this letter is left out of consideration, it must be admitted that Grant gave all the information that could have been wanted. Most companies, in the event of a lost shipment, offer to trace the material which they are supplying; but since the Molyneux Iron Works could have done this as well as the Central Steel Castings, there is nothing about the particular statement concerning the shipment that should have irritated Mr. Harkness.

The elements of the letter that did annoy him were rather nebulous, but they are there. He didn't exactly locate the cause of his displeasure at the first reading, but after looking over the letter again, he determined what was objectionable about it. In the first place, Mr. Grant had begun his letter with the cold and formal "Dear Sir." The second thing that Grant had omitted was the number of the Molyneux Iron Works order on the subject line. It gave Harkness the feeling that the Central Steel Castings cared nothing about the manufacturer who placed the order; that their interests never went beyond their own company.

In the body of the letter Harkness came upon two words that he disliked. The first of these was "allege." The precise dictionary definition of "allege" is "to affirm; to assert; to state positively." In an earlier letter to Grant he had done just that; he had stated positively that the flywheels had not arrived. On the surface and according to the definition, he had no reason to object to what Mr. Grant had said. But—"allege, allege"—it was one of those words that the examining attorney used when he was interrogating the criminal. "You allege that you were at home on the night of June 16?" "You allege that you were not in the company of this woman?" The jury and the spectators in the courtroom at once feel that the man on the stand must be lying; that he *was* in the company of whatever woman is being referred to, and that he was *not* at home on the night of June 16. "Allege" seemed to imply subtly that Harkness was lying; that the flywheels *had* arrived.

The second annoying phrase was "we contend that." Harkness liked a firm to give a direct statement of fact, but "we contend that" made it seem that the writer wanted to argue about his company's business procedure—a very bad practice in letter writing.

The following examples are phrases that make people get subconsciously angry. Most persons are quite unable to say exactly what there is about them that is unpleasant but often they carry a hostile air.

We maintain that   If this is the case
It is our position that   Although you assert that
We contend that

There are a large number of phrases of this sort that the technical man should omit if he wants to keep the good will of his correspondents. Most words of this type do one of two things: they either appear to cast doubt upon the truthfulness of the correspondent, or else they put him ever so slightly on the defensive. Both effects are unpleasant.

COMPLETENESS

Earlier in this chapter, the discussion of headings for second sheets pointed out that the completeness of the message is always more important than the number of pages. Lack of complete, specific information often makes necessary the exchange of other letters. Consider the following illustrations.

Assuming that the addressee of the letter is acquainted with oil diffusion pumps from reading about them in the standard texts, does this letter tell him all he should know? It instructs him clearly

---

CENCO SCIENTIFIC COMPANY
Watervliet, Maine

September 14, 19--

Mr. William E. Haskins
Kartheon Uranium Corporation
594 East Sixth Avenue
Marion, Ohio

Dear Mr. Haskins: Subject: High Vacuum Pump

I was sorry to hear that you had experienced trouble with the high vacuum, oil diffusion pump which we recently delivered to you.

From your letter I gathered that the difficulty did not lie with the pump itself, but rather with your house vacuum system. I feel that your system has not been creating sufficient vacuum to enable this style of pump to operate properly. If this defect is remedied, I am sure that the pump will perform as warranted.

Very sincerely yours,

A. R. Keith

A. R. Keith
Sales Engineering

ARK:ru

CENCO SCIENTIFIC COMPANY
Watervliet, Maine

September 14, 19--

Mr. William E. Haskins
Kartheon Uranium Corporation
594 East Sixth Avenue
Marion, Ohio

Dear Mr. Haskins: Subject: High Vacuum Pump

I was sorry to hear that you had experienced trouble with the high vacuum, oil diffusion pump which we recently delivered to you. From your letter I gathered that the difficulty did not lie with the pump itself, but rather with your house vacuum system.

Oil diffusion pumps require a fairly high degree of vacuum into which to pump, and the type which you have will not perform properly if the pressure into which it is required to exhaust is greater than 50 microns, or 0.05 millimeter. If your pump has failed, I suggest that before putting heat under the pump to activate it you make arrangements to hang a McLeod gauge on the exhaust system which backs the pump. If readings on the gauge indicate a pressure of 75 microns or above, I believe you should examine the oil pump you are using. Without knowing anything more precisely about your trouble I would recommend a change of oil to a somewhat heavier type, although there is a possibility that the lubricant in the oil pump has become emulsified with water.

I hope that my suggestion will be of help to you. Write me if you find that your difficulties with the pump persist, for the corporation will be glad to give you every assistance it can.

Very sincerely yours,

A. R. Keith

A. R. Keith
Sales Engineering

ARK:ru

that the writer thinks something is wrong with the house vacuum system, but are there enough details to aid him in getting the pump into operation? The letter obviously needs to be rewritten.

These two letters really say about the same thing. Both tell Mr. Haskins that the trouble with the high vacuum pump is that it is being required to pump into too great a gas concentration. But in the first letter the writer merely told Mr. Haskins where he thought the trouble lay. In the second he offered him enough suggestions to enable him to find the trouble. He did this without giving offense; he left the final determination to Mr. Haskins. The added details make a much more effective letter. All letters should be complete as well as concise.

Summary

In this chapter we have followed the technical man's progress in learning the essential parts of the letter, the several styles, and the mechanical details. We have pointed out some problems in dictation, have analyzed the methods of planning the letter, and have discussed the intangibles that often are inherent in the composition of a letter. We have tried to show the costs of errors in some cases and the pay-off for success in others. We have tried to give you, in other words, ideas concerning the essentials of the successful business letter, whatever the industrial field.

Discussion Questions

1. What does a dictator need to know about the writing of business letters if he is to perform his job acceptably?
2. What are the basic parts of a business letter?
3. What are the acceptable forms for the salutation and the complimentary close?
4. Defend or refute the need for subject lines in business letters.
5. Why should enclosures be mentioned in the body of a letter as well as in the enclosure line itself?
6. Why is open punctuation almost universally used in American business letters?
7. What are the two most popular styles for the form of business letters? Describe each style.
8. Why should the style of letters, the system of punctuation used, and the address on the envelope be consistent?
9. Discuss what method you would use in paragraphing business letters.
10. Describe how you would fold a standard sheet of paper (8½ by 11 inches) for an envelope 3⅝ by 6½ inches; for an envelope 4⅛ by 9½ inches.

11. What procedure should the careful dictator observe when he prepares to dictate answers to letters?
12. What is the typical pattern for the plan of a letter?
13. In the letter to Mr. Hepburn on p. 41, how does the writer indicate that he is a tactful individual?
14. In using a dictating machine, what principles should the dictator observe regarding his dictation?
15. What does proofreading a manuscript involve?
16. Why is the *you* point of view superior to the *I* point of view in business writing?
17. What qualities would you like your own correspondence to have?
18. Discuss the qualities of language that should be found in first-class business letters.
19. Give some examples of overworked words and phrases, as well as euphemisms, that you have observed in letters you have read.
20. Why should the length of a letter always be of lesser importance than its completeness of information?

Writing Assignments

1. Proofread the following letter for the proper placement of its parts, for organization of material, and for exact, original phrasing and tone. Make any changes that would improve the letter; then rewrite it.

```
Mr. Alfred Francis,
Estes Chemical Co.
  Manson Bldg.
Norton, South Dakota

  Dear Mr. Francis

Per your March 13th request enclosed you will find technical
information and formulations on our water reducible metal
primers.  It is indeed a pleasure to have this opportunity to
forward to your attention a gallon sample each of our

          70-808 Synpol  (formerly 1808)
          70-809   "        "      1809
          90-120 Expol   (formerly 3120)
          90-370 Plapol  (formerly 3370)

      Also, no doubt you will be pleased to find attached a copy
of our current price list MD-8923.

After you have had a chance to review our literature and
    evaluate our samples I will be sure to contact you so that, if
you agree, we can discuss their possible application.

Yours truly,

    DAKOTA CHEMICALS, INC.
    James T. Blair
```

2. Make diagrams that show the preceding letter written in the balanced block style and the semiblock style. Put in a subject line, and place this line in a different position in each illustration.
3. Write a letter in semiblock style to inquire whether your company, the Harnwell Manufacturing Co., may borrow a film dealing with dictation practices from the Joplin Office Equipment Co., Joplin, Missouri.
4. One of your friends has asked you to explain the placement of the various parts in a letter. Write the letter of explanation.

3

Types of Technical Letters

This chapter will discuss the major kinds of business letters with which technical men should be familiar and will analyze how they are planned and how they achieve their effects. Although each letter you write presents an individual problem, the type of letter to be written will govern in large measure the planning of your dictation. Because you will have to answer a number of inquiries during your career in business, we shall offer first some suggestions for the planning and dictating of the letter of inquiry.

Letter of Inquiry

Every company daily receives letters of inquiry from its customers. A great many of such letters have to do with technical matters. The questions asked must consequently be answered by technical personnel, for often the inquiries deal with equipment or ask for quotations on equipment, or they may deal with design problems, with manufacturing problems, or perhaps with defects in equipment.

Sometimes such letters are like the one reproduced below, in which a student wants information from a personnel director. Sometimes the inquiries relate to patents or to the use of machines. Whatever the purpose of the letter of inquiry, however, its pattern remains fundamentally the same.

This pattern could be outlined as follows:

1. The opening paragraph should state the purpose of the letter. It should include the request and the reason for it.
2. The second paragraph should give, if necessary, any background information regarding the request. Such information would include telling what use the writer wishes to make of the information that he hopes to receive. Many firms refuse to answer inquiries that come from people who are not customers unless they know why the writer wants the information. A letter might properly combine points 1 and 2 into a single para-

graph, such as "I am in need of information about new developments in jet engines for a paper which I am preparing to submit to *Aeronautical Engineering Review*." Such an opening informs the company of the request and of the application which is to be made of the facts that may be given.

3. If the inquiry involves several points, these points should be numbered for the convenience of the addressee. Each point should be specific in statement.

4. Before closing the letter, the writer should express his appreciation for any consideration which the addressee may give his request. If he is going to publish the information requested, he should ask permission to use that information and should offer to send the person who gives him data a copy of his printed results. In fact, whenever the inquirer can give something in return for information, he will be more likely to obtain what he wants.

5. It is well to make the answer as easy as possible for the addressee to comply with. Sometimes this is done by the enclosure of a return envelope. Sometimes, if an inquiry can be answered by a simple "yes" or a series of check marks, the writer can make use of the questionnaire. A simple covering statement and a return envelope or card should accompany this type of inquiry.

Observe how the pattern is carried through in the letter below.

Shaw Residence Hall
Michigan State University
East Lansing, Michigan
September 28, 19--

Mr. L. Saxon Graham
Personnel Director
The Reed Motor Company
Lansing, Michigan

Dear Mr. Graham:

One of my instructors, Mr. F. R. Patterson, has assigned me a study dealing with the following problem: "What are the retention rates for female employees in the automotive industry?"

I would appreciate your giving me data concerning two questions relating to this problem, if such information is easily available:

1. What is the retention rate of female employees in your shops?

L. Saxon Graham   -2-   September 28, 19--

    2. What is the retention rate of female employees in your
       offices?

    Answers to these questions will help me materially in
validating my study.

    I am enclosing a stamped return envelope for your con-
venience in replying.

                              Very truly yours,

                              Arthur P. Hambleton

                              Arthur P. Hambleton

Enclosure

The writer loses no time in stating his request in the opening paragraph and in phrasing his points in paragraph two. This paragraph
also expresses appreciation of any data which Mr. Graham may give.
The writer avoids the stale phrase "Thanking you in advance," for
such a phrase implies that the writer is so certain of a favorable
answer that he takes it for granted. The result is that it is often *not*
granted. The ending explains what use will be made of the data and
offers the courtesy of a return envelope.

    The letter addressed to the manager of the Sun Drug Store has a
slightly different organization. The opening paragraph gives the
reason for the inquiry, complete background information, and the
nature of the inquiry. The final paragraph offers to send a copy of
the results of the study when the work is done. The letter is straightforward and concise, for it is always well to make inquiries as short
as possible.

                              College of Pharmacy
                              Wayne State University
                              Detroit 26, Michigan
                              June 6, 19--

Manager, Sun Drug Store
2938 Pontiac Avenue
Detroit 6, Michigan

Dear Sir:

    As one of the projects of our pharmacy course, the students
in Wayne State University have been asked to make a survey of

Manager, Sun Drug Store   -2-   June 6, 19--

labor costs as they apply to drug stores. I have been assigned
the Detroit area. It would help me greatly if you would
indicate on the enclosed postcard the number of people working
in the departments mentioned and the approximate total costs
of their labor.

   If you would like to know the results of this study so that
you may compare your costs with others throughout the country,
as well as in Detroit, we shall be glad to forward a copy of
the results to you when the work is completed.

                                    Very sincerely yours,

                                    George P. Robertson

                                    George P. Robertson

Enc.--Postcard

   The postcard (Fig. 4) indicates what can be done with the simple
questionnaire for inquiries. Such a form, properly filled out, gives
the inquirer all the information he wants and does not unduly use
the time of the businessman.

DEPARTMENT	TOTAL EMPLOYEE HOURS PER WEEK	APPROXIMATE WEEKLY WAGES
Prescription	_____	_____
Fountain	_____	_____
Tobacco and Candy	_____	_____
Cosmetics	_____	_____
Notions	_____	_____
Baby Department	_____	_____
Prepared Medicines	_____	_____

Fig. 4. Simple postcard questionnaire.

   In writing a letter of inquiry, aim to incorporate the following
qualities:

1. Be *concise*. Make your request, if possible, in the opening paragraph.
2. Be *specific*. Ask precisely for what you want.
3. Be *reasonable*. Ask for what can be given without unusual trouble.
4. Be *fair*. Tell what use you intend to make of the information.
5. Be *considerate*. Make the addressee's task as easy as possible.

Letter of Quotation

Closely related to the inquiry is the letter of quotation, often written in answer to customers' inquiries. This type of letter features the most important qualities of a product and the quotation of prices. Complete description of the product or piece of apparatus is usually given in an accompanying bulletin. Technical men connected with sales engineering have to write this kind of letter frequently. A typical letter of quotation follows:

MEDICAL ELECTRIC CORPORATION
Anagog, Tennessee

June 24, 19--

Dr. Arthur E. Hutchins:
625 Aiken Avenue
Mono, Illinois

Dear Dr. Hutchins:

Our field representative, Mr. Alfred Munk, has told us of your interest in our X-Ray Generator and the Shockproof Mobile X-Ray Unit. At his request, we are sending you the enclosed bulletins.

The following information gives complete details on the prices of the various pieces of equipment:

Item #1 1--Transportable Model Ultra-Short Wave Generator

      List price each $990.00
      Discount--40%
      Net price each (freight prepaid) $594.00

Item #2 1--Complete set of Soft Rubber Condenser Electrodes

      List prices per set .... $ 75.00
      Discount--10%
      Net price per set .... $ 67.50

Arthur E. Hutchins   -2-   June 24, 19--

Item #3   1--Complete set of Glass Condenser Electrodes

              List price per set $125.00
              Discount--10%
              Net price per set $112.50

Item #4   1--Upright adjustable stand to hold the above

              List price each .... $ 75.00
              Discount--10%
              Net price each (freight prepaid) .... $ 67.50

Item #5   2--Cords for Glass Electrodes

              List price for two .... $ 15.00
              Discount--10%
              Net price for two (freight prepaid) .... $ 13.50

    Shipment can be made within ten days after receipt of the order at our plant.

    Terms are 2% in 10 days.

    As you review the accompanying bulletins, the relation which the various parts bear to each other will become evident. This apparatus, when properly installed, will provide you with a satisfactory unit and will, we feel, fulfill all the demands which Mr. Munk has told us you will probably make on it.

    Mr. Munk will be glad to discuss this equipment further with you on Monday, July 8, if that will be convenient.

    If you have any other questions about the apparatus, we shall be glad to answer them by letter from the plant, or Mr. Munk will probably be able to give you the needed information.

                              Very sincerely yours,

                              E. W. Hanslowe, Manager

                              E. W. Hanslowe, Manager
                              X-Ray Division Sales

EWH/de
Encl.--3

This letter is principally concerned with the following up of the personal call which the corporation's representative has already made on the customer. The additional offer of a special service through the representative is an added appeal.

Sometimes a letter of quotation recommends a product briefly and relies on an enclosed bulletin to give the customer all the data about the product, as well as current prices. The letter below, regarding laminates, offers merely a brief statement about each one.

RICHMAN CHEMICALS, INC.
Omaha 6, Nebraska

December 10, 19--

Mr. F. L. Mossman
Easton Corporation
476 Beacon Street
Iowa City 15, Iowa

Dear Mr. Mossman:

Knowing your interest in laminates, we would like to bring to your attention several of our new high temperature resistant phenolic resins described below.

Plyophen 23-900 (5900) has been approved by the government under MIL-R-9299 Specifications. It has been used in many components of rockets and various types of missiles.

Plyophen 23-900 (5900) is an epoxy modified phenolic resin.

Plyophen 23-017 (SF-2947-34) is a phenolic silicone resin which is superior to the straight phenolic resins and to the epoxy modified resins for exposure to high temperatures for fairly long periods of time.

Plyophen 23-057 (SF-4057-10) is a polyamid modified phenolic resin which was developed especially to withstand ablation and burn-through resistance when the material is exposed for short periods of time to temperatures in excess of 6000° F.

Data sheets and current prices are shown in the enclosed printed list.

Very truly yours,

RICHMAN CHEMICALS, INC.

John F. Golden

John F. Golden

JFG:af
Enc.

This kind of letter relies on the customer's established interest in laminates. Because of this interest, he would examine the enclosed list in detail.

Letter of Instruction

Technical men who are in positions of some authority are often required to write letters of instruction to field engineers, foremen, or others who are working under them. These letters must give information concisely, accurately, and, above all, clearly.

Although clarity is necessary in all business communications, it is the most important single element in giving instructions. Clarity may be achieved by precision in the choice of words and their placement. The good writer will outline his letter of instruction logically before dictating it; he will make the letter complete; he will tabulate his instructions wherever possible. Complete sentences are preferable to phrases for giving instructions.

The following letter illustrates the essential points of any letter of instruction.

KINSELLA MANUFACTURING CORPORATION
Seattle 5, Washington

August 27, 19--

Mr. E. C. Spanos
Spanos Testing Laboratories
124 Eastern Avenue
Las Vegas 16, California

Dear Mr. Spanos: <u>Imperial Irrigation Company—Turbine-</u>
<u>Generator Tests</u>

This letter is to outline the final tests of our turbine-generator, Style #344825. Since you have agreed to act as observer for us on these tests, you should know the exact conditions under which they are to be made. The procedure which follows represents the requirements of the customer, the Imperial Irrigation Company.

1. Trip the breaker, disconnecting the transformers from the high voltage system.

E. C. Spanos   -2-   August 27, 19--

2. Check the operation of the voltage relay by both visual inspection and voltmeter test.

3. Admit steam to the auxiliary generator. It must come up to both normal operating speed and voltage in 20 seconds.

4. Connect the meters of one bus section to the generator terminals 20 seconds after steam has been admitted to the auxiliary generator.

5. Connect the meters of the second bus section to the generator terminals two seconds later (22 seconds after steam has been admitted to the auxiliary generator).

6. See that the generator voltage as registered by a recording voltmeter does not drop below 75% of the rated voltage of 2300 at any time after step 3 has been completed.

If the turbine-generator fails in any particular to meet these requirements, please wire me at once.

Very truly yours,

William C. Hummel

William C. Hummel, Superintendent
A-C Engineering Division

WCH:yr

In his letter of instruction Mr. Hummel has left nothing to chance. The entire procedure for the testing of the turbine-generator has been set down logically, proceeding in a time sequence of operation. The words are clear and precise, and each test has been described in sufficient detail to enable Mr. Spanos to know exactly what the requirements are.

Technical men often write letters of instruction concerning shop-testing and manufacturing processes. The following illustrates a letter from an engineer to a foreman, giving directions for the testing of gages about which complaints have been received.

Internal Correspondence

OXON GAGE COMPANY

To: B. E. White, Foreman   From: R. H. Ilsley, Manager
      Section JU   High Vacuum Engineering
                                     Date: August 27, 19--

                                     Subject: Test procedures for
                                               Pirani gages

CC: Edwin D. Peterson, Inspector
      4G-47

      R. E. Grantham, Manager
      Returned Materials Dept.
      8-L-34

Several of our customers have complained lately that the Pirani
gages purchased from the Oxon Gage Corporation have leaked.
This leakage has occurred immediately upon their being put into
service, so we may assume that the fault is in our testing
procedure.

To make certain that these complaints do not continue, I have
outlined test specifications which I should like to have you
follow.

1. Examine the seat of the gage. If irregularities are
   apparent, return the complete assembly to the shop for
   further machining.

2. Mount the gage on the vacuum testing rack, using Neo-
   prene rubber for the gasket seal. Tighten holding bolts
   firmly. At least 6 should be used.

3. Pump the gage for a minimum of 6 hours at a pressure of
   1 micron or less, as read on the test rack McLeod gage.
   A greater length of time is acceptable if it is not convenient to make the test at the expiration of the 6-hour
   period.

4. Close all valves to shut off the pumping action from
   the gages being tested. Allow them to remain closed for
   2 hours.

5. Close the 8 in. valve at the end of 2 hours, thus shutting
   off the evacuating pump from the test rack.

B. E. White, Foreman   -2-   August 27, 19--

6. With the test rack at a pressure of less than 1 micron, open any valve connecting a gage which is to be tested to the entire test rack. After waiting at least 1 minute and not more than 5 minutes, read the pressure on the McLeod gage connected to the rack. If the leakage shown is greater than 2 microns for the 2 hours, consider the gage defective and return it to the shop.

This procedure, if carefully followed, should prevent us from sending out any more defective gages. If you can put this method of testing into operation by September 1, we shall have an adequate check on its efficiency.

An effective letter of instruction should:

1. Have a covering statement at the opening which explains the situation and gives the reason for the writing of the letter.
2. Be in parallel grammatical construction. The imperative should be used for the verb forms.
3. Be set up in a tabular form whenever possible to aid clarity.
4. Under certain circumstances, specify a date by which the instructions should be complied with.

Letter of Transmittal

Every technical man writes reports of investigations he has undertaken. Although the forms of reports will be considered later (pages 106–107), the covering letter, called the letter of transmittal, will be taken up here.

This letter acts as an introduction to the report, and should be as short as is consistent with clarity. If work continues on the project after a first report has been made, the second letter of transmittal may summarize the progress which has been detailed in the first report.

The first paragraph of a letter of transmittal gives the title of the report and often mentions the authorization under which the work was conducted. The authorization, however, may also be cited in the second paragraph. The letter of transmittal indicates too that the work either is in progress or is completed.

The writer's status in a firm determines the tone of the letter of transmittal. The following letter is an example in which an employee is writing to his superior, with whom a direct contact is comparatively easy.

ACHESON RESEARCH LABORATORIES
Chicago 32, Illinois

September 2, 19--

Mr. Arthur F. Braun, Director
Marketing Research
Acheson Research Laboratories
Chicago 32, Illinois

Dear Mr. Braun:

The enclosed report contains our findings on "Problems of
International Commodity Agreement on Petroleum."

The investigation was authorized by Dr. A. E. Parsons, Associate
Director of the Research Laboratories, on June 16, 19--, with a
view to determining the procedure of existing international
commodity agreements and the possible reaction of consumer
countries to such agreements.

Respectfully submitted,

Carll Wilson Doxsey

Carll Wilson Doxsey
Engineer-in-Charge
Petroleum Division

In the letter following, the authorization and scope of the work are mentioned in the first paragraph. But Mr. McMullen has added information from the report itself in the second paragraph, calling attention to certain pages that will interest the Vice-President. He has also summarized his recommendation by pointing out that manufacturing can be profitably continued at the plant. The letter also specifies methods of increasing efficiency at Swampscott and suggests changes. Frequently, the more important conclusions and recommendations of a report are a part of the letter of transmittal.

PENDRAY and SAMSON
CONSULTING ENGINEERS
151 Broad Street
Philadelphia 21, Pennsylvania

August 18, 19--

Mr. Arthur L. Maine
Vice-President in Charge
  of Maintenance
Ruud Manufacturing Corporation
Pittston, West Virginia

Dear Mr. Maine:

In accordance with your letter of June 24, 19--, we have
made a complete examination of the Ruud Manufacturing Corporation's physical plant in Swampscott, New Jersey, to determine
whether its condition warrants continuing manufacturing
operations there.

The accompanying report lists the conditions in detail, but
you may be interested to know that, in our opinion, the plant
can be rehabilitated at comparatively small cost. The report
suggests on pages 17 and 18 two methods for lowering factory
costs and increasing efficiency at Swampscott by the addition
of a ramp and a short spur of railway.

Very truly yours,

PENDRAY and SAMSON

W. L. McMullen

By W. L. McMullen
Chief Viewer

WLMcM:ss
Enclosure

In many instances a field engineer has little personal contact with
his supervisor. Under these circumstances, the only way in which his
work may become known is through his reports. It is consequently
to his advantage that he make recommendations in his letters of
transmittal, for usually his superior will read only the letter and forward the report itself to those concerned with the specific problem
with which it deals.

The letter from Mr. Thomas Altman to Mr. Albert Frome illustrates what can be done in a letter of transmittal to recommend the contents of a report to the person who authorized it.

THOMPSON STEEL CORPORATION
Pittsburgh 10, Pennsylvania

August 18, 19--

Mr. Albert F. Frome, Manager
Waterville Plant
Brown and Price Furnace Co.
1892 Remington Building
Newark 8, New Jersey

Dear Mr. Frome:

Acting on your instructions of July 20, I have prepared the enclosed report, "Effect of Design Modifications on Flow Distribution in Operating and Cold Open Hearth Furnace Regenerators."

On page 3, the measurements given confirm the existence of severe channeling, and even recirculation, of gases in the single pass checker system of the standard design. Erection of baffle walls above and below the checker chimneys of an operating furnace was found to eliminate this maldistribution almost entirely, and at the same time to improve furnace performance and fuel rate.

Pages 10 through 12 give a method for computing flow distributions on the basis of pressure and temperature measurements.

Mr. A. P. Monroe and Mr. P. J. Kron have given me much help in this investigation and a number of constructive suggestions.

The findings in the report should be taken into consideration when you redesign your regenerators.

Very truly yours,

Thomas A. Altman

Thomas A. Altman
Research Engineer

Enclosure

Letter of Sales Recommendation

Technical men are sometimes called on to recommend equipment on the basis of their knowledge of performance data and the way in which the equipment will fit the needs of particular customers. The following letter makes a diplomatic suggestion about an air conditioning system designed to give a customer the satisfaction he expects.

THE HEATING CORPORATION
Cincinnati 5, Ohio

September 10, 19--

Mr. George Plummer
White Top Restaurants
1673 Riverdale Avenue
Birmingham 4, Alabama

Dear Mr. Plummer: <u>Air Conditioning System</u>

Thank you for sending us such a specific outline of your needs regarding a complete air conditioning system for your new restaurant in Birmingham.

We notice that the specifications you enclosed are similar to those used as the basis for building a system in your Philadelphia restaurant. Several customers living in Birmingham, however, have found our Type SL11 Heat Pump installations the most efficient on the market.

The conventional air conditioning system is designed for cooling purposes. Because temperatures in the Alabama climate sometimes fall as low as 20 degrees Fahrenheit, it is advisable to have a unit that will heat as well as cool your restaurant. We should like to stress that the SL11 Heat Pump installation is the only air conditioning system that can maintain temperatures at a constant 68 to 70 degrees Fahrenheit all the year round without the use of an extra heating unit. If you will look at page three of the enclosed pamphlet, you will find the detailed specifications of the system. We should like you particularly to notice the estimated decreased operating cost of the SL11 over any conventional unit.

One of our engineering representatives, Mr. T. E. Naismith, will be in Birmingham on September 20 and will call on you to

George Plummer   -2-   September 10, 19--

explain the features of this installation. He will be pleased
to answer any questions you may have.

                              Very truly yours,

                              H. N. Beatty

                              H. N. Beatty, Superintendent
                              Air Conditioning Department

HNB:tn
Enc.

This letter is diplomatic in phrasing. At no time does Mr. Beatty suggest that Mr. Plummer has the wrong ideas about an air conditioning system suited to his needs, nor does he reject entirely the specifications sent. He does not even say that he or his company believe that the heat pump installations have been efficient. Instead, he cites the satisfaction of customers.

Because a pamphlet is enclosed with the letter, he mentions only a few of the advantages of the heat pump installation, preferring to rely chiefly on the pamphlet to persuade the customer to accept the system. The engineering representative should do the rest. He is really the one to expedite the customer's decision.

Letters of this type have a relatively simple plan. They can be reduced to the following points:

1. Acknowledgment of any previous correspondence.
2. Introduction of suggestions concerning equipment to suit the customer's needs.
3. Brief statement of the advantages of the recommended equipment.
4. Some device to help the customer make a decision.

Letter of Complaint

The letter of complaint is written to secure an adjustment of a claim which the writer feels he has upon the supplier of services or materials. To obtain the adjustment, a letter of this sort must be courteous. Although a company has sent defective equipment or a railroad over which a shipment was made has been careless, there is no point in becoming angry. The main effort should be directed toward a suitable adjustment. This can be gained more quickly by the exercise of tact and discretion than by the exhibition of bad temper.

The following letter of complaint illustrates the proper tone to be employed. It is firm but polite. By giving the date when he had specified he needed the transits and by quoting the shipment clause

---

THE UNIVERSITY OF THE NORTH
Burlington, Maine

September 5, 19--

Mr. Rexford A. Pendleton
Sales Manager
Engineering Supply Co.
1282 Weston Building
Passaic, New Jersey

                         Transits: Serials #53672-53687
Dear Mr. Pendleton: Your Order No. SX573

On June 10 I ordered fifteen transits for the use of our students in surveying classes and specified that I needed them by September 1. Your original letter of quotation contained the clause, "Shipment can be made within sixty days from the time your order reaches our Passaic Works."

Although the University was invoiced for this equipment on August 20, I have not as yet received it. Since the Fall term will begin September 24, our instructors in surveying will be seriously handicapped if the transits are not received on or before September 15. We cannot teach surveying without having students do as much field work as possible before the weather becomes too severe.

Please let me know by wire when the shipment left your Passaic Works and when I can expect delivery . If the transits do not reach Burlington by September 15, I shall have to cancel the order and obtain used equipment from government surplus.

                         Very truly yours,

                         H. F. Bender

                         H. F. Bender, Head
                         Department of Civil Engineering

HFB:ss

---

included in the letter of quotation, the writer places the responsibility for the delay on the Engineering Supply Company. In no place has he become angry or abusive. He has indicated, however, the reason he needs the equipment before September 15 and has explained under what conditions the order will have to be cancelled. This approach should apply the needed spur to make the company do its utmost to supply the transits on time. The request that the company wire information should further expedite action.

The company's answer follows, showing the results which the letter obtained.

ENGINEERING SUPPLY CO.

Passaic, New Jersey

September 7, 19--

Professor H. F. Bender, Head
Department of Civil Engineering
The University of the North
Burlington, Maine

Dear Professor Bender:

Our telegram to you, dated September 6, stated that we immediately put a tracer on the shipment of transits sent out from our Passaic Works on August 18. The Union Railroad has assured us that you will receive this shipment before September 15.

Unfortunately, our Shipping Department sent the transits to Burlington, Vermont, instead of Burlington, Maine. We have instructed the Union Railroad to send them on to you immediately.

Please accept our sincere apology for the delay and inconvenience you have experienced. Since you have always received efficient service from us in the past, we hope you will not allow this one instance of inefficiency to influence your opinion of our company. We shall do our best to see that you get prompt delivery of all future orders.

Sincerely yours,

Rexford A. Pendleton

Rexford A. Pendleton
Sales Manager

RAP:mp

This answer attempts to keep the business relationship between the company and the University on a cordial basis. In the opening paragraph, the writer is careful to let the Professor know the answer to the question "When shall I receive the transits?" Since the answer to this question is more important than the explanation for the delay, the explanation comes logically in the second paragraph. The final paragraph stresses the company's desire to be efficient.

Sometimes letters of complaint concern the disappointment of customers regarding equipment. The following letter records such disappointment. The answer aims to explain why the equipment cannot be expected to meet the customer's needs and to suggest another type.

ZELIENOPLE OIL & REFINING CO.
Chicago 28, Illinois

December 1, 19--

Mr. Frank C. Kalter, Director
Scientific Equipment Company
1894 Berger Building
Kansas City 10, Missouri

Dear Mr. Kalter:

The specifications you have sent me for the custom-made MacMichael Viscosimeter fail to meet the requirements I set down in my letter of November 10.

After examining these specifications, I find that the Viscosimeter will not meet my need for speeds coninuously variable between 0-600 rpm. I also wanted a quotation on a Powerstat, but to date I have not received it.

Unless you can give me a unit that will suit the operating conditions I set forth, I shall have to go to another company for equipment.

Sincerely yours,

Thomas F. Amos

Thomas F. Amos
Director of Research

TFA:fs

To meet the customer's objections and to satisfy his requirements, Mr. Kalter wrote this reply:

SCIENTIFIC EQUIPMENT COMPANY
Kansas City 10, Missouri

December 6, 19--

Mr. Thomas F. Amos
Director of Research
Zelienople Oil & Refining Co.
1983 La Salle Street
Chicago 28, Illinois

Dear Mr. Amos:

I regret that the specifications sent you for the custom-made MacMichael Viscosimeter fail to meet your requirements. Investigation reveals several reasons why this type of Viscosimeter will not suit your needs.

When I telephoned the manufacturer of the motors used in such a unit, he told me that he cannot supply a single motor to give the range of speeds you requested. He can, however, supply three separate reduction gear heads, with ratios to cover the range in three steps. This would make it necessary for you to employ three Viscosimeters to cover the range 0-600 rpm.

I also asked about the possibility of using a Powerstat to vary the speed instead of the governor which is presently used. This he definitely did not recommend.

Another matter suggested itself to me that might cause trouble even if we were able to get the speeds you need. At the upper range of speed on the Viscosimeter, the fluid under test-- as well as that in the bath—would be thrown to the sides of the cup by centrifugal force. This would lower the level of the test fluid in the center of the cup, changing the depth of immersion of the spindle. This would give you a lower viscosity than is the actual case. (There is also, unfortunately, the chance that liquid might even be thrown up and out of the cup by centrifugal force.)

If the spindle revolved, instead of the cup, this problem would not occur. The Brookfield Viscometer, modified to have a continuously-variable speed motor (instead of 4 speeds) would therefore meet your needs better than our MacMichael unit. The Brookfield uses a revolving spindle, and the torque is indicated on a scale graduated in centipoises.

Thomas F. Amos   -2-   December 6, 19--

    I am sorry that we could not work something out on the
MacMichael unit, but I believe you can get some concrete assist-
ance from Brookfield. Since we are not dealers for the
Brookfield, perhaps it would be best if you contact the
Laboratories. The man to write to is: Mr. R. A. Mansfield, Sales
Manager, Brookfield Engineering Laboratories, Inc., 240
Cushing Street, Stoughton, Massachusetts.

    Although I am disappointed that the MacMichael unit will
not suit your requirements, I am hoping that we can be of
assistance to you in the future whenever you need our equipment.

                  Very truly yours,

                  Frank C. Kalter

                  Frank C. Kalter
                  Director of Research

FCK:tm

    This answer is designed to apologize for the failure of the specifi-
cations to meet the requirements of the Zelienople Oil & Refining Co.,
to explain why no single motor will cover the range of speeds called
for, and to answer the question about the Powerstat. Because of the
customer's special requirements, Mr. Kalter points out, the Mac-
Michael Viscosimeter cannot give the best service possible.

    The help he offers is planned to create good will. The Brookfield
Viscometer, though it is manufactured by a competitor, should meet
the customer's requirements; therefore Mr. Kalter recommends it. To
expedite the customer's getting the equipment he wants, Mr. Kalter
cites the name and address of the man to be contacted. The letter
is both diplomatic and helpful.

    Whether letters of complaint deal with faulty equipment, failure to
meet shipping promises, inadequate specifications, or other matters,
this type of correspondence should:

1. Be courteous and good-tempered in attitude.
2. State the grounds for complaint.
3. Give specific information.
4. Indicate the good faith of the writer, or justify the legitimacy of
   the complaint.
5. Specify, when necessary, the time by which an adjustment
   should be made.

Letter Refusing a Request

It is sometimes necessary to refuse requests made in letters of complaint. If a customer has abused a machine, for instance, the supplying company is justified in levying costs of repairs on him. If a delay in shipment has been caused by the customer's failure to send complete data when he ordered equipment, he should suffer any losses occasioned by the delay. In such instances a company has to inform a customer that his request cannot be granted, but it also has to keep his goodwill.

The letter answering a complaint must:

1. Be handled speedily in order to convince the customer that the supplying company is interested in his problem.
2. Express the willingness of the company to do anything it feels obligated to do.
3. Be polite and conciliatory. It should express concern over the inconvenience caused the customer.
4. Make a positive recommendation of action which may be taken.
5. Keep good will.

Interoffice and Intershop Communications

Interoffice and intershop communications may be written to individuals working in the same plant, or in subsidiary plants of the company. The form of stationery used for such correspondence is usually standardized within the company. The heading of this stationery is generally similar to the one reproduced below, although each company may have its own variation of the form.

Internal Correspondence

UNITED STATES STEEL CORPORATION

To: From:

Date:

Subject:

CC:

Interoffice and intershop communications require no salutation or complimentary close. And they are rarely meant for one person only; often the distribution list of individuals to receive carbon copies may run to fifteen or twenty names. The tone is strictly businesslike.

Often internal communications take the form of orders, which may be either general or special. Special orders are addressed only to certain individuals; they are not applicable to the shop as a whole. The form used in both kinds, however, is the same as that below.

Internal Correspondence

UNION ELECTRIC CORPORATION

```
To:  Mr. E. W. Sims        From:   Office of the Vice-
     Superintendent                President, 11-N-17
     Works Transportation
     Division               Date:   June 23,  19--

                            Subject:  Works Transportation
                                      Electric Trucks

CC:    R, H. Glenn, Medical Division, 1-G-43
       W. L. Bates, Metal Fabricating, 6-L-19
       E. D. Ropp, Insulating, 1-G-14
       H. A. Daerr, Winding, 3-CR-4
```

A number of our employees have been injured lately from being run down by the trucks which make up a part of our shop transportation system. In some cases, of course, these accidents have resulted from carelessness on the part of the injured persons, but we have a number of sharp corners where it is impossible for our employees to see the trucks until they are nearly upon them. In order to lower the accident rate within the shop, I now ask that mirrors be hung at these blind corners in such a way as to enable both the trucker and the worker who is on foot to see the condition around the corner.

Your cooperation will be appreciated.

                              E. C. Kaiser, Vice-President

                              E. L. Grosser
                              _____

                              E. L. Grosser

ELG:jfm

A good example of general orders is this letter.

CRESCENT

General Sales Dept. Letter 872

Date: March 24, 19--

To: Entire SD List

From: F. P. Bergman
Location: Akron Plant

Subject: TOOL STEEL GRADE CODES

All Tool Steel grade codes will be changed during the Year 19--.
Aside from providing more accurate descriptions of grades in
question, these refinements will result in better inventory
control, a direct savings to the Company.

The first such change became effective January 1, 19--, and
covered all REX High Speed Steel Grades--the 1100 and 1700
series. This change will cover all nonHigh Speed Grades and
will complete the grade code change-over--series 1300, 1400,
1500, 1600, and 1700.

Please note that the code book changes now show grade, temper,
carbon range, and whether the grade is standard or nonstandard.
Future inquiries and orders should show grade code, grade name
and carbon range. These changes make current tapes obsolete.
New tapes should be generated for mill business after April 1,
19--.

Open orders will be changed by the Tool Steel Sales Division,
Bethel Plant, Chicago.

Please refer questions concerning this subject to Mr. William
K. Butler, Tool Steel Division, Bethel Plant.

F. P. Bergman
Director of Sales

/ef

The full block form is most efficient for this type of internal letter,
for every line begins at the left-hand margin, including beginnings of
paragraphs. The handwritten signature would be placed above the
typewritten signature, as in a letter going outside the plant. Only the

stenographer's initials are given in the stenographic reference. Because offices have to send many internal communications each day, this form helps speed output.

Letter of Invitation

During a technical person's career he is called on to write a few types of letter that are not strictly technical in content, yet they are the kind that an educated person should know how to compose. One of these is the letter of invitation.

The commonest example of this type is the letter which invites someone to a function—perhaps to address a meeting, as in this illustration.

GASPE ELECTRIC COMPANY
Ogden, Utah

March 1, 19--

Mr. Frank Catalano, Director
Electrical Research Institute
1956 Arroyo Boulevard
Los Angeles 24, California

Dear Mr. Catalano:

The Ogden Branch of the Institute of Electrical and Electronic Engineers has been fortunate in having a number of outstanding speakers address the members. Some of these speakers have been distinguished researchers in electrical engineering. Your recent paper on "The Monorail--Answer to Cities' Transportation Problems" has drawn a number of interested comments from our members. If you could come to Ogden to speak to our group, we would be honored to have you.

We hope you will develop some aspect of transportation problems in cities, but if you prefer to speak on some other topic please feel at liberty to exercise your preference.

We should like you to choose which of the following dates will suit your schedule: September 8, 15, or 22. Our meetings are held in the Union Club at noon. Luncheon is served before the program begins, and the meeting always ends by 2 p.m. If you talk for 20 or 30 minutes, you will then have a little time left for audience discussion. Our average attendance is approximately 100.

Frank Catalano, Director   -2-   March, 1, 19--

     We shall be happy to offer you an honorarium of \$150 and expenses. If you will let me know the time and place of your arrival, I will meet you and escort you to the Club.

     Can you let me know within ten days whether you can accept this engagement and which date will suit you?

                   Very truly yours,

                   Frank T. Bates

                   Frank T. Bates, Secretary

FTB:tp

     In trying to persuade someone to accept a speaking engagement, use a little deft flattery. Mr. Bates has done this by implying that Mr. Catalano should consider himself one of the outstanding persons mentioned. He stresses what an honor it will be to have this speaker. Further, he mentions why the members would like to hear Mr. Catalano and cites one of his articles. These references should gratify the prospective speaker.

     Few speakers like to be invited to address a meeting without having a definite idea of what they are supposed to talk about. Mr. Catalano is asked to speak on a specific subject, one related to his special interests.

     It is most important to give the speaker such necessary details as the date of the meeting, the place, the time, the expected length of the talk, and the approximate size of the audience. If possible, add some information about the interests of the audience and their age level. So often, details of this sort are neglected.

     If your organization cannot afford an honorarium, let the speaker know so that, if he has a policy to speak only for a fee, he can decline graciously. Organizations incur the ill will of speakers if those speakers accept invitations to lecture with the idea that they will be paid for their efforts and afterward get nothing. Even though some organizations cannot afford to pay speakers, lecturers of national importance are sometimes willing to talk without a fee to people who have a community of interests with them.

     It is wise to provide for the acceptance or rejection of the invitation by setting a specific time limit in which the invited guest should notify the organization. If the limit is set well in advance of the actual speaking date, the person responsible for the program can try to get another speaker.

A well-planned letter of invitation should:

1. Use some device to make the addressee eager to accept.
2. Extend the invitation and either name the subject of the talk or suggest the general area of audience interest.
3. Indicate the place, the date, and the time of the meeting, the size and type of audience, and whether the speaker will be offered a fee.
4. Offer to meet the speaker and make arrangements for his entertainment.
5. Name a time limit within which an answer will be accepted in order that another speaker may be obtained if the first invitation is declined.

Letter of Congratulation

When a fellow worker receives a promotion, a special honor, or some other distinction, the occasion calls for congratulation. If the individual thus honored cannot be complimented personally, a letter of congratulation should be written.

Provided that the writer is sincere, a note of congratulation brings lasting pleasure to the addressee. Most of us know and admire men whose achievements are outstanding. We are glad to hear of their success and sincerely want them to advance even further. What we say to them on paper will be appreciated.

Notes of appreciation should be kept short. A few well-chosen remarks are better than fulsome praise. The note below accomplishes its aim in a few sentences.

AMERICAN CHAIN & CABLE CO., INC.
Des Moines 14, Iowa

December 10, 19--

Mr. Lawrence Monet
Aluminum Research Laboratories
New Kensington, Pennsylvania

Dear Mr. Monet:

I have been much interested in your recent paper, "Column Strength of Various Aluminum Alloys." The tests which you have devised will be the basis for future work on column studies.

Lawrence Monet   -2-   December 10, 19--

    You certainly deserve the recent award given you for this
and previous studies. The Aluminum Company of America has
fittingly recognized your significant contributions to research
in an important field.

    Please accept my sincere congratulations and best wishes
for continued success.

                                    Sincerely yours,

                                    Harvey S. Rankin

                                    Harvey S. Rankin
                                    Vice-President

HSR:st

    Mr. Rankin's letter has the proper delicacy and precision of phrase
needed to convey his sincere feelings about the paper and the award.
He has avoided overdoing his praise. A letter of congratulation gains
by understatement rather than overstatement of the writer's feelings.
    The following example illustrates the tone of a sincere letter dealing
with a fellow worker's promotion.

                                            October 15, 19--

Dear John,

    I was pleasantly surprised to hear that you have been
promoted to Vice-President in charge of Public Relations.
Congratulations! Your past record with our company certainly
merits this deserved recognition.

    All good wishes.

                                    Cordially,

                                    Ed

855 Elmhurst Road
Lebanon, Pennsylvania

    This letter represents a more informal style than that used for
regular business correspondence. The writer is obviously a close
friend, for he uses "John" in the salutation and closes the note "Cor-

dially." He uses only his own first name in the signature, and places his address in the lower left-hand corner of the sheet. Many individuals would write such a note by hand, but today the arbiters of etiquette would also approve a typewritten note.

The letter of congratulation demands that:

1. The writer be sincere.
2. The letter be short and concisely phrased.
3. The letter be specific but not profuse in its compliments.

Letter of Application

If you have not as yet begun your working career, an important letter for you is the letter of application. If you have had considerable experience, you may wish to change your job at some future time. Again, the letter of application will play a part in getting you another position.

A letter of application will not of itself get you the job you want; but it will, if it is competently written, secure an interview with the personnel director of the company in which you are interested. Knowledge of how to write this letter is important.

If you are inexperienced, to whom should you direct the letter of application? In almost all large corporations letters of this type are addressed to the personnel director, whereas in small companies they are often sent to the individual most concerned. The large corporation generally makes it a rule that no hiring may be done except in the personnel office, although the personnel director is usually quite willing to take recommendations from men in responsible positions within the organization. If, when you are making application for your first job, you know some member of the firm, his recommendation to the personnel director will often help you.

Once you have determined to whom you should write, you are faced with a number of questions. What should you write? Should you include specific information about yourself in the letter, or should you give details in a data sheet and send it with a covering letter? How much should you say about your education? your extracurricular activities? your experience? Should you mention salary expected, or should you leave this matter for the interview?

Before answering these questions, let us examine a letter of application sent by a technical student to Mr. Henry W. Fisher, the personnel director of the Ames Turbine Company.

Letter of Application by a Nonexperienced Person

---

187 Spring Street
Chicago 16, Illinois
April 16, 19--

Mr. Henry W. Fisher
Personnel Manager
Ames Turbine Company
Montgomery 10, Alabama

Dear Mr. Fisher:

During the December meeting of the American Society of
Mechanical Engineers, you told Dean T. E. Holbrook, of the
Illinois Institute of Technology, that the Ames Turbine Company
might have openings for a limited number of young engineers this
summer. Since I expect to receive my bachelor's degree in June,
I should appreciate being considered for one of these positions.

As you will notice from the enclosed data sheet, I am
especially interested in steam generating plants and turbines
and in problems connected with power engineering. You might like
to know that during the past year I took all my elective courses
in this field and wrote my thesis on a problem allied with it.

My extracurricular activities in the Society and my part-
time work have taught me much about human relations. In addition,
my rank as master sergeant in the Air Force gave me responsibilities which I was able to carry successfully.

Should you wish me to come to Montgomery for an interview,
my professors have assured me that I can do so at your convenience.

Respectfully yours,

Charles N. Dailey

Charles N. Dailey

Enclosure

PERSONAL RECORD SHEET

of

Charles Norton Dailey
187 Spring Street
Chicago 16, Illinois

April 16, 19--   Telephone: EV 2-1673

Personal Data

Age: 24   Unmarried
Height: 5 ft. 8 in.   Nationality: American
Weight: 145 lbs.   Thirty months of
Health: Excellent   military service

Education

Will be graduated with the degree of Bachelor of Science in
Mechanical Engineering from the Illinois Institute of
Technology, Chicago, Illinois, in June, 1962.

Standing in class: in the upper fifth of a class of 182.

Extracurricular activities[1]

Member of Student Council, the governing body for all students
    in the Institute.

Reporter for Tech News, student newspaper.

Member of Sigma Tau, national honorary engineering fraternity.

Special Interests

Steam generating plants and turbines.

Senior thesis: "An Investigation of the Steam Losses Through
                       Various Types of Insulating Materials."

[1] The registrar of one of our large midwestern universities inquired of the
seventy-five largest corporations in the country what they looked for in students
about to be graduated from college; students whom they might wish to hire. In
declining order of importance, they wanted:
    a. Personality
    b. Extracurricular activities
    c. A satisfactory academic record
    d. Competence in a given field

Personal Record Sheet   -2-   April 16, 19--

Experience

September, 1960 to date	Gasoline attendant for Sun Oil Company. This part-time work brought me into contact with various types of people and taught me how to appreciate the customer's point of view.
January, 1959 to September, 1960	Night watchman for the Dow Chemical Company. While I worked for this company, I had the chance to prove my dependability.
June, 1956 to December, 1958	Worked up through the ranks to Master Sergeant, USAF. My military experience taught me the need for discipline, trained me to handle men, and showed me how to assume responsibility.

References

I have permission to use the following references:

Professor E. T. Deakin, Head
Department of Mechanical Engineering
Illinois Institute of Technology
Chicago 16, Illinois

Dean T. E. Holbrook
Illinois Institute of Technology
Chicago 16, Illinois

Mr. A. P. James
Personnel Director
Sun Oil Company
Chicago 7, Illinois

Major W. H. Christian
Missile & Space Systems Division
Douglas Aircraft Company, Inc.
Santa Monica, California

Date of Availability

Any time after June 15, 1962.

This letter handles the problem competently. The young man demonstrates that he knows the mechanics of a good business letter. Further, he has not used the stationery of the Sun Oil Company, for which he is still working. He recognizes that plain white paper of a good quality (20- or 24-pound bond) is preferable for the letter of application.

The letter is carefully planned. The first paragraph mentions the reason for writing, names the source of the writer's information about the job, and gives the writer's application for the opening. (Incidentally, many applicants forget to apply formally for a position when they write.) The use of Dean Holbrook's name is an advantage because Mr. Fisher has known the Dean for a long time.

Paragraphs 2 and 3 are the most important sections of the letter. They call attention to the data sheet and try to sell Dailey's personal services. The paragraphs also help to obtain the interview because they mention not only his interest and abilities in engineering but also his extracurricular activities, his military experience, and his personal qualities. His self-appraisal indicates that he has a proper degree of self-confidence but not an undue amount of egotism.

The self-appraisal should include statements about the writer's major field of interest. A corporation realizes that it will get more efficient and more worthy service from its employees if it places them in positions where they can best use their training and education. What a man enjoys doing is what he does best. Personnel men know this and will try to place each applicant to the greatest advantage.

Dailey's letter exhibits another good quality. He avoids the negative suggestion that he lacks work experience in his major field. Instead, he makes the most of his extracurricular work at the Institute, as well as his military rank and its implication. Positive factors like these should be emphasized.

Dailey's enclosure is a personal data sheet. These data are arranged under headings that are self-explanatory, such as "Personal Data," "Experience," etc., and each is underlined. If the personnel director wanted only to survey Dailey's education and experience, he could pick out those headings at a glance. The personal data most needed are age, height, weight, marital status, draft status, and health. Unless you are asked for information about your religion, salary expected, or lodge memberships, omit it. Membership in professional societies should be included.

The second heading, "Education," is a section with which the technical man just being graduated should be most concerned. It is unlikely that he will have much work experience to offer his prospective employer. He should therefore include any honors he has won in college, any extracurricular activities that have given him valuable experience, his approximate class standing (if it reveals him to be a good student), and any other information that would interest a personnel director.

Under "Experience," the writer should include in chronological sequence (from the most recent to the most remote in time) any summer jobs he has had or any work he has carried on during his school terms. All the "References" should have been asked whether they would be willing to recommend him. Usually three to five references are enough, unless the prospective employer asks for a stated number. These references should be persons of some standing in their professions. Their names and titles should be written exactly.

The last heading, the statement of availability, lets the prospective employer know when he may reasonably expect the applicant to go to work if it is decided to employ him.

Dailey's letter has done everything which an effective letter of application should do. It has aimed to sell the applicant's services to the prospective employer. It has answered the questions raised when the section of this chapter dealing with the letter of application was first introduced (page 85). Its plan could be set forth as follows:

I. Introductory paragraph
   A. Source of information about the position
   B. Formal application for the position. (If you are applying for a specific position, name it: chemical engineer with stainless steel production experience, laboratory technician in physics, registered pharmacist, etc.)
II. Body of the letter: selling the writer's services
   A. Reference to enclosed data sheet
   B. Amplification of two or more points which will best sell the applicant's services
   C. Consideration throughout of the employer's needs
III. Concluding paragraph
   A. Request for an interview, if this would be physically possible.
   B. Naming of times when the applicant is free, subject to the convenience of the employer.

Letter of Application by an Experienced Person

Letters of application written by men with technical and professional experience have to follow a slightly different pattern, although the essential elements are the same. Mr. Uhl's letter, below, illustrates this difference.

                                         322 Rheims Avenue
                                         Columbia, Missouri
                                         April 14, 19--

Mr. J. E. Shaffer
Supervisor, Personnel Department
Byers Steel Pipe Corporation
Ambridge, Pennsylvania

Dear Mr. Shaffer:

   Mr. E. T. Phelps, field engineer for your corporation, was
passing through Columbia recently and called to see me. During
our conversation he told me that the present Superintendent
of your powerhouse was being retired, and suggested that I
might like to apply for the position. Since I have been interested
in this type of opening for a long time, I would like to have the
opportunity to become associated with the Byers Steel Pipe
Corporation. Please consider this letter as my formal application.

   Although I have enjoyed working as Assistant Superintendent for the Columbia Gas and Electric Company, I have few prospects
for advancement here. The present superintendent is only three
years older than I, his work for the company is most satisfactory,
and his family ties will probably keep him in Columbia.

   From glancing through my experience record on the enclosed data sheet, you will observe that I have held several
positions of responsibility. These have all had to do with
the supplying of electric power; therefore I feel myself
conversant with the problems of electrical distribution.
This experience should fit me to undertake the operation of your
powerhouse.

   If you are interested in my qualifications, I shall be
pleased to come to Ambridge for an interview, at which time you
can judge my fitness for the position.

                                  Very truly yours,

                                  Robert F. Uhl

                                  Robert F. Uhl
                                  Assistant Superintendent
                                  COLUMBIA GAS AND
                                  ELECTRIC COMPANY

RFU:tv
Enclosure

PERSONAL RECORD SHEET

of

April 14, 19--   Robert Findlay Uhl   Business
                      322 Rheims Avenue   Telephone: 341-2200
                      Columbia, Missouri   Residence
                                            Telephone: 266-5861

Personal Data

Age: 42   Married: three children
Height: 5 ft. 10 in.   Nationality: American
Weight: 175 lbs.
Health: Excellent

Education:

Graduated with honors from Massachusetts Institute of
Technology, with the degree of Bachelor of Science in
Electrical Engineering, 1938.

Master of Science, The Pennsylvania State University, 1944.

Experience:

February, 1948   Assistant Superintendent in Charge of New In-
     to   stallations, Columbia Gas and Electric Company,
    date   Columbia, Missouri.

                  This position involves the supervision of the
                  installation of new generating equipment in the
                  hydro-electric station at the Cold River Dam.
                  In addition, I have charge of all minor installa-
                  tions to be made by the company. At the present
                  time I have seventy-five employees under my
                  direction.

July, 1944   Superintendent of Electrical Equipment, Louis-
     to   ville Coal and Coke Company, Louisville,
February, 1948   Kentucky.

                  I had charge of all installations of electrical
                  equipment. I was required also to oversee repairs
                  made on major items of equipment and to make
                  recommendations on purchases. As a result of a
                  survey which I made, the company decided on more
                  extensive electrification.

Personal Record Sheet   -2-   April 14, 19--

        This position was considered necessary to the
defense effort in World War II.

July, 1942   During this period, I was a graduate student at
    to   The Pennsylvania State University and was work-
July, 1944   ing for the Master of Science degree.

July, 1940   Foreman in charge of Wilkinsburg Substation,
    to   Duke Light Corporation, Pittsburgh, Pennsylvania.
July, 1942

        I was responsible for power production and trans-
mission to the Wilkinsburg-Edgewood circuits
of the Duke Light Corporation. I also had
charge of the maintenance of alternators and
other equipment in the substation. I had twelve
men under me.

June, 1938   Lineman, Union Gas and Electric Company, Boston,
    to   Massachusetts.
July, 1940

        I worked as a lineman for this company for two
years. There were no supervisory duties connected with this job.

References

    I have permission to use the following names as references:

        Mr. E. H. McCafferty, Superintendent
        Columbia Gas and Electric Company
        Columbia, Missouri

        Mr. Joseph F. Coffield, President
        Louisville Coal and Coke Company
        Louisville, Kentucky

        Professor Robert C. Gorham
        Department of Electrical Engineering
        The Pennsylvania State University
        University Park, Pennsylvania

        Charles H. Schultheis
        Algonac Research Laboratories
        Columbia, Missouri

Date of Availability

    I shall have to give my present employer at least two months'
notice.

The emphasis in Uhl's letter is on what the writer believes to be his best selling point—his experience. Although he has an excellent educational background, which includes a master's degree in science, his practical qualifications are represented by his successful industrial experience. He has worked for the Union Gas and Electric in a less important capacity than for any of the other companies; hence he lists his references from those concerns which have known him as a supervisor rather than as a power line worker. He includes in the data sheet his experience with the Union Gas and Electric, for it indicates that he is acquainted with the actualities of power line transmission rather than merely knowing them academically. The emphasis in the "Experience" portion of the data sheet is on the fact that Uhl is ready for a position of some responsibility.

INTERVIEWS

You may wonder why the letters of application to this point have not mentioned salary. The reason is that the letter of application is not intended to secure a job for the writer. Its main effort is on getting an interview. During the interview the candidate can get salary information. This is also the time to get a precise idea of the duties expected of the employee, the working hours, what may reasonably be looked forward to in advancement and salary increments. It is in this interview that the applicant's personal appearance, speech, and alertness are evaluated.

The chapter on speech outlines the preparation necessary for the interview. At this point, however, it may be stressed that every applicant should anticipate the types of questions he may be asked. He should have his answers ready.

Sometimes an interview is supplemented by a series of tests. A reproduction of the final score sheet of a representative test is shown on the opposite page.

This sheet is to some extent self-explanatory. The Otis test indicates the technical man's ability to secure information from printed sources; mechanical comprehension (the Bennett test) is a test which determines the understanding of mechanical devices; aptitudes for learning are measured by the Minnesota test, and the mathematical training and ability of the applicant are gaged by the test in mathematics.

The personality inventory shows under "Stability" whether the individual being tested has those qualities which will enable him

Ability
    Otis (Mental Ability) 94.3
    Bennett (Mechanical Comprehension) 89.0
    Minnesota (Aptitude) 88.0
    Mathematics 91.0

Personality Inventory
    Stability 93.0
    Self-sufficiency 70.5
    Dominance 62.0

Vocational Interests in relation to successful practicing
    Engineers 79.5
    Production Managers 68.0
    Personnel Managers 83.0*

---

* These figures represent deviation from median. Fifty is the average score of persons who have previously taken the tests.

---

to withstand sudden changes in circumstances without losing his mental equilibrium. In testing for self-sufficiency, the aim is to find whether the applicant can carry out his own plans. Dominance indicates his control over others; but any experienced personnel man will tell you that if the dominance value on a personality chart is too high, the individual being tested is not likely to succeed in any work which requires close cooperation with his fellows, as such a person is too certain of the correctness of his own views.

The vocational interests indicate how well the applicant will compete with other successful men in the same field.

Although tests of this kind are widely used, they are by no means the determining factor in the acceptance or rejection of the applicant. The effect of his personality on the interviewer is important.

Some applicants, however, never have the opportunity to take the tests or to have the interview. Their letters disqualify them. Since letters of application are screened several times by employers and personnel men to eliminate those written by the obviously unfit, such a letter as that on page 96 would be thrown out at the first screening.

On one piece of evidence alone—the tone of the letter—any employer would refuse to consider Ertman as an applicant for a responsible position. To test whether you have assimilated the principles underlying first-class letters, go through Mr. Ertman's letter to find

PHI NU PSI
397 South Advent Avenue, Mauch Chunk
Idaho

July 2, 19--

Mr. James A. Lowry, Personnel Director,
Iowa Agricultural Cooperatives
Des Moines, Iowa

Dear Sir,

I am just out of college and looking for a job. Therefore,
I request you to consider my following qualifications.

Although I have not had any experience in your line of work,
I feel that I can handle almost any assignment in the field of
agricultural engineering because I have been a Student at Mauch
Chunk Agricultural and Mechanical Institute, majoring in
agricultural engineering, for the past four years. My college
training has been good. I have taken courses in Physics, Chemistry, College algebra, differential and integral calculus,
soil analysis, farm machines, and many other courses pertaining
to the field of Agricultural Engineering.

My experience has been limited, but not more so than most
young graduates. In the summer of 1959 I worked for the Superior
Foundries. They were pleased with what I did, and I hope will be
glad to recommend me. In the summers of 1960 and 1961 I was
visiting in Chicago and got a job with Allis-Chalmers. I spent
the next summer helping my professor of soil analysis equip a new
laboratory in Mauch Chunk Institute. He commended me for my
industry.

In view of my training and experience, I feel that I would
be justified in asking a beginning salary of $6500 a year. I might
be willing to take less after I have talked with you.

I can be reached any day in the week at 621-9374, as I am
staying with my cousin.

Hoping for an early reply, I am

Cordially yours,

Charles R. Ertman

out what he has done wrong and to suggest how the letter can be improved.

Fortunately, few technical men would write such a letter as this. They would analyze their abilities and make a direct sales appeal to the employer. The letter on page 98, which answers an advertisement in a technical journal, illustrates such an analysis and sales appeal.

Solicited Letter of Application

In answer to an advertisement in *Industrial Engineering*, the applicant, Mr. Brennan, makes the most of his training and experience. Writing to the prospective employer, he takes care to observe a procedure that will satisfy every item asked of him in the advertisement.

INDUSTRIAL ENGINEER

Wanted: industrial engineer, under 30, familiar with general shop practices and capable of organizing a shop transportation system. Write, giving education, experience, and references, to R. E. Grant, President, The Garrett Corporation, 1976 Ellison Avenue, Firman, North Dakota.

First, Brennan has to read the advertisement carefully, noting down each required item. He is not yet thirty, so he satisfies the age requirement; he is a graduate in industrial engineering; he has had practical experience in shop practice and the organization of transportation systems; therefore he is applying for a position for which he knows he is capable. Having noted all the requirements set forth in the advertisement, he lays out his data sheet, being sure to stress those aspects of his education and experience which show him to be a qualified man. His most difficult step is to analyze his abilities and training so that he can prepare the data sheet to buttress the points by which he will sell his services in the accompanying letter. The letter and the data sheet he composed are on the following page.

The three effective letters which have been discussed all have one purpose. They aim to get the applicant an interview, not a job. Once a technical man gets in the personnel office of a corporation, it is

3740 Decatur Street
Chicago 18, Illinois
April 10, 19--

Mr. R. E. Grant, President
The Garrett Corporation
1976 Ellison Avenue
Firman, North Dakota

Dear Mr. Grant:

In the April issue of INDUSTRIAL ENGINEERING, your corporation advertised for a junior industrial engineer who could organize a shop transportation system. Since my training and experience fit me for this type of work, I should appreciate being considered for the opening.

While I was a student in Duke University, Durham, North Carolina, I was given thorough training in industrial engineering. The curriculum emphasized proficiency in mechanical drawing and layout, as well as courses in such fields as time and motion study, corporation organization, production equipment, labor relations, and wage plans. Because I realized that an engineer must have a broad knowledge of other matters than purely scientific studies, I elected several courses in economics, political science and English. These have helped me to appreciate contemporary problems.

In the enclosed data sheet I have indicated that I am at present employed by the Chicago Interurban Railways. Although the position has taught me a great deal, it offers advancement only through the retirement or death of my superior. The work has nevertheless improved my understanding of industrial problems and has made me exercise my ingenuity; consequently, I can apply this added knowledge to the problems of your company.

If you would care to have me come to Firman for an interview, I would appreciate your setting the date for such a meeting somewhat in advance, as I must make arrangements for absence from the office.

Very sincerely yours,

Frederick P. Brennan

Frederick P. Brennan

Enclosure

PERSONAL RECORD SHEET

of

Frederick P. Brennan
3740 Decatur Street
Chicago 18, Illinois

April 10, 19--   Business telephone:
                                        313-1300
                                        Residence telephone:
                                        241-1893

Personal data

    Age: 28   Unmarried
    Height: 6 ft.   Free to travel
    Weight: 190 lbs.   American
    Health: Excellent

Education

    Graduate of Duke University, Durham, North Carolina, with
the degree of Bachelor of Science in Industrial Engineering.

    Night School training, Downtown Branch, Northwestern
University, leading toward the Master of Science degree.

Experience

August, 1957   Assistant engineer, Time and Motion Study
  to date   Department, Chicago Interurban Railways,
                    Chicago, Illinois. This position requires me
                    to make time and motion studies in the shops. It
                    also carries the supervisory responsibilities
                    for the shop transportation system.

September, 1954   Student, Duke University, Durham, North Caro-
    to   lina. Graduated with the Bachelor of Science
June, 1957   degree in Industrial Engineering, June, 1957.

June, 1953   Private first class, United States Army Signal
    to   Corps.
August, 1954

September, 1952   Student, Duke University, Durham, North Caro-
    to   lina.
June, 1953

<u>References</u>

I have permission to use the following names as references:

Professor F. N. Beauregard
Department of Industrial Engineering
Duke University
Durham, North Carolina

Mr. M. F. McVey, Industrial Engineer
Time and Motion Study Department
Chicago Interurban Railways
Chicago 23, Illinois

Mr. E. F. Adams
Vice-President in Charge of Personnel
Chicago Interurban Railways
Chicago 23, Illinois

Professor F. B. Stanihurst, Head
Industrial Engineering Department
Northwestern University, Evening Division
Chicago 11, Illinois

<u>Date of Availability</u>

My present employer should be given one month's notice.

---

then his problem to sell himself.[2] The three letters also aim to make the addressee feel that the applicant:

1. Is neat and precise in the use of letter forms.
2. Can analyze what his education and experience have done to fit him for the job.
3. Knows how to appraise his personal qualities and potentialities.
4. Keeps the needs of the reader in mind by using the *you* rather than the *I* point of view.
5. Has been successful enough to have others think well of him.
6. *Understands how to sell his personal services.*

If a technical man can do these things, he has a good chance of getting the job he wants.

[2] See pages 346–349 for an example of the technique of the interview.

Letter of Refusal

After he has had his interview and has been offered a position, he must either accept it or reject it promptly. Accepting a position is relatively easy. Refusing it is the more difficult task. Notice how Brennan wrote his letter of refusal.

The tone of his letter is pleasant. Brennan has stated the main reason for his refusal of the job in a polite but concise way. He does not waste Mr. Grant's time by making a too detailed analysis of his reasons; yet he is specific. As an added touch, he expresses his appreciation of the considerate treatment he has received. Such a letter should make a favorable impression on any recipient.

When the technical man has occasion to draft a letter of refusal, he should remember to write pleasantly to the man who has offered him a job, to give specific but not too detailed reasons for the refusal, and to make the entire tone of the letter sincere and cordial.

The following letter, written by Mr. Brennan, centers its refusal around the offer of a promotion by the Chicago Interurban Railways. Since it is clear to Mr. Grant that Brennan had not used the offer of a position by the Garrett Corporation merely as a means to obtain an advancement within the Railways company, his refusal is logical and acceptable.

                                              3740 Decatur Street
                                              Chicago 18, Illinois
                                              April 28, 19--

Mr. R. E. Grant, President
The Garrett Corporation
1976 Ellison Avenue
Firman, North Dakota

Dear Mr. Grant:

As a result of our interview of April 20, you were kind enough to offer me the position of junior industrial engineer.

For the past few days I have given the matter serious consideration. Since talking with you, however, I have been offered a promotion by the Chicago Interurban Railways. This resulted from the resignation of Mr. J. N. Nugent, my immediate superior. I have also been assured of future advancement by the officials of the company. Because of this unforeseen change in my status, it will be to my advantage to stay in Chicago.

R. E. Grant, President   -2-   April 28, 19--

    I enjoyed talking with you while I was in Firman, and carried away with me pleasant memories of your courtesy.

Very sincerely yours,

Frederick P. Brennan

Frederick P. Brennan

Letter of Acceptance

Since the Garrett Corporation had to have an industrial engineer as soon as possible, Mr. Grant interviewed Herbert Manwiller and offered him the position. His letter was simpler to write than was Mr. Brennan's, for it is easier to accept a position graciously than to reject one diplomatically. Refusals are so likely to offend employers that the greatest tact must be exercised. Letters of acceptance, on the other hand, may be too profuse in expressions of gratitude.

1263 Maple Avenue
Iowa City, Iowa
May 8, 19--

Mr. R. E. Grant, President
The Garrett Corporation
1976 Ellison Avenue
Firman, North Dakota

Dear Mr. Grant:

    It was pleasant to meet you on May 4 and to talk over with you the problems connected with the organization of your shop transportation system as well as the duties of the junior industrial engineer. I appreciate your offer, which I received in this morning's mail.

    I am glad to accept the position and I shall do my best to prove myself a progressive employee. As you suggest, I shall plan to be in Firman on Friday, May 21, so that I can take up my duties the following Monday.

    You were kind enough to give me all the information I need at present. If there is anything further, will you address me here until May 20, when I shall leave my present position?

Very sincerely yours,

Herbert Manwiller

Herbert Manwiller

In writing this letter, Mr. Manwiller no doubt found that one of the most difficult things to do was to make the tone not too subservient. After all, he had much to offer the Garrett Corporation. Yet he did want to say that he was glad to work for them. Keeping a balance between subserviency and proper self-evaluation is the real achievement of the letter. Manwiller also maintains the *you* point of view, even though, of necessity, he has to refer to himself throughout the letter.

First of all, he had to phrase a statement of pleasure about the interview he had had in Firman. He realized, too, that he ought to express his appreciation for the offer. He wanted, he knew, to accept the position and give a date when he could report for work.

Letters of application and letters of acceptance and refusal are difficult to terminate. Often the writer, finding no convenient way to stop, is inclined to say too much. No letter of acceptance, for instance, need be longer than Manwiller's, which runs a little over a hundred words. A subtle compliment to the reader (as Brennan's "I . . . carried away with me pleasant memories of your courtesy") or the giving of pertinent information of special use to the reader (as ". . . will you address me here until May 20, when I shall leave my present position") form convenient ways to conclude. In every circumstance, the technical man must exercise his common sense in deciding what the ending should be.

Summary

The types of letters treated in this chapter are those which most technical people use often. The letter of inquiry is one means of obtaining necessary information from other individuals and companies. The letter of quotation gives customers vital data and prices about products or apparatus. The letter of instruction communicates important directions and procedures to those who have the responsibility of carrying out orders. As an introduction to a report, the letter of transmittal can frequently recommend reports to the attention of executives and can direct them to those sections of greatest interest. How equipment can suit a customer's needs is set forth in letters of sales recommendation, and defects in equipment or omissions in specifications are explained in letters of complaint. Knowing how to deal with complaints and to make equitable adjustments for customers requires both tact and discretion. The skilled writer must make the most of his knowledge of human relations, particularly if he has to refuse a customer's request. Most of all, however, technical people have to write interoffice and intershop communications. To take care of the amenities, now and then they may write letters of invitation or congratulation. At any stage of experience, they may have to write a letter of application and to accept or refuse the offer of a position. Without knowledge of how to write such letters, technical people would be handicapped in day-to-day business.

Discussion Questions

1. What qualities should an acceptable letter of inquiry have?
2. In a letter of inquiry, why is it advisable to explain what you will do with the information you are seeking?
3. Should a letter of quotation go into detail regarding a piece of apparatus or a product?
4. Why is it advisable to tabulate material in a letter of instruction?
5. Where is the letter of transmittal most commonly used, and to whom is a letter of transmittal most often addressed?
6. Why should an authorization be mentioned in the letter of transmittal?
7. In what ways can a good letter of sales recommendation foster satisfactory human relations?
8. Why should letters of complaint be handled speedily?
9. Why should courtesy be a primary consideration in the letter of complaint?
10. Cite a few situations that would require interoffice and intershop communications.
11. What matters should always be mentioned in a letter of invitation to a speaker?
12. Why should letters of congratulation be short and tend to understatement rather than overstatement?
13. Why are data sheets commonly used to accompany a letter of application?
14. If you were answering an advertisement of a position, what procedure would you follow?
15. What points would you be sure to cover in a letter of application if you were trying to get your first job?

Writing Assignments

Write the following letters:
  a. To E. N. Dugdale, Personnel Department, Birmingham Steel Corporation, Birmingham 4, Alabama, applying for a position as junior engineer. You have heard of this opening through E. N. Irish, a friend employed by the United States Steel Corporation.
  b. To E. S. Carlson, Consulting Engineer, 157 Fordham Building, Chicago 17, Illinois, asking him to examine Lot 1571 in Aurora, Illinois, to determine whether it will be a good location for a steam gage manufacturing plant.

c. To Paul R. Anderson, Superintendent, Oregon Timber and Construction Company, Talooka, Oregon, asking him for an adjustment on a shipment of defective 2-by-10-inch joists.

d. To R. N. Charlesworth, Vice-President, Vanadium Coal Company, Scripps Building, Philadelphia 16, Pennsylvania, telling him that you have examined his ground in Warren County, Pennsylvania, for iron ore and are enclosing a report. Mr. Charlesworth authorized you to do this work.

e. To Mr. E. C. Calkins, Foreman, Andover Power Company, Andover, Ohio, asking him for information on the amount of replacement necessary on the company's high tension lines.

f. To S. T. Jenkins, Jr., 273 Ridge Street, Cleveland 10, Ohio, instructing him how to determine the efficiency of a piece of apparatus.

g. To one of your instructors in a technical subject, sending him a letter of transmittal to cover a report you have written.

h. To E. J. Hemingway, Director, Akron Research Laboratories, Akron, Ohio, asking him to speak to your technical society.

i. To X-243, NEW YORK TIMES, applying for a position advertised as follows:

INDUSTRIAL ENGINEER
Experienced in time study and wage incentive application. Write stating age, qualifications, and other pertinent information.

j. To Mr. N. F. MacInerny, Superintendent, Electrical Department, Kaiser Shipyards, Tacoma, Washington, refusing his offer of employment as junior engineer. You have already had an interview with him.

4

The Formal Technical Report

Necessity for Formal Reports

Although reports vary widely in their subject matter, their intentions, their audiences, and their forms, they can generally be divided into two major types, formal and informal. Usually, you will be called upon to write many more informal reports than those of the formal kind. Reports upon any undertaking in industry and business call for information to be presented according to a definite plan. If you have spent three months working on some project for your employer, your report will show what you undertook to do, what you actually did, what conclusions you were able to come to, and what recommendations you made. With such a large body of material as would probably result from so lengthy an investigation, an organizational plan to guide the writer is a necessity. In any report, firm organization of ideas is a valuable first step in the preparation to write.

Form of the Report

If we may assume that you are obligated to transmit a large body of information to the officer of the company to whom you report, you will find it advantageous to lay out in your mind the order of the parts of the report. Although usages differ somewhat from company to company, the formal report will generally be found to consist of the following major parts:

1. The cover sheet
2. The title page
3. The table of contents
4. The foreword or letter of transmittal
5. A short, often nontechnical, summary or abstract
6. The body
   a. Purpose of the report (or introduction)
   b. Historical survey of the subject (if needed)

    c. Detailed analysis, giving all data necessary for a full under-
standing of the problem
7. Conclusions
8. Recommendations
9. Appendix
    a. Bibliography
    b. Charts, maps, graphs
    c. Supplementary mathematical data
    d. Other supplementary material

The items just given are not necessarily included in all reports. It is quite possible, for instance, that the nature of the work done was such that no recommendations would be essential; on the other hand, the report might stretch to such a length that it should include an index, so that minor items which would not have a place in the table of contents could be looked up with ease. Perhaps no supplementary mathematical data would be needed, yet, under the heading of "Other supplementary material," you might find it of value to include a large number of photomicrographs.

Nor is the suggested order of the parts an inflexible one. It is generally true that if you are asked to report on a project which has involved the time and effort of a dozen people for three or four months, you are likely to be in a position of some trust within your company. The executives who read your work will assume that you have done the laboratory experimentation adequately; what they will be concerned with will be your findings and the conclusions which these findings have enabled you to come to. To save such readers as these time and trouble, you may want to present your conclusions and recommendations in the early part of the report, perhaps immediately after the abstract or summary. In fact, some large American corporations require that conclusions and recommendations of major reports appear very early, before the body of the reports.

General Qualities of Formal Reports

As you may have inferred from the discussion regarding the usual order of formal reports, that order does not necessarily follow set rules, although some companies require a specific ordering of the parts of reports. In other words, fashions vary in reports as they do in women's clothes, although by no means so abruptly. For example, Julius Caesar wrote a lengthy and thoroughgoing report on his military campaigns in what is now France and Germany under the title *De*

Bello Gallico, a piece of writing that many of us suffered through when we took our second-year Latin. That it was an adequate report in its time is indisputable, but one may be sure that the officers of your company would not look with delight on your casting reports in the form which Caesar gave to his.

Different types of work to be reported on will require different management in the writing of the report. Different audiences for the information which the report carries will demand different treatment of the subject matter. If you must make a lengthy sales report, for example, it is apparent that your treatment of material must differ from that which you will use if you are making a statement of your findings in the laboratory. A report on the construction of a breeder reactor will necessarily differ in treatment from one dealing with the financial condition of your company. Yet in spite of such variables as these, the following characteristics are the ones likely to be found in any good formal report.

SINGLENESS OF PURPOSE

All reports have a central purpose; they must present an organized body of facts relating to a specific problem. Every idea, conclusion, recommendation, and illustration must center upon that problem. Extraneous thoughts, no matter how brilliant, should be excluded. As the reader goes through the report, he must be kept aware at all times of its dominant purpose.

CLARITY AND CONCISENESS OF EXPRESSION

A report that is clearly and concisely written creates in the reader's mind a favorable impression regarding the soundness of the work and reasoning which have gone into the report, and the reliability of the conclusions and recommendations. A report that is clumsily and wordily written, or that is ambiguous, suggests muddled thinking and casts doubt on the quality of the work and the ability of the writer.

COHERENCE OF ARRANGEMENTS

An effective report is so arranged that every part fits in with and leads toward the following parts. The reader must be made aware of the coordination of the parts. Repetition should be avoided, unless the writer feels that a preceding statement of fact necessary to a full understanding of the matter under discussion is so far removed that the average reader may well have forgotten it. The best way to ensure coherence is to follow a rigorous outline which has been thoroughly tested before the writing begins. (For a discussion of outline methods, see "Language Essentials," pages 267–270.)

TACTFUL PRESENTATION

1. Language. The technical writer must keep in mind those for whom the report is prepared. Their technical knowledge, their practical acquaintance with the problems involved, and their mastery of the specialized vocabulary must be gauged, and the report written in the language they can understand. It is easy for a technical man to become so well acquainted with a certain problem, its special terminology, and its special features that he forgets others do not possess this familiarity. They may become confused when reading a report full of technical or local terminology.

2. Evaluation of Existing Conditions. Many of the investigations conducted and reported on by technical men are written to improve existing procedures, facilities, and methods. Such studies may involve evaluating these, and the report may not be complimentary to their originators. In the wording of his report the technical writer must take pains not to use remarks that are undiplomatic, or which would reflect adversely on the persons responsible for the existing order of things. The truth, of course, is of supreme importance: facts must be given, but the expression of those facts should be couched in diplomatic and inoffensive language.

The opening statements of a report might read: "The finishing process for this product involves a method which is both obsolete and costly. The increase in annual production of this product from 1,000,000 to 5,000,000 tons forecast for the immediate future necessitated a critical review of the present process. Newly developed finishing equipment, manufactured by the ABC Company, was investigated to determine the feasibility of its use to cut manufacturing costs." The criticism implied in the opening sentence of this statement is not softened by the sentences immediately following which state that it is the increasing production demands which have made it necessary to examine the process critically. A more tactful and equally truthful approach would have omitted the first sentence entirely. It casts reflection on the man who originated the process.

One can never improve his own situation by depreciating the work of others.

JUDGMENT

The element of primary importance in report writing is judgment. The characteristics already mentioned touch on it but do not encompass it. Precise definitions of judgment are difficult, but the word includes the art of knowing what to say and what not to say, the ability to put oneself in the reader's place and speak his language, and the knack of handling cold facts persuasively and of coming to legitimate conclusions about them.

Poor judgment in writing the technical report will obscure the finest skills and the best of technical information and may render useless the most thorough investigation.

The Parts of the Formal Report

THE COVER SHEET

Although your actual writing process will follow a different order from that which we shall follow in this section, it will be convenient to examine the parts of the formal report in the order which the reader of such a report would observe. In practice, before you would write the abstract or summary, you would necessarily have written the body, the conclusions, and the recommendations. But when you put the different parts of the report together, they would probably appear in the order that we shall follow in the analysis of the components of the formal report.

Formal reports that are at all lengthy are likely to be bound in some type of folder to allow of their being filed in a library. Those which represent extensive studies and matters of considerable importance may be permanently bound. Decisions as to the type of binding are based on such varied considerations, however, that they cannot be taken up in such a text as this. Nevertheless, almost every report cover will give the following information:

1. The title of the report
2. The name of the author
3. The date of submission
4. The name of the company and the department to which the writer belongs
5. The number of the report (optional).

The example on page 114 [1] includes these and other pertinent points. In addition to such of these items as are applicable, student reports should carry the title of the course in which the report is submitted.

Some companies have found it advantageous to combine the cover and the title page of reports. The summary of the report should be easily accessible; hence, they have a definite space for this on the title page–cover sheet, as well as appropriate notations for the title of the report, its author, etc. The Dow Chemical Company title page– cover sheet is reproduced on pages 112–113.

THE TITLE PAGE

The title page should list the following information:

1. The title of the report, with any subheads that may be necessary
2. The name of the individual or company which has authorized the report, or if it is a student report, the name of the instructor to whom the report is addressed
3. The name of the writer of the report (if it is an industrial report, the name of the writer and his position within the company)
4. The date of submission
5. The report number (optional)

Since the title page should make a pleasing appearance, the writer should give considerable attention to proper spacing. It is a temptation to overfill a title page, just as it is to add too much advertising and informational material on a letterhead. A good deal of white space on the title page helps to improve its appearance. The National Tube report title page is an acceptable example (page 114).

THE TABLE OF CONTENTS

The table of contents indicates the major sections of the report and the pages where they may be found. It presupposes that the report will be accurately paginated and that the writer is capable of indicating sufficiently descriptive titles for the sections. Often subheads are needed under section heads, so that a reader can see how the major head is divided and is to be developed.

Sections are usually numbered in Roman numerals, with the pages in Arabic numbers. Introductory material is indicated by small Roman numbers (i, ii, iii, etc.). Subheads are indented under the section

[1] By permission of the United States Steel Corporation.
[2] Reproduced by permission of The Dow Chemical Co.

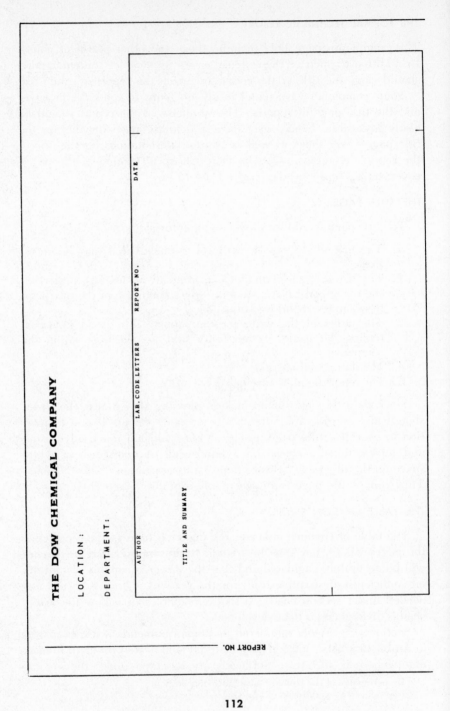

THE DOW CHEMICAL COMPANY

LOCATION:

DEPARTMENT:

AUTHOR   LAB. CODE LETTERS   REPORT NO.   DATE

TITLE AND SUMMARY

REPORT NO.

112

TYPE OF REPORT: _____ PAGES: _____

(e.g. INTERIM, SUMMARY, SERVICE, CALL, ETC.)

RESEARCH CLASSIFICATION: MATERIAL _____ USE _____ TYPE _____ STAGE _____ DISTRIBUTION _____

DISTRIBUTION: (* COMPLETE REPORT)

* MIDLAND CRI (3 Copies)
  EXECUTIVE RESEARCH

FOR USE OF DOW EMPLOYEES ONLY

113

NATIONAL TUBE

DIVISION

UNITED STATES STEEL CORPORATION

REPORT ON

THE USE OF OXYGEN IN THE BESSEMER CONVERTER

DATE: January 7, 19—

BY: W. T. Rogers, Research Engineer

REPORT No. 270

APPROVED BY: E. F. Ketterer

NATIONAL TUBE COMPANY — LORAIN WORKS

heads of which they are a part. The following example shows a representative table of contents.

TABLE OF CONTENTS

Some technical schools as well as some industries prefer to use a different type of outlining, the decimal method. (For this, see the chapter on language essentials, pages 267–270.) If the preceding table of contents were set up in this way, it would appear as follows:

THE LETTER OF TRANSMITTAL

This has been taken up in detail under "Types of Technical Letters," pages 67–70.

THE SUMMARY, ABSTRACT, AND SYNOPSIS

As the terms indicate, all three of these items are intended to give the major ideas of a given report or article in a highly shortened form. In general, the abstract is the one most commonly used in the report, and it is almost invariably shorter in length than either of the other two.

In addition to the fact that the abstract is an essential part of the formal report, there is another compelling reason for learning to write good abstracts of your own reports. Assume that you are executive vice-president in charge of development in a large corporation. It would be by no means unusual that on a given day you would receive twenty reports, each of which might present two or three hundred pages of reading. Unless you are uncommonly gifted, you cannot read four or five thousand pages of material in a day—certainly not if you are going to get much of anything else done. But if each report has a good abstract, you are immediately able, after reading it over, to decide who should deal further with each report, or whether the material contained in some of them is of such importance that you must examine it in detail yourself.

Very often, the abstract is the only part of a report read by high executive officers. If your report is one upon which you would like to have action taken, you must present your abstract well enough to attract attention at the level where it will do most good.

Remember that your major effort in writing an abstract is to bring together the primary ideas of the report in a minimum of words. You are immediately faced with the problem of determining what the important ideas are, and it is at this point that you begin to have trouble when you write your first abstract. You want the reader to follow your major points, but you are afraid that he will not fully grasp them unless you add certain details. After you have gone through this process of "feeling that it must be put down" several times, the abstract has grown so unwieldy that it may occupy 12 pages.

The simplest way to go about the preparation of an abstract is to make as concise an outline as possible of your paper. Then after you have made this concise outline, make it more concise. Say to yourself, "Does a reader have to understand subpoints 3, 4, and 5 to follow my major idea?" If your answer is an unqualified "Yes!" then you must include these subpoints in your abstract. But if it is instead, "Well, probably," then take them out.

Consider the following abstract of an article. Although its language is slightly technical, and perhaps in a field that is foreign to you, try to decide exactly what the article itself has as its major sense.

Eliminating the bran-weighing procedure and equipping a 5-gram micro-mill with a detachable hopper resulted in a 200% increase in the number of samples that can be evaluated for milling quality in a day, and significantly reduced operator fatigue.

For one trained in cereal chemistry, this abstract makes an exact, clear point; it is apparent that the writer is recommending the elimination of the procedure formerly used (bran weighing) in favor of a micromill with a detachable hopper. The abstract states the results achieved by the authors with this departure from the usual procedure. If one had a problem in the brewing or flour industry which stemmed from the inability of the laboratory to evaluate samples rapidly enough, he might well go on to read the article itself and discover in detail what the new process is.

A highly technical abstract is the following, reprinted from *The Review of Scientific Instruments* and written by D. S. Miller of the Research Laboratory of the United States Steel Corporation of Delaware. Its technical language can be understood clearly only by persons who are working in the field.

A RECORDING TORQUE MAGNETOMETER

This instrument produces, automatically, a curve of torque *versus* angle of orientation for a thin iron or steel disk in a strong magnetic field. A resistance strain gauge converts the torque acting on the disk specimen to a small d.c. voltage, which is recorded on a "strip-chart" recording potentiometer. The specimen is rotated in synchronism with the translation of the chart paper, both being driven by synchronous motors. A torque curve is completed in six minutes.

An abstract which has been written for the general reader is reproduced below. In this the author has tried to avoid bringing in technical terms because the abstract must be read by the average stockholder of the railroad company which is considering installing a new type of safety device on its locomotives.

The safety factor in the operation of trains can now be increased, not only by a system of cab signals which tell the engineman when to reduce speed and when to stop, but also by an automatic method of applying brakes if the engineer and the fireman fail to notice the display of the cab signal. Not only can the entire train be brought to a stop without any action on the part of the train crew, but its speed can be automatically decreased to whatever is called for by a predetermined safety factor.

The signaling apparatus, as well as that to activate the brakes, is carried in the engine and is made to operate by a series of electrical impulses carried along the rails on which the train is running. This electrical current is interrupted at certain rates which are determined by the amount of traffic which is on the track ahead of the train receiving the impulses. If there is a great deal of traffic ahead, the current is no longer interrupted, but becomes a steady flow. This applies the brakes in an emergency fashion, causing the train to come to a complete halt. If there is a breakdown in the signaling system and no current whatever is transmitted the brakes are also applied at once. If there is only a small amount of traffic ahead, yet so much as to make running at high speeds dangerous, the interruption of the electric current is lessened and the automatic apparatus in the cab puts on the brakes only enough to obtain a safe running speed.

Sometimes a combination of the two types of vocabulary is used in abstracts, summaries, and synopses. Then the writer assumes some acquaintance with technical language on the part of his readers, yet not so much as he himself has. Such summaries usually will be phrased without mathematical data, however, for it is here that executive officers may find themselves unable to follow the technical man's thought. Most executives, even if they do not have a technical education, learn a great deal about the language of the technical fields they are called upon to work in.

The following summary is a semitechnical form of the nontechnical one which you have just read. Rather than being designed for the stockholders of the company, this form is meant to be read by persons who are conversant with the railroad business.

Increased safety of train operation is effected by the continuously controlled cab signals which may be augmented by means for applying the brakes automatically in case cab signal changes calling for a reduction in speed are ignored or predetermined speed limits are exceeded. The engine-carried apparatus is inductively linked and selectively responsive to coded alternating current in the running rails, the frequency of coding determining the cab signal indication displayed and being dependent upon traffic conditions ahead. Absence of rail current or the presence of uncoded current establishes the most restrictive speed conditions.

Sometimes a summary which merely states the problem which was investigated and follows this with a short note of the conclusions spends most of its space upon the recommendations advanced for the consideration of the executive officers of the company. This type of summary is sometimes sent separately to these officers. It is an advis-

DEWATERING OF PRODUCT X

SUMMARY

This investigation was directed toward finding methods to increase the dewatering efficiency and to reduce the high labor costs involved in the filtration and repulping steps in the manufacture of Product X.

Recommendation:

It is recommended that an Ansco Machine Company, 40-in. diameter, high-speed, suspended-type centrifugal filter constructed of rubber-covered steel be purchased and installed to replace the three filter presses now used in the dewatering of Product X.

Anticipated Results:

The use of the batch centrifugal filter will:

1. Decrease the annual labor cost in this operation by $3400

2. Increase catalyst recovery worth $450 annually

3. Yield cake solids of 38% instead of the present 22% in the drowned slurry filtration step

4. Produce a 9% higher cake solid on the final filtration

5. Effect reductions in operating cost of $447.50, representing a 20% return on the proposed $2237.50 investment.

Prepared by:

A. N. Newton

A. N. Newton, Industrial Engineering

Approved by:

E. K. Chesterville

E. K. Chesterville, Superintendent, Industrial Engineering

able one when the report has been discussed with members of the staff and their full agreement has been obtained. Usually such a summary carries a notation of approval, as does the preceding one.

Lengths of abstracts vary considerably. Some corporations impose a 75-word limit on them, as does E. I. du Pont de Nemours and Company, whereas another corporation may have a maximum limit of 225 words. You will have to be guided in the length of your report's abstract by the usages of the company for which you work.

In addition to eliminating the superfluous ideas which are not essential to your reader's understanding of the central theme of your report, you will want to examine carefully the wording of the abstract you have written. Consider the following abstract, which deals with stress relaxation of special polymers for high-temperature use.

As a result of the tests performed upon them, it was apparent that Silicone and Viton A stocks exhibited very good stress retention in a 10,000-minute test which was performed at 120° Centigrade. On the other hand, Viton A-HV illustrated a lower stress retention in similar tests. Of all the high-temperature elastomers tested, however, butyl rubber exhibited the lowest retention of stress in the group.

Although this is not a very long abstract, it is capable of considerably greater compression. Observe what economies can be effected by a judicious cutting-out of unnecessary phrases and words, and by combining sentences.

Silicone and Viton A stocks had very good stress retention in 10,000-minute test at 120° C. Viton A-HV had lower stress retention, and butyl rubber the lowest retention of stress among the high-temperature elastomers tested.[3]

Although the advice does not apply only to the writing of abstracts, but to reports in general as well as to all types of technical writing, you should always try to cut out the "deadwood" in your phrasing. There are certain kinds of sentences which give you signals that they can be revised to advantage; they are the ones that start with "it" and "there." For example:

It has generally been thought advisable to use caution.

Revise this into:

Caution is generally advisable.

Or:

There are three seed blankets in that reactor.

Revise this into:

That reactor has three seed blankets.

Often you will find that you can cut a clause down into a phrase and make your sentence more effective and more exact than it originally was.

The high-pressure turbine which was located in the East Building . . .

[3] By permission of the Firestone Tire and Rubber Co.

Revise this into:

The high-pressure turbine in the East Building . . .

In general, when writing abstracts, you must remember that the central ideas of the report must be presented, but details or material of proof need not be. Write the abstract concisely and exactly, without wasting words.

THE BODY OF THE REPORT

Since the body of the report contains the detailed information you wish to supply, since the abstract or summary and the conclusions and recommendations cannot be written until after such time as the body of the report is complete, and since it is upon the body of fact you present that you will be judged by your fellow workers, it seems best to examine the entire procedure of report writing under this general head.

EARLY PLANNING NECESSARY. If you begin to plan your report from the first day that you advance the idea upon which you will work, or on the day when you are assigned to a given investigation, you will cut down the total energy you will have to put into this complicated process. And if you plan early for your report, you will not fall into the trap sprung on so many technically trained men—that of having the investigation done, and not a word written when the finished report is actually due. Many executives with whom the authors have corresponded have said that getting reports in on time from their staffs is one of their most difficult problems, and that often an excellent piece of work is wasted because the report on it is so late as to be of no value to some new process which is being worked out.

In this early planning stage, there are certain central ideas that you should be quite clear about.

1. Why does whatever you are planning on doing (and writing a report on) need to be done? You must be sure of this. What is the aim of the work that has been authorized? Being certain of this is not only a help in writing your report, but is a great assistance in carrying out the investigation, no matter what sort it may be. It will keep you out of blind alleys and point you to the path you will need to follow.

2. Who needs to learn what you have found out? In no case does one write a report for himself; he writes it for an audience of some sort. You must know long before you write who the members of this

audience are, and what sort of people they are. You must ask yourself how much they know about the subject you are concerned with, for if their acquaintance with the technical language of your field is non-existent, you must then undertake the task of translating your symbols into words that will carry the sense of what you want to say. If the audience is limited to people who have a similar background to yours, you may indulge in the special language of your field as much as you please; in fact, this is the kind of language you will have to use.

Again, a determination of your audience will tell you to what extent you must go into detail. If your audience is unfamiliar with technical matters, you may have to explain at some length what is everyday knowledge to people who have the same technical training that you do.

Usually, if you are writing a formal report of some length, you may determine which other people, aside from those who originally authorized your work, should receive a copy of the report. It is a good thing to detail such a list and then talk with your supervisor about the distribution list for the report. He may wish to add people whom you do not know, or who you thought would have no interest in the subject you are pursuing.

3. How can you interest your reader? Although this query is allied to the preceding one, it needs to be thought out carefully. If you are to make a good report, it is plain that you will want the recommendation you offer to be acted upon and put into practice. You must find ways by which you can keep your reader sufficiently interested in the report to induce him to perform the necessary action. Your report may have in it a method of cutting down maintenance costs, but you must write it in such a way that the maintenance director will read it eagerly. You must appeal to his interests; the report must show him how he can carry out a better operation more cheaply. Or perhaps your investigations have led toward a newer and better method of producing a given product more cheaply. Again, you must attract your reader's interest in what you have to say.

4. How can you organize your work as it progresses? The first answer to this question is a relatively simple one: discuss the problem and the possible avenues of attack on it with your supervisor. Essentially, that is what he is there for, and his longer experience may suggest many time-saving devices. The second phase of the answer sounds a little extreme: *write* down the answers to these questions, at least as far as you can.

Why am I doing this work?
Who is going to read my report?
How can I best tell them about what I am doing?
What (as exactly as possible) am I trying to do?

Writing the answers to these questions will almost surely give you an outline, not only of the work itself, but of the report which will come out of that work.

Another method of organizing your ideas as your work progresses is to plan the sequences which you think the work will follow. You will not be able to do this exactly every time, but you will at least have a tentative guide to help you along.

Another help in organizing your work as it goes through successive stages is to take careful notes on what you are doing. This is not to suggest that you should sit down at the end of the day, and in the last half-hour, write down the day's activity. The nearer the writing to the time you have done a given thing, the more explicit and exact your note will be. And it is always best to write those notes in reasonably full sentences. If you merely jot down a word or a short phrase "to remind," you will find that this serves admirably while the subject is still fresh in your mind, but by the next day, these cryptic words may not serve to stimulate your memory, and you may find that you have totally lost the sense that the words were intended to recall.

Although many technically trained people seem to abhor the idea, taking these notes on cards is a time and effort-saving way of recalling to your mind what you have done. Cards may be shuffled so that a part of the process which you are engaged in may be noted on the day a certain phase of the work is completed. Then these cards may be moved into the main organization of your report, even though that organization does not follow the chronological sequence which you originally were pursuing. Your cards may be headed under the general idea being examined; as work progresses further and further, you will be able to head them more specifically. The card notes may be placed under the sequences you originally planned; if the work does not follow these sequences, the cards may be moved to an appropriate heading.

The answers to the questions on this page will have already given you some idea of the total outline of your problem, but as work goes on, you will find that you can amplify and perhaps vary this outline. As you work, try to keep the outline of the work (and hence of your final report) up to date.

Finally, to continue your organization as your work goes on, you should try to evaluate the elements that you consider of greatest importance to the central idea you are investigating. If you have used cards for your notes, you have only to develop a system in which an asterisk (*) indicates matters of most importance, a plus sign (+) matters of lesser importance, a zero (0) those of little or no importance, and a question (?) to mean that you are not yet able to evaluate these ideas.

GUIDES TO CLARITY. As in all types of prose writing, technical or otherwise, clarity stands supreme in importance. No matter how impressive the big words that you know may look, it is always better to use words as simple as possible to convey your ideas, for these simple words are more easily understood by more readers than any other kind. Again, as has been noted, you should remember your audience.

Consider the following quotation and try to determine its major meaning.

> Identifying ourselves with those who take cognizance of, and align themselves against, what appears to be a fast-growing tendency toward oversimplification and overgeneralization, we hasten to qualify, to an extent commensurate with the actual degree of disparity found to be existent among certain of our intermediate findings, the conclusion which otherwise we might be accused of having embraced without due consideration to pertinent uncontrolled variables.

If a person is willing to invest the time to find out what this communication means, he can probably do it, but his effort would probably be better spent rubbing butter into his hair.

There are a few elementary rules to follow if you wish to write simple, lucid prose. The most important of these are:

1. Remember that although an idea may be perfectly clear to you, this does not mean that it is at all clear to your reader. First, when you revise, put yourself in the place of the person who is *reading* the report, and who does not have your background of knowledge about the material it contains. Will that reader understand the report?

2. Ask your colleagues who have not been working on this or similar material to read your report and criticize it. But remember that people do not like to hurt each other's feelings; you will actually have to *want* constructive criticism, and you must prove this to your fellow workers.

3. Examine the length of your sentences critically. If they are over 30 words in length, either prune them fearlessly or make two sentences of any lengthy one.

4. Keep your paragraphs short. Doing this lets more light onto the the page and makes the work appear easy to read.[4] Whenever you have a chance to begin a new paragraph, always take it; even if you doubt whether you should begin a new paragraph, do it anyway.

5. Don't use too many participial phrases to open your sentences. They do not convey the important idea of your sentence, yet they occupy the attention-getting part of it. Further, they are traps for the unwary in that they may "dangle"; that is, you may neglect to write down something for them to modify.[5]

6. Choose your words carefully. Don't limit yourself to two- or three-syllable words, but be sure the words you use mean exactly what you are trying to tell.

7. Try to avoid "weasel" words, such as ". . . gives rise to the possible conclusion that . . . ," ". . . would seem to indicate . . . ," ". . . may tend to . . . ," and ". . . affords at least some support for the position. . . ."

8. Be sure that your major idea is expressed in your independent clause. Never let it go into a subordinate clause, for if it occurs here, the reader will be almost certain to misinterpret your meaning.

The body of the report is its most important section. From it stem the conclusions, recommendations, appendixes, summary, and abstract, and it is in the body that most of the illustrative techniques are used. Since these techniques apply, however, to both the report and the article, they are taken up in some detail in Chapter 6.

CONCLUSIONS AND RECOMMENDATIONS

It is in the conclusions and recommendations that the discrimination and judgment of the technical man are revealed. These two elements are the most important parts of the report; they are the result of the thought of the author as he interprets his facts. Anyone acquainted with scientific techniques and methods can gather adequate data on any problem, but only the intelligent author can evaluate them. The conclusions are gathered directly from the de-

[4] To discover personally how repelling long paragraphs are to a reader, look at Sir Thomas More's *Utopia* in the Harvard Classics edition, pp. 151 to 166.

[5] For a consideration of the dangling participle, see the Index to English Usage, pp. 374, 394.

tailed analysis of the report; they show the ability of the writer to use inductive (from particular to general) logic. The recommendations are the writer's considered ideas of what should be done about the problem, viewed in the new light thrown upon it by his conclusions.

It is in these two important sections of the report that the writer must be most careful about his phrasing. If his sentences, as a result of bad construction and slipshod grammatical usages, may be interpreted in ways he has not intended, the value of all the work done may be nullified.

APPENDIX

An appendix is mainly applicable to a long formal report. It contains explanatory material which cannot be given in the text of the report without interfering with the logical and orderly progress of the paper. If a formula has been given, and the explanation of the method by which it was worked out is not appropriate in the text, the explanation should be relegated to the appendix. The bibliographical details—the books, magazines, and files used—should be listed here and labeled "Bibliography" under the appropriate appendix heading. Additional charts, maps, and graphs which aid in clarifying the data, but which are not absolutely necessary in the text, may be included in this part of the report and form another appendix heading. Only in elaborate reports is an index added.

Sometimes the appendix of a report necessarily contains matter whose purpose is to show that one or another process attempted in the course of an investigation was a complete failure. In the body, you need only mention that the process *was* a failure, but you should then indicate by a footnote the reference to the appendix in which the full explanation can be found. Likewise, supplementary graphs or figures should also be footnoted and the reader referred to the appendix.

Following is a report of the Jones and Laughlin Steel Corporation.[6] It represents one of the activities that many technical men are often called upon to take part in—the carrying out of research in the actual manufacturing process itself rather than in the confined and almost academic surroundings of the research laboratory. In this report, the writer describes the results of using special atmospheres in the process of treating various steel products.

[6] Reproduced by permission of the Jones and Laughlin Steel Corporation.

Notice that the report begins with a concise summary which tells the reader what types of steel have been treated in the furnace, and what work and tests have been performed. Thereafter, the writer begins his discussion, which may be thought of as the body of the report. He has been careful in this to draw the attention of his readers to each of the major heads (which have already been set out in the summary) by underlining and numbering them. Further, he has used the same nomenclature in the discussion as he did in the summary in order that no reader may become confused over terms.

The conclusions drawn appear in full at the end of the report proper, although they are given in a shortened form under heads B and C in the summary.

The appendix consists of two parts, with Appendix A having four photomicrographs as exhibits to show the different surface structure of the skin of steel bars before and after they have been treated in the special atmospheres. Appendix B is made up of tables identifying the products and giving physical data about them.

JONES AND LAUGHLIN STEEL CORPORATION
PITTSBURGH, PA.

January 12, 19—

Mr. E. C. Mears, Vice-President
Jones and Laughlin Steel Corporation
Pittsburgh, Pennsylvania

Dear Mr. Mears:

The following report, "Results of Operation of Controlled Atmosphere Furnace at Hazelwood Cold Finishing Department," gives the procedures followed and the conclusions reached in the course of my work with this problem.

One of the more important conclusions reached and one in which you have already indicated your interest was that carbon can be restored to the decarburized skin of steel bars.

Respectfully submitted,

W. E. Lawlor

W. E. Lawlor
Staff Research Engineer

Letter of Transmittal (*sent separately*)

JONES AND LAUGHLIN STEEL CORPORATION
PITTSBURGH DIVISION
PITTSBURGH, PA.

January 12, 19—   Report No.   38

Results of Operation of Controlled
Atmosphere Furnace at Hazelwood
Cold Finishing Department

prepared for

Mr. E. C. Mears, Vice-President
Jones and Laughlin Steel Corporation
Pittsburgh, Pennsylvania

by

W. E. Lawlor
Staff Research Engineer

JONES AND LAUGHLIN STEEL CORPORATION

RESULTS OF OPERATION OF CONTROLLED ATMOSPHERE FURNACE AT HAZELWOOD COLD FINISHING DEPARTMENT

By W. E. Lawlor, Staff Research Engineer

1. Summary

A. Types of product treated in the furnace to date include:

(1) Carbon restoration anneal
(2) Anneal before cold drawing
(3) Intermediate anneal
(4) Bright anneal
(5) Stress relief anneal
(6) Normalizing.

B. Further development work, including full anneal, spheroidize anneal, and case carburizing, is yet to be done.

C. Mill test results have been satisfactory. Customer reactions and specific requirements are to be fully developed.

2. Discussion

The subject "Controlled Atmosphere Furnace" is a car bottom type, designed and installed by the Surface Combustion Corporation. The installation incorporates two types of gas generators: one for manufacturing an inert, protective nitrogen atmosphere (NX) used for scale free and bright annealing; the other for producing a cracked natural gas mixture of hydrogen, carbon monoxide and nitrogen (RX). This atmosphere provides the carbon potential required for carbon restoration and high carbon case carburizing. The carbon potential is controlled by regulating its dew point.

3. Types of products ordered and processed to date include carbon restoration annealing and normalizing before cold drawing; intermediate annealing between successive cold drawing operations; bright annealing; and sub-critical temperature strain relieving of cold drawn bars. These orders did not include products specifying spheroidized, specific annealed or normalized structure developments, or high carbon case carburizing, which have yet to be developed.

-2-

4. Following is a brief description of the types of product, method of
treatment required, and results obtained on those processed to date:

A. <u>Carbon Restoration Anneal</u>

Purpose—Restoration of carbon in the decarburized skin of bars.
This can be performed before or after cold drawing, but for economical
operation we find it preferable to treat the full mill length rough stock
before cold drawing.

It is necessary to pickle and lime the rough stock before treating.

Developments have shown that best results are obtained by loading
the bars in layers with separators between layers as compared with loading
in lifts or bundles. In addition to permitting a maximum uniformity of
distribution of the controlled atmosphere to all parts of the charge, a more
efficient heating and cooling cycle is realized.

A typical carbon restoration cycle is controlled as follows:

The charge is heated to 1500° F in an NX gas atmosphere. At
this point the carburizing R gas is substituted in place of NX. The charge is
soaked for four hours at 1600° F. During the soaking period the dew
point of the RX gas is controlled to maintain the required carbon potential
for the grade of steel being treated. After soaking, the RX gas is replaced
with NX gas when the charge has cooled to 1400° F. When the charge has
further cooled to 1000° F, the car is pulled and the charge permitted to
finish cooling in the air.

Before and after photomicrographs showing the restoration of
carbon to the decarburized skin of the bar are shown in figures #1 to #4;
#1 and #2 are representative of a coarse grain and #3 and #4 a fine
grain steel.

-3-

The ladle carbon of the heat of coarse grained steel was 0.52; the carbon content of a 0.010″ depth removed from the bar surface checked 0.28 carbon; a similar check on the carbon restored stock showed 0.58 carbon, a very satisfactory performance. Carbon checks were not made on the fine grain stock figures #3 and #4, but the comparative photomicrographs show conclusive evidence of an excellent carbon restoration action.

B. Anneal before Cold Drawing

Purpose—To develop a relatively lower hardness suitable for aiding in cold drawing and/or customers' fabrication of material which would otherwise be too hard in the cold drawn state. It is not to be confused with full annealing or the development of specific annealed structure requirements. For this treatment we used an intermediate temperature between the upper and lower criticals. The satisfactory softening effect obtained is shown in table No. 1.

C. Intermediate Anneal

Purpose—To eliminate the work hardening of cold drawing to permit further cold drawing operations. Temperature used is slightly below or above the lower critical, depending on requirements.

D. Bright Anneal

Purpose—To relieve cold working stresses and retain the size accuracy and smoothness of finish of the cold drawn stock. Surface discoloration is not important in most instances, but relatively bright finishes are required in others. This should be fully developed as a matter of guidance in the processing of this type of product. This type of treatment is usually performed at temperatures slightly below, at, or slightly above the lower critical. A typical satisfactory relieving of the cold drawn hardness is shown in table No. 2.

E. Stress Relief Anneal

Purpose—To relieve cold worked stresses to meet desired hardness or mechanical properties. A particular item treated required a higher temperature than can be processed without scaling in our continuous strain drawing furnaces and has been, in the past, confined to the Strip Mill Annealing Department. Results obtained in our new furnace indicate a satisfactory performance and that a relatively lower temperature and shorter time cycle can be realized.

—4—

F. Normalizing

Purpose—To relieve stresses introduced in rolling or forging operations. Material is heated and soaked at a temperature usually above the upper critical and cooled in air from this temperature. Before and after results on hardness vary according to amount of stresses and size or mass effect in cooling. However, regardless of any change by direct before-and-after comparison, the resultant product has a decidedly improved overall uniformity. Typical results showing no appreciable change on the 1-1/32″ and 1-5/32″ sizes and an appreciable softening of the 1-17/32″ size are shown in table No. 3.

5. Conclusions

Results to date for the types of products treated indicate acceptable performances have been developed. There is still considerable development work required to complete the potential products to be processed. In addition, it will be necessary to have the benefit of customer reactions, and a full knowledge of specific requirements in order to assure the development of satisfactory products.

–5–
APPENDIX A

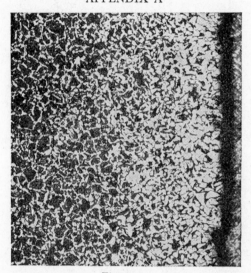

Figure 1
As Rolled Decarburized Surface

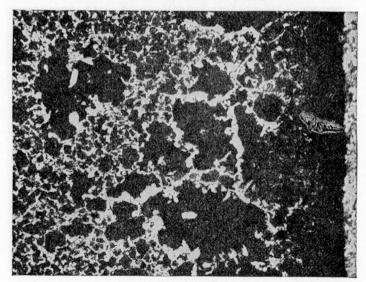

Figure 2
Carbon Restored Surface

Before and After Photomicrographs—C–1045 Grade—Coarse Grain Steel
100X   Nital Etch

	As Rolled (Fig. 1)	Carbon Restored (Fig. 2)	Ladle
.010″ Ring Tests-Carbon Check	0.28C	0.58C	0.52C

APPENDIX A

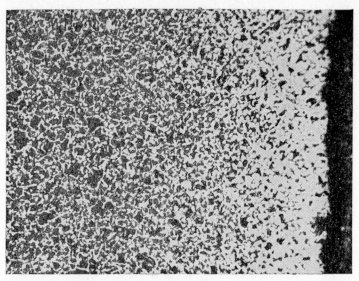

Figure 3
As Rolled Decarburized Surface

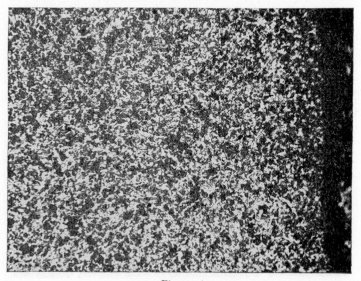

Figure 4
Carbon Restored Surface
Before and After Photomicrographs—C-1049 Grade—Fine Grain Steel
100X   Nital Etch

–7–

APPENDIX B

TABLE No. 1

Annealed Before Cold Drawing

Grade	Size	Hardness: As Rolled	Annealed
C–1144	1–3/4″ Rd.	R_b 88	R_b 57
C–1144	1–3/4″ Rd.	R_b 85	R_b 50
C–1080	2.020″ × .270″ Flat	Brinell 311	Brinell 212
C–1080	2.005″ × .205″ Flat	Brinell 321	Brinell 212
C–1050	27/32″ × 7/32″ Flat	Brinell 228	Brinell 163/166

TABLE No. 2

Bright Annealed

B–1113	.517/.520″ Rd.	R_b 94	R_b 80/83
.40 Carbon Bessemer	"	Brinell 228	Brinell 187

TABLE No. 3

Normalized Before Cold Drawing

C–1029	1–1/32″ Rd.	Brinell 146	Brinell 140/149
C–1029	1–5/32″ Rd.	Brinell 146	Brinell 143/149
C–1029	1–17/32″ Rd.	Brinell 153	Brinell 131/137

The Formal Student Laboratory Report

Student laboratory reports have an entirely different aim than do these submitted by technical men employed in industry. These latter reports present a body of facts dealing with hitherto unknown matters; they attempt to show what a process will or will not do, or what qualities a piece of apparatus may have, or what a new method of manufacture or a new material flow system will do for a corporation. The student report, on the other hand, is an attempt to convince the instructor that (1) the student is acquainted with the proper laboratory techniques and apparatus, (2) he knows the theory behind the experiment, (3) his calculations are correct, and (4) he is acquainted with the form and development of a good report. It is rare in undergraduate school that an instructor will assign a laboratory problem calling for a report if he is not perfectly sure himself of the approximate results that may be obtained from it.

The following report may act as a good model of a student report in a technical field. The writer has been clear in his thought and phrasing, and painstaking in his work.

Report on

Calorific Value of Knoxville Natural Gas

for

Mechanical Engineering 146

***

Submitted on

January 17, 19—

by

John Alexander

School of Engineering

University of Calydon

Calydon 13, Illinois

University of Calydon
Calydon 13, Illinois
January 27, 19—

Mr. Arthur A. Hanawalt, Instructor
Mechanical Engineering Department
University of Calydon
Calydon 13, Illinois

Dear Mr. Hanawalt:

In compliance with your instructions of December 17, 19—, I have made as careful an investigation as possible on the calorific value of Knoxville natural gas.

The enclosed report shows that the higher and lower heating values are in close agreement with the values you specified.

I wish to express my obligation to Mr. Walter E. Murphy for his guidance in my laboratory work.

Respectfully submitted,
John Alexander
John Alexander

SUMMARY

This experiment determined the calorific value of Knoxville natural gas to be 1065 Btu/cu ft for the higher heating value and 1005 Btu/cu ft for the lower heating value. These figures are in close agreement with the values of 1050 Btu/cu ft and 1000 Btu/cu ft issued prior to the test.

Calorific Value of Knoxville Natural Gas

Object

The object of this experiment was to determine the higher and lower heating value of Knoxville natural gas by using the Sargent gas calorimeter.

Theory

Heating value is the amount of Btu given off for a definite quantity of fuel measured at standard conditions. The heating value as determined directly from the calorimeter readings is called the higher heating value. In most types of combustion apparatus the heat absorbed by the water formed from the burning of hydrogen is not recoverable; therefore this hydrogen heat loss is not accounted for on the calorimeter readings. To obtain the lower heating value, the condensate of the burning gas is collected and a correction is made by subtracting from the higher heating value the heat liberated by the condensation of this vapor.

Description of Apparatus

A Sargent gas calorimeter (Junkers Type) was used in this experiment. It contained a combustion space for a bunsen burner, flue gas passages, and a water jacket for the fluid to circulate. A wet type gas meter was used to measure the quantity of fuel consumed. Pails to catch the water, platform scales for weighing, three 220° Fahrenheit thermometers, and a 100 cc graduate cylinder to collect the condensate were used in measuring and computing the data.

Procedure

The equipment was set up as illustrated in Fig. 1. The gas meter was connected directly to the main gas supply line. The gas regulator pressure tank was placed between the meter and the bunsen burner so that a wide variation in the gas pressure would be eliminated. Thermometers were placed at point 1 to measure the water inlet temperature, point 2 to measure the water outlet temperature, and point 3 to measure the gas temperature. The water flow through the calorimeter jacket and the heat of the bunsen burner were regulated so that the water outflow was approximately at room temperature. When the temperatures became steady, the run was started. Temperature readings were taken every two minutes of the inflow and outflow of the water and of the inflow of the gas. The gas pressure was also recorded at the two-minute intervals. The water and fuel quantities used for the entire test were measured after the ten-minute run period was completed. A barometer reading was taken so the gas volume could be corrected to standard conditions.

Results

The higher heating value for Knoxville natural gas as determined in this experiment was measured to be 1065 Btu/cu ft. The lower heating value was calculated to be 1005 Btu/cu ft. These results are in close agreement with the specified value of 1050 and 1000 Btu/cu ft issued prior to the test.

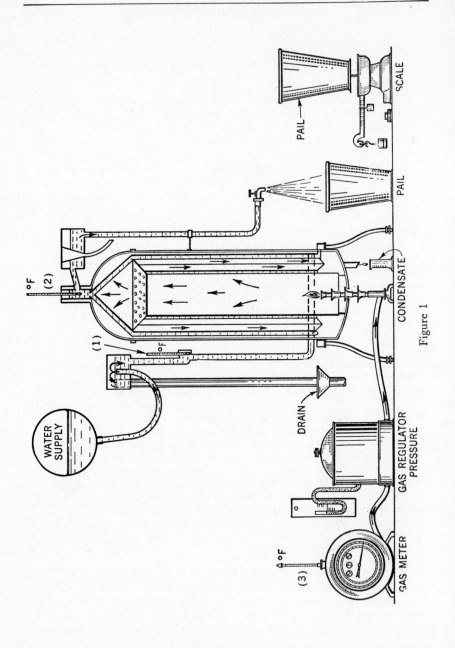

Figure 1

APPENDIX

Data

Time (minutes)	Gas Pressure (inches of water)	Gas Temp. °F	Water Temp. °F in	out
0	0.95	82.0	81.3	92.2
2	0.95	82.0	81.4	92.2
4	0.95	82.0	81.4	92.3
6	0.95	82.0	81.4	92.4
8	0.95	82.0	81.4	92.4
10	0.95	82.0	81.4	92.4

Volume of gas used	0.310 cu ft.
Weight of water	28.57 pounds
Weight of condensate	7.50 grams
Barometer reading	29.210 inches of mercury

Calculated Results

Standard volume of gas burned	0.291 cu ft
Heat absorbed by water	310 Btu
Heat released by condensate	17.2 Btu
Higher heating value of gas	1065 Btu/cu ft
Lower heating value of gas	1005 Btu/cu ft

Calculations

Standard conditions   30 in. of Hg
                      60°F

Standard volume of gas
Barometer correction = Gas Pressure ÷ sp gr Hg + Barometer reading

$$= \frac{.95 \text{ in.}}{13.6} + 29.21 \text{ in.} = 29.28 \text{ in. of Hg}$$

$P_1 = 29.28$ in. of Hg
$V_1 = 0.310$ cu ft
$T_1 = 82°\text{ F} + 460°\text{ F abs} = 542°\text{ F abs}$
$P_s = 30.00$ in. of Hg
$T_s = 520°\text{ F abs}$
$V_s = ?$

$$\frac{P_1V_1}{T_1} = \frac{P_sV_s}{T_s}$$

$$V_s = \frac{P_1V_1T_s}{T_1P_s} = \frac{29.28 \text{ in.} \times 0.310 \text{ cu ft} \times 520°\text{ F abs}}{542°\text{ F abs} \times 30.00 \text{ in.}} = \underline{0.291 \text{ cu ft}}$$

Heat absorbed by water—
From steam tables—
   h_f of water at outlet temp. of 92.3°F = 60.29 Btu/lb
   h_f of water at inlet temp. of 81.4°F = 49.42 Btu/lb
                  h_f absorbed = 10.87 Btu/lb
Water collected = 28.57 lb
Total heat absorbed = 28.57 lb × 10.87 Btu/lb = 310 Btu

Higher heating value—

$$\text{Higher heating value} = \frac{\text{Heat liberated}}{\text{Volume of fuel at standard conditions}}$$

$$= \frac{310 \text{ Btu}}{.291 \text{ cu ft}} = \underline{1065 \text{ Btu/cu ft}}$$

Lower heating value—

Lower heating value = H.H.V. − (latent heat × wt condensate)

$$\text{Weight of condensate} = 7.5 \text{ grams}$$

$$= \frac{7.5 \text{ g}}{1} \times \frac{1}{454 \text{ g/lb}} = 0.0165 \text{ lb}$$

Heat loss = 0.0165 lb × 1040 Btu/lb = 17.20 Btu

$$\text{Lower heating value} = \frac{310 \text{ Btu}}{0.291 \text{ cu ft}} - \frac{17.20 \text{ Btu}}{0.291 \text{ cu ft}} = \underline{1005 \text{ Btu/cu ft}}$$

Final Example of the Formal Report

As a final example of the formal report, we reprint the following one on the Stirling engine by the courtesy of the American Rocket Society. The report begins with a short abstract and then moves into an introduction and general considerations. A large number of headings, such as those on system description and cycle considerations, are used to indicate the organization of the report. The report ends with a series of conclusions, followed by the references.

After you have read over the entire report, you will be able to see that the abstract really gives its essence. The introduction is largely concerned with stating the problems which the writers of the report hope to be able to solve. Such a procedure enables the writers to know definitely what their aims are. Such a statement of aims also, to a large extent, acts as an outline and guide for the writers as they organize the body of the report in preparing it for publication. Within the body, the major headings help the reader to know what phase of the effort is being taken up within a particular piece of the report. The conclusions follow logically from the material in the body of the report and actually act almost as a summary. The references are indications that the authors have examined the materials in the field in which they are working. These references act to buttress the material presented in the report and give it validity in the eyes of readers who are acquainted with the general material which the report is considering.

AMERICAN
ROCKET
SOCIETY

A national association
for the advancement of
rocketry, jet propulsion
and astronautics

500 FIFTH AVENUE • NEW YORK 36, N. Y.

Stirling Engine Development for Space Power

by

M. D. Parker and C. L. Smith
Allison Division, General Motors Corporation
Indianapolis, Indiana

1315-60

This research program is supported
by the Wright Air Development Division,
United States Air Force.

Presented at the ARS Space Power
Systems Conference, The Miramar
Hotel, Santa Monica, California,
September 27-30, 19--.

STIRLING ENGINE DEVELOPMENT FOR SPACE POWER

By M. D. Parker*and C. L. Smith**

ABSTRACT

Progress in the adaptation of the Stirling engine to supply power to an orbital space capsule is reviewed.

The basic Stirling cycle is reviewed with respect to its advantages and limitations for space power applications. An engine design for space power is discussed with particular emphasis on problems associated with the space environment. Conditions for exact balance of dynamic forces are examined. Design and development approach to the lubrication and sealing problems in a zero gravity environment for long periods of unattended operation is outlined. Finally, a Stirling cycle engine, designed and constructed by the Allison Division of General Motors Corporation, is discussed.

I. INTRODUCTION

Within the last two years the Stirling engine has emerged as an energy converter with considerable potential for application to space power systems, especially where the energy source is solar. A paper describing the general system characteristics and performance of the Stirling engine was presented at the American Rocket Society 14th Annual Meeting in Washington, D. C. in November 1959 (Reference 1). Since that time, the Allison Division has been actively engaged in research and development work on the engine and other major system components for a solar energized 3- to 5-kw satellite application. In this paper a progress report of the engine design and development is presented. This engine has been designed as part of a program which was originally sponsored by the Advanced Research Projects Agency; however, the initial program has been expanded and is now solely sponsored by the Wright Air Development Division.

The unusual performance characteristics of the advanced Stirling engine are the result of 20 years of research work conducted by the Research Laboratories of the N. V. Philips Gloeilampenfabrieken of Eindhoven, Netherlands. The

* Sr. Project Engineer, Research Activity, Allison Division of General Motors
  Corporation

** Sr. Project Engineer, Technical Services Activity, Allison Division of
   General Motors Corporation

Allison Division of General Motors Corporation, with the support of the General Motors Research Laboratories, is actively engaged in the further development of the engine for space power systems.

II. GENERAL CONSIDERATIONS

Extensive studies, which have been made relative to space solar power systems, have shown that the Stirling and Rankine cycles are the two most practical choices for thermomechanical systems. Both meet the space requirement that the cycle must be closed, and each is capable of utilizing any form of external heat source. The Rankine cycle uses a two-phase working fluid which introduces limitations with respect to maximum and minimum cycle temperature. For example, the mercury Rankine cycle power system is best suited for operation with a sink temperature in the range of 500 to 600°F. In general, this feature is well suited to space power systems since minimum radiator size is associated with high sink temperatures.

The Stirling cycle engine, on the other hand, has complete freedom with respect to maximum and minimum cycle temperatures because its working medium is a pure gas. The choice of the operating temperatures can be selected solely on the basis of system optimization and practical design limitations. Analysis has indicated that the minimum weight for the Stirling engine solar power system is obtained with a radiator temperature of approximately 150°F when the maximum cycle temperature is 1250°F. When designed for the same radiator surface area as that required for the mercury Rankine cycle, the radiator temperature increases to approximately 270°F. From the over-all system standpoint, the thermodynamic characteristic of the Stirling cycle has much to offer.

III. SYSTEM DESCRIPTION

The application which will be considered in this presentation is an orbital satellite requiring an auxiliary power source in the 3- to 5-kilowatt output range. A typical orbit would be one which circled the earth in 100 minutes. Of the total duration, 65 minutes would be in the sun and the remaining 35 minutes in the shade of the earth. Solar energy would be the source of heat.

A sketch of a typical solar-heated space power system is shown in Figure 1. The general arrangement is one in which all of the major rigid components (engine, heat reservoir, collector, and radiator) are grouped into one assembly. The Fresnel mirror system is positioned to reflect the sun rays into the absorber. The entire system is oriented with the collector directed toward the sun.

Figure 1. Solar-heated Space Power System

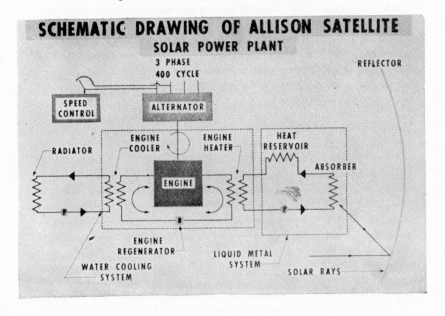

Figure 2. Schematic Drawing of Allison Satellite Solar Powerplant

The sun rays are collected by a mirror and focused on the absorber surface (See Figure 2). Heat absorbed by a liquid metal stream is transferred to the engine heater section. During exposure to the sun, excess heat is stored in the reservoir in the form of the heat of fusion of lithium hydride. The stored heat is released to the engine when the space capsule is in the shade of the earth. The engine waste heat is rejected into space by the radiator. Engine speed control is achieved by maintaining a constant load on the engine, regardless of power requirement, and radiating the excess energy, not required by the satellite, to space.

IV. ENGINE CHARACTERISTICS

While the general characteristics of the engine were presented in Reference (1), it is desirable to review them again. First and foremost is the high efficiency of the engine. With a maximum cycle temperature of only 1300°F, shaft output thermal efficiencies of higher than 40 percent have been demonstrated (excluding combustion losses). The high efficiency of the engine has a very important effect upon the weight of other system components which far overshadow the difference in weight between the Stirling engine itself and the equivalent mercury turbine. Comparable studies for a specific application of the Stirling and mercury Rankine cycles is summarized for a space solar application in Table I. For comparable designs, including all structure required to adapt the power system to the vehicle, the weight of a mercury Rankine system is 42 percent higher than the corresponding Stirling system.

TABLE I.

Stirling and Mercury Rankine Cycle Design Data Comparison Optimized

For Minimum Weight

(300 Nautical Mile Earth Orbit)

	Stirling	Rankine
Engine Efficiency—%	37.5	13
NaK Inlet Temperature—°F	1250	1250
Radiator Temperature—°F	150	500
Radiator Area—Sq Ft	160	96
Solar Collector Area—Sq Ft	283	816
Solar Collector Diameter—Ft	19	32.3
Weight Breakdown—Lb		
Solar Collector	112	310
Absorber	20	53
Reservoir	45	124
Radiator	36	25
Power Conversion System	237	126
Structure	75	115
Liquid Inventory	42	55
Total - lb	567	808

For comparable designs optimized for minimum weight, the Stirling system
has a larger radiator surface area than the mercury Rankine system, since
the effect of lower radiator temperature overshadows the higher efficiency.
However, when the Stirling system is designed for the same radiator surface
area as the corresponding mercury Rankine cycle, only a moderate weight
increase is encountered. The normal increase in radiator temperature
required to accomplish this introduces no problem. Comparative data are
shown in Table II which indicates the Stirling system is 23 percent lighter in
weight than the Rankine system.

TABLE II.

Stirling and Mercury Rankine Cycle Comparison

(Identical Radiator Surface Areas)

	Stirling	Rankine
Radiator Surface Area—Ft^2	96	96
System Weight—Lb	622	808
Weight Difference—-Lb	186	

The Stirling engine employs a closed cycle using externally supplied heat.
Since no valves are required and piston side loads are nonexistent, maximum
reliability can be achieved for long durations of time at rated output conditions.
The Stirling engine is adaptable to mechanical arrangements which can be
balanced with respect to shaking and torsional vibrations. Torque and gyros-
copic forces can be cancelled. The engine requires no spark ignition, does
not exhaust, and does not have sudden pressure changes in the cycle. This
results in a powerplant free from noise and electrical disturbances which
would cause unacceptable interference in the space capsule equipment.

V. CYCLE CONSIDERATIONS

The thermodynamic cycle involves compressing, heating, expanding, and
cooling a gaseous working medium. Typical ideal pressure-volume and
temperature-entropy diagrams for the Stirling cycle are shown in Figure 3.
A description of the various processes involved is presented in Reference 1.

The mechanical arrangement of the advanced Stirling engine for space power
is illustrated in Figure 4. A cylinder which is closed at one end and sealed
at the other by a work piston is used. A displacer piston is enclosed within
the cylinder between the closed end and the work piston. The function of the
displacer piston is to transfer the gas from one end of the cylinder to the
other through ports in the cylinder wall. The ports at each end of the cylinder

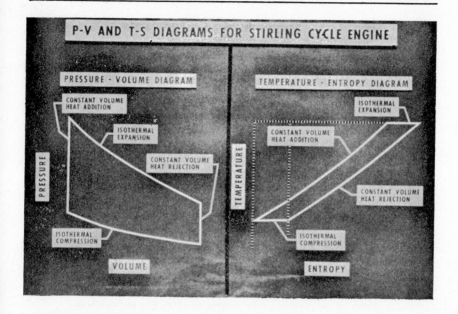

Figure 3. P-V and T-S Diagrams for Stirling Cycle Engine

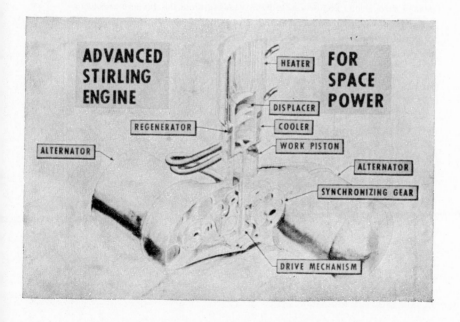

Figure 4. Advanced Stirling Engine for Space Power

are connected by a passageway comprised of a heater, a regenerator, a
cooler, and connecting tubes.

Functionally, the engine operates in the following manner. The operational
cycle (Figure 5-a) is started with the displacer piston against the closed end
of the cylinder and the power piston at the bottom of its stroke. This position
of the pistons allows the greatest amount of gas in the "cold space" and is also
the maximum cylinder volume position. The gas is compressed within the
cold portion of the engine by moving the power piston toward the closed end
of the cylinder while holding the displacer piston fixed (see Figure 5-b).
After compression, the displacer piston is moved toward the power piston
displacing the relatively cool compressed gas from the "cold space", causing
it to be heated as it passes through the regenerator and heater (see Figure 5-c).
At the end of this constant volume heat addition portion of the cycle, the
pressure level of the gas is considerably higher than it was at the end of the
compression. By moving the work piston and the displacer down together
on the work stroke, as shown in Figure 5-d, the working medium is caused
to expand in the "hot end" of the engine. Cycle pressure bears on the top of
the power piston at all times because the ports in the cylinder are never
blocked by either of the pistons. After expansion of the gas is completed,
the displacer piston is returned to the closed end of the cylinder forcing the
gas from the "hot space" to the "cold space". Heat is added to the gas as it
passes through the heater and is then removed from the gas and stored in
the regenerator matrix. The energy stored in the matrix of the regenerator
is available for heating the gas during the reverse flow. This completes
the cycle.

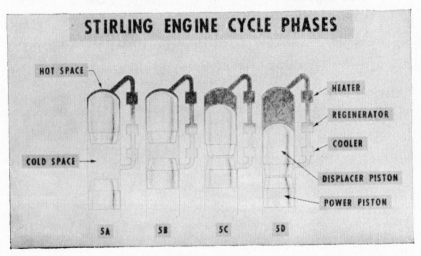

Figure 5. Stirling Engine Cycle Phases

In reality, the thermodynamics of the engine are considerably more complex than that given in the simplified explanation above. A significant departure from the elementary cycle stems from the use of a drive mechanism which produces an overlap of the processes. This must be accounted for in the thermodynamic calculations.

VI. DESIGN OBJECTIVES

The basic design objective of the Allison Stirling cycle engine program was to design an engine, which in principle, embodied those features required of a solar space powerplant. The design was influenced to a considerable degree by the need for maximum flexibility of the various components. The design concept included the following primary criteria:

1. Maximum thermal efficiency

2. Maximum engine reliability for at least one year operation at rated conditions

3. Minimum engine vibration

4. Minimum engine operating noise level

5. Minimum engine weight consistent with other requirements

6. Component compatibility to space operation

To integrate these parameters into a practical machine, numerous design investigations, both thermodynamic and mechanical, were made.

VII. MECHANICAL DESIGN CONSIDERATIONS

A feasible mechanical design, incorporating features which would satisfy the requirements imposed by the thermodynamic prarameters and the unusual problems associated with operation in space, provides a unique challenge. Basic design problems which must be solved are:

1. Lubricating the engine moving components under a gravity free field

2. Sealing the working fluid and lubricant within the engine

3. Selection of a working fluid compatible with maximum engine efficiency in a space atmosphere

4.   Balancing of all shaking and torsional vibratory forces

5.   Control of the powerplant in a space environment

These problem areas in the Stirling engine design are discussed separately
in detail in the following paragraphs.

LUBRICATION

The problem of lubricating an engine whose drive components consist of both
reciprocating and rotating parts in a gravity free field is most critical. This
problem is compounded when reliable operation for long periods of unattended
operation is a prerequisite. Maximum output operation is required for a
period of at least one year to be considered acceptable for satellite applications. The evaluation of a particular lubrication system becomes extremely
difficult inasmuch as terrestial test facilities cannot reproduce a zero gravity
environment. To date, weightlessness conditions can only be simulated in
special test aircraft for a fraction of a minute.

Various systems which appear attractive as a means of lubricating the Stirling
engine have been surveyed and analyzed. The possibility of running the
crankshaft bearing surfaces with some means of dry lubrication was investigated and does not appear to be practical due to the high loading requirements.
Likewise, it has also been found that grease packed antifriction bearings for
the connecting rod journals are not feasible due to the physical size of the
bearings required for extended operation. Analysis has narrowed into two
basic systems. These are:

1.   Pressure lubricated system incorporating a means of retaining a
     relatively stable oil sump

2.   Controlled mist system

The pressure lubricated system must contain an oil pump, a unit to separate
the oil droplets from the crankcase atmosphere, and a device to direct the
separated oil into a sump. A typical system is shown in Figure 6. As will
be noted, this system incorporates an oil pressure pump and an oil centrifuging fan. During operation, the oil and gas mixture enters the eye of the
centrifuging fan and is thrown outward into an annular collector ring. The
oil is then returned to the pump inlet where it is pressurized and fed through
an oil cooler into the main and connecting rod bearings.

The oil droplets that are thrown off from the bearings are again picked up
by the centrifuging fan. This completes the cycle.

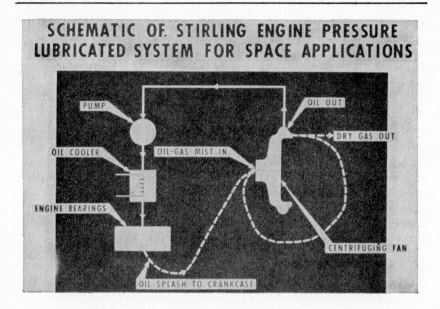

Figure 6. Schematic of Stirling Engine Pressure Lubricated System for
Space Applications

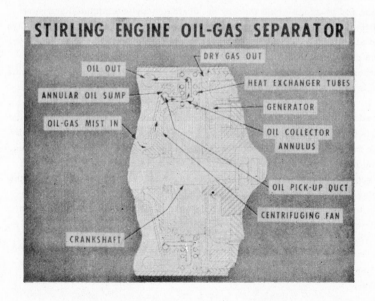

Figure 7. Stirling Engine Oil-Gas Separator

Currently, bench tests on such a system are in process. Preliminary investigations indicate that approximately 80 percent of the oil can be removed from the gas-oil mixture. The principle advantage of this system is that conventional plain bearings can be utilized with a corresponding high load rating. A typical design of a centrifuging fan mounted on the engine crankshaft is shown in Figure 7. Also illustrated is the annular sump and the oil pick-up duct.

Lubricating by a controlled mist appears to be a very attractive system for a space Stirling engine. One significant advantage of a mist system is its relative insensitivity to a gravity field. This permits development testing in a one "g" field with reasonable assurances that the effects of a zero "g" environment on operation of the system will be negligible. In a mist system, however, the available information on the exact bearing load limits is lacking. Experimental evaluation will be necessary to verify this design approach.

Establishing and maintaining a satisfactory oil mist requires the designer to provide wall surfaces close to the rotating engine components. Either plain or antifriction needle type bearings could be utilized in such a design. For a plain bearing configuration, the crankshaft can be made to perform as the oil mist pump by incorporating drilled passageways in the journal. Oil mist would enter a hole located in the center of the main journal and be thrown out by centrifugal force to the passageway located in the crank throw. The connecting rod bearings would thereby be lubricated under simulated pressure condition. An alternate design incorporating antifriction needle type bearings could also be utilized. These bearings would be lubricated by mist generated by the crank mechanism. In both cases, it is mandatory that the crankcase incorporate minimum clearance between the walls and the moving components, to maintain a satisfactory mist.

One additional design consideration associated with a space powerplant is the effects of the lubricant on the electrical generators operating in the crankcase under mist conditions. To provide for extended reliable operation, the complete engine must be hermetically sealed to prevent the loss of the working fluid. The generators must, therefore, be contained inside the crankcase where the windings are in contact with the lubricant. The solution to this problem appears to be in the proper selection of an oil type which is compatible with the electrical requirements and has good lubricating properties. Petroleum oils, free of additives, are suitable for this application.

Discussion of the piston lubrication is covered in the subsection entitled "Seals".

SEALS

In the Stirling engine, high pressures must be maintained in the working zone
to achieve maximum efficiency.   The lubricant must also be prevented from
entering the regenerator matrix by use of adequate seals.   In a basic one-
cylinder engine configuration, four critical seal locations warrant serious
consideration.   The location and function of these seals are as follows:

1.   Displacer Piston - To prevent the flow of gas between the hot and
     cold end

2.   Power Piston - To prevent gas leakage from the working space

3.   Displacer Piston Shaft - To prevent the loss of working fluid to the
     crankcase and to prevent the flow of lubricant into the working zone.

4.   Power Piston Shaft - To prevent the loss of buffer zone gas to the
     crankcase and to seal oil from entering the buffer zone

The various seal locations are shown schematically in Figure 8.   From Figure
8 it can be seen that sealing off of the gas at the piston-to-cylinder interface
is accomplished by a completely dry operating seal.   This eliminates the
need for lubricants in the engine working zone which might foul the regenerator
matrix.   Sealing of the working fluid must be achieved while maintaining
minimum friction load during engine running.

A seal design which has demonstrated satisfactory performance is a seal
consisting of a special soft metal coating on the piston.   A slight amount of
dry lubricant is integrated into the alloy during plating.   The piston is fitted
to the cylinder wall with a minimum of diametral clearance.   At first inspection, a dry seal operating with such close tolerances in an engine does
not appear feasible; however, with the rhombic drive, pure rectilinear motion
can be achieved which results in no piston side loads.   With no side loads,
satisfactory operation is obtained under these close tolerance conditions.
Initial rig tests with this type of seal configuration have been very promising.

During actual engine running, one additional problem must be taken into consideration.   The cylinder pressure fluctuations cause deflections in the cylinder
walls which increase the piston clearance resulting in a performance loss.
The design incorporating the soft metal seal must, therefore, utilize a thick
cylinder wall to minimize the deflections.   The temperature of both cylinder
wall and piston are maintained within close limits and lengthwise temperature
gradients in the cylinder wall are held to low values throughout the rubbing
zone.

The shaft seals, whose primary function is to prevent oil from entering the
buffer zone and to prevent gas leakage into the crankcase, are also most critical.
A design, which is considered feasible, utilizes a babbitt ring loaded by a finger
type spring. A hydrodynamic wedge is developed which pumps oil towards
the crankcase as the shaft reciprocates.

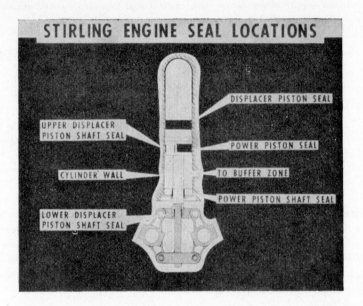

Figure 8. Stirling Engine Seal Locations

Seals of different designs, which are currently being evaluated, are also
worthy of mention. Piston and shaft seal rings made of teflon impregnated
with glass or graphite appear attractive for this application, due to the low
coefficient of friction and the ability to run dry. A test program is currently
in progress to evaluate the merits of these type seal configurations.

WORKING FLUID

The type of working fluid used in the Stirling engine has a considerable effect
on the engine efficiency as illustrated in Figure 9. From this chart, hydrogen
appears to be the most desirable. What is not apparent is the difficulty encountered in containing this gas. Hydrogen diffuses readily through most
metals. Should this gas be utilized in the Stirling engine a continuous de-
gradation in engine power would result due to diffusion. Helium on the other
hand is not limited by these considerations. The resulting loss in efficiency
when using helium is but a small penalty to pay for the advantages derived.

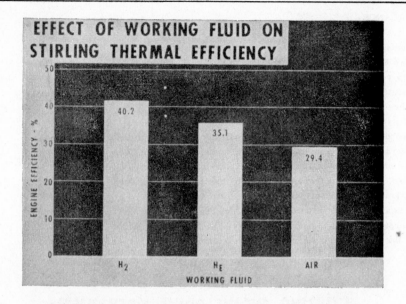

Figure 9. Effect of Working Fluid on Stirling Engine Thermal Efficiency

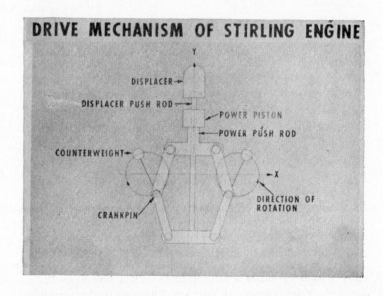

Figure 10. Drive Mechanism of Stirling Engine

BALANCE

For space systems extremely low vibration is essential. The drive mechanism
(See Figure 10) of a Stirling engine is well suited to meet this requirement.
The rotating components can be completely balanced by attaching proper
counterweights to the two synchronized crankshafts, and by meeting certain
other conditions.

In order for the engine to be balanced, there must be no shaking forces in the
lateral, vertical, and longitudinal directions. It is intuitively obvious that
the sum of the inertia forces in the lateral, or x-direction (See Figure 10) is
zero, because the forces produced by the left half of the drive are equal in
magnitude and opposite in direction to the forces produced by the right half.
It is also obvious that the inertia forces are zero in the longitudinal direction
(perpendicular to the plane of the sketch). It is less apparent that the sum
of the forces in the verical direction is zero or can be made equal to zero.

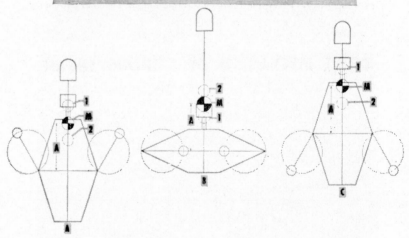

Figure 11. Various Positions of Stirling Engine Drive Mechanism

The principle by which the engine is balanced in the vertical direction will
now be discussed. First, assume that the mass of the power piston assembly
(power piston, push rod, yoke, and associated parts) is concentrated at its
center of gravity at point "1" (See Figure 11-a). Second, assume that the

mass of the displacer assembly (displacer, push rod, yoke, and accessories) is concentrated at its center of gravity at point "2". The engine is designed such that these two masses are exactly equal in magnitude.

It can now be assumed that the sum M of these two masses is concentrated at their center of gravity half-way between them. The location of this mass M, which is the total reciprocating mass, is found to be a vertical distance "A" from the two crankpins. Next, applying the same procedure in locating the center of gravity of the total mass M when the drive is in other positions (see Figures 11-b and 11-c), it is found that the center of gravity is still located a vertical distance exactly equal to "A".

With this relationship of the mass M being established to be a fixed vertical distance from the crankpins, the motions and forces are examined. The vertical y-location of the crankpins varies with harmonic motion as they rotate around the crank circle at constant speed. The combined mass M must, therefore, reciprocate with like motion, for it is always a constant vertical distance from the crankpins. As the mass M moves with harmonic motion, it produces a force which varies sinusoidally with time (see Figure 12).

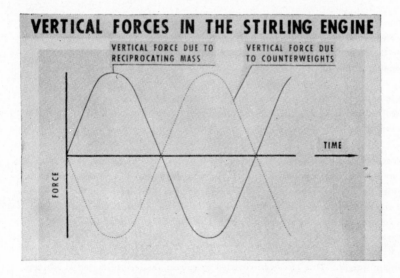

Figure 12. Vertical Forces in the Stirling Engine

To have zero force in the vertical direction, it is necessary to build into the system vertical forces exactly equal in magnitude and opposite in direction to the force produced by mass M. This is done by use of a counterweight

attached to each crankshaft (See Figure 10). Proper sizing of these counter
weights produces a desired counter-acting force with a vertical component
varying sinusoidally exactly equal and opposite to the force produced by the
reciprocating mass M.

To maintain a high degree of balance each component part of the drive mechanism
must have mass values which will satisfy the foregoing conditions. In addition
the geometry of the system must be precisely maintained. The length of the
power piston yoke must be equal to the displacer yoke; the length of the power
piston connecting rods must be equal to the length of the displacer connecting
rods; and the counterweights must be precisely located 180 degrees around
the axis of rotation from the crankpins.

By taking all precautions in the design and manufacture of the drive mechanism,
extremely low levels of vibration can be attained, as demonstrated by actual
operating engines. In addition, the engine can be isolated in a satellite installation by properly designed mounts to reduce any forces being transmitted
to other components aboard the satellite where vibration is undesired.

CONTROL

Various methods of controlling the engine output for solar space power have
been analyzed. For the system described in Section III, it would appear that
for the most part the satellite electrical power requirements are relatively
constant. Any deviations from maximum output are quite small.

It is not the intent of this paper to delve deeply into the complex problems
involved in various control modes; however, the selected system is outlined
briefly.

To achieve a reliable control system for a typical space capsule, it is desirable
to have minimum complexity. A system whereby the engine is operated at its
design point at all times meets this requirement. The system selected utilizes
an engine sized to match the known satellite equipment load. Should the load
be reduced at any period, the excess engine output is radiated into space.
A system such as this requires no valves or complex equipment. The additional
radiator required is of minor importance in relation to the over-all satellite
system weight. This has been verified by recent studies conducted at Allison.

VIII. ALLISON STIRLING ENGINE

In the previous sections, the primary design considerations necessary to
adapt the Stirling engine to a satellite secondary power system have been
discussed in a more or less general manner. The practical application of

these general parameters as integrated into an engine design are described in the following paragraphs.

The Allison Division of GMC has recently designed and built a Stirling engine, which in principle, embodies those features required in a space auxiliary power plant. The only significant departure from this concept in the Allison engine, currently under development, is that a nonspace type lubrication system was incorporated to facilitate early development of the various other engine components. A conventional lubrication system dependent on a one "g" environment to maintain the oil sump was utilized. The space type oil system development was conducted on a bench test facility independent of the engine with the plan of incorporating the resulting configuration into the assembly at some later date.

The mechanical configuration of the Allison development Stirling engine is shown in Figure 13. This design incorporates test equipment type components so that the engine can be used as a development tool in the evaluation of the significant parameters. Attempts were made to integrate the greatest possible flexibility into the engine. The disassembled engine components are shown in Figure 14.

In this engine, heat is supplied by NaK (sodium potassium) and rejected in a water coolant system. A pressure lubrication system is utilized in which lube pressure is obtained by use of a positive displacement gear type pump.

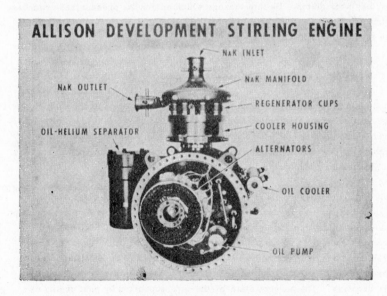

Figure 13. Allison Development Stirling Engine

Figure 14. Allison Stirling Engine Components

Conventional automotive type SAE 10 oil is used as the lubricant. The NaK flows past the heater tubes and is exhausted in an annular manifold. Water enters the cooler housing and absorbs the engine rejected heat. The working fluid, helium, flows from the cavity between the two pistons through the cooler tubes, regenerator matrix, heater tubes, and into the cavity above the displacer piston. Helium leakage which enters the pressurized crankcase from the buffer zone is reclaimed by the oil-helium separator mounted on the side of the crankcase.

IX. CONCLUSIONS

In summary, it has been shown that the characteristics of the Stirling engine are well suited to applications where engine efficiency has a large effect on over-all system weight. Satellite solar power very clearly falls in this category. The Stirling engine appears superior to competing power sources in the smaller outputs.

One important facet of the engine design is that high efficiencies can be obtained at relative moderate temperatures. It is also noteworthy to mention that the primary moving components, such as generators, pistons, and bearings operate in an environment conducive to long life. To date, no problems have been encountered which would forestall or limit the future development of the Stirling engine. In short, no scientific breakthroughs are required. The present state-of-the-art, supported by past engine experience, ensures the utmost in reliability.

REFERENCES

1. Welsh, H. W., Poste, E. A., and Wright, R. B.   The Advanced Stirling Engine for Space Power.   ARS 1033-49 (November 1959).

2. Rinia, R., and DuPre, F. D.   "Air Engines."   Philips Technical Review. Vol. 8 No. 5 (May 1946), pp. 129-160.

3. De Brey, H., and van Weenen, F. L.   "Philips Air Engines," Automotive Industries.   Vol. 97, No. 12 (15 December 1947), pp. 24-28.

4. "Philips Air Engines."   Philips Technical Review. (September 1958).

Summary: The Formal Report

In the introductory part of this chapter, we have indicated how learning the techniques of good report writing is valuable to the technical man. We have discussed the general characteristics of reports, and divided them into three major types, noting at the same time that this division was made chiefly for instructional purposes. You should remember that reports do not follow set rules for construction or type, but that, instead, if they have the qualities of singleness of purpose, exactness of data, clarity and conciseness of expression, coherence of arrangement, tactful presentation, and judgment, they are likely to fulfill the essential requirements of report writing. We have indicated the parts which are most likely to be found in the formal report; we have offered several samples of these reports for your consideration. Because the formal type of report is somewhat more likely to follow set rules than is the informal type, we have taken it up first; the following chapter will examine informal and memoranda reports.

Discussion Questions

1. The formal report is usually confined to what sort of work?
2. Give the major parts of a formal report.
3. Why is the order of the elements of the formal report flexible?
4. Why is the singleness of purpose of the report emphasized?
5. What is the advantage of a decimal system of outlining?

6. Why is it essential that you learn to write adequate abstracts?
7. Why are abstracts intended for the general public likely to be longer than those intended for a technically trained audience?
8. What are three ways by which one can cut down the number of words in an abstract?
9. Why is it necessary to be sure that the work you are planning on doing needs to be done?
10. Why is it so necessary to analyze the audience that will read the report?
11. Why is emphasis given to writing down material as the work progresses?
12. Why are card notes particularly useful?
13. State six rules which will help you to write simple, lucid prose.

Writing Assignments

1. Draw up an outline, using the decimal system, of a report which you might offer one of your instructors in some technical subject you are taking.
2. Write a report showing the good and bad qualities of some apparatus in one of your laboratories.
3. Write a report giving the progress of one of your own investigations in some technical subject.
4. Make an examination of one of the buildings of your school from the point of view of student safety in the event of enemy attack. Add recommendations to the report which you will write on the building.
5. Write a short report, employing all the parts of the formal report, on one of the following:
   a. Safety devices in the school laboratory
   b. Progress of a model farm or home
   c. Safety devices in some manufacturing concern you have visited recently
   d. The water system of the town in which you live
   e. Possibilities of using incentive systems in industries you know well.

5

Informal and Memoranda Reports

The informal report is usually suited to matters of limited interest and importance, or to problems which are merely parts of larger projects. The first complete report reproduced in this chapter, for instance, discusses whether or not a steam line already in existence will be large enough to handle the heavier load which will be put upon it if the Hammer and Forge Shop is moved to a new location. This is only one of many problems which the technical men of the Jones and Laughlin Steel Corporation will have to solve in order to relocate the shop. The Carson Electric Corporation report (page 179), on the other hand, discusses a problem which would concern only a relatively small number of technical people. Generally, such informal reports are brief.

Like the formal report, the informal type should have a clear statement of purpose, logical presentation of data, and exactness of phrasing.

Form

Although the formal report is almost always lengthy enough to justify most of the parts cited in Chapter 4, the informal report dispenses with as many of these parts as it can, and often combines parts. Information that would be included in the cover sheet, the title page, and the letter of transmittal of the formal report is often telescoped into a mere heading placed before the opening of the informal report. Two typical headings occur on pages 166 and 167.

The subject and the originator of the report, as well as the date of submission, are included in these headings. In formal reports this information would be given on the cover, the title page, and the letter of transmittal. Since more than one person will receive these reports, a distribution list is given.

PORTLAND CEMENT COMPANY
MONACA, WISCONSIN

Report No. X1582

SUBJECT: HARDENING TIME ON EXPERIMENTAL MIX #34S5

TO: J. A. Williams, Vice-President in Charge of Production, Home Office

           M. P. Monteverde, Research Director, Mansfield Plant

           G. C. Acheson, Division Engineer, Home Office

FROM: F. B. Schoenberg, Research Engineer

DATE: March 5, 19—

It is usual in most large corporations and companies to indicate the report number, such as the one placed at the right-hand side of this illustration. Numbers of this sort are assigned to each division within a company.

As in the formal report, it is common practice to head each division and to call attention to it by underlining. The writer will have to make such heads as will suit his material and clarify his organization for the reader. *Purpose, Conclusions, Recommendations,* and *Analysis* are typical notations. Occasionally, writers may feel that their reports are so short that the organization is self-explanatory and that division heads are therefore unnecessary.

Typical Reports

The Jones and Laughlin report on pages 167–169 [1] answers a relatively simple question. Its form and organization exemplify good industrial practice.

In this report Mr. Wood, the engineer, presents a direct statement of his problem which he labels "Study." The question asked under "Study" is answered specifically by the citation of adequate data.

[1] By permission of the Jones and Laughlin Steel Corporation.

JONES & LAUGHLIN STEEL CORPORATION
PITTSBURGH WORKS

DISTRIBUTION:

Mr. K. L. Grand, Chief Engineer
423 New Office Building

Mr. E. T. Keene, Superintendent
Power and Steam Division
325 New Office Building

Mr. R. K. Borros, Foreman
Hammer and Forge Shop

March 30, 19—

STEAM PRESSURE LOSS IN 14″ LINE
RELOCATION OF HAMMER AND FORGE SHOP

by

L. L. Wood, Engineer, Power and Steam Division

STUDY:

Is the present 14″ line from the Central Boiler House to the No. 11 Mill of adequate size to handle the steam load of the Hammer and Forge Shop, if it were moved to the Tie-Plate Building?

CONCLUSIONS:

The 14″ line is large enough to handle the additional load.

PRESENT FACILITIES:

A 14″ line approximately 3500 ft. long connects the Central Boiler House with the No. 11 Mill. At present, it supplies only two steam consumers:

(1) The No. 11 Mill engine

(2) A miscellaneous load beyond No. 11 Mill
(tar tanks, gas producers, air compressors, etc.).

The steam pressure at the boiler house header is maintained at 150 psi. An indicator card taken by the Steam Efficiency Department shows that steam at 144 psi is available at the No. 11 engine. This pressure drops to 132 psi at the cut-off. With the installation of the proposed receiver at the engine, the pressure will drop to only 138 psi.

A flow meter is located in the 14″ line at the boiler house. Since the No. 11 Mill does not run on week-ends, an accurate estimate can be made of the engine load and also the miscellaneous load.

STEAM PRESSURE LOSS IN 14″ LINE—
RELOCATION OF HAMMER AND FORGE SHOP   -2-

PRESENT FACILITIES (Cont'd)

The Steam Efficiency Department reports that, although the steam leaves
the boiler house with 100° F. superheat, it arrives at the No. 11 Mill
dry, without superheat. This may be due largely to the present small
steam flow through such a large, long line. With increased steam flow,
the steam should arrive at the engine with superheat. This, of course,
will decrease the pressure drops as calculated.

There are two 8″ gate valves installed in the 14″ line at the Tie-Plate
Building—one at the south end, and the other at the middle. These will
form a loop for the relocated Hammer and Forge Shop; but, in the
calculations, it was assumed that all of the steam would go through the
valve at the south end.

The following additional assumptions were made in the calculation of
pressure drops:

(a) Steam available at 150 psi

(b) Equivalent line length (boiler house to 8″ gate
valve at south end building) .... 3300 ft.

Equivalent line length (8″ gate valve to the
No. 11 engine) .... 1000 ft.

Total equivalent length of 14″ line .... 4300 ft.

(c) Steam flow, lb./hr.   Av.   Max.

	Av.	Max.
No. 11 engine	30,000	40,000
Miscellaneous	28,000	30,000
Present load	58,000	70,000
Hammer and Forge Shop	40,000	45,000
Proposed load	98,000	115,000

FLOW IN 8″ LINE TO HAMMER AND FORGE SHOP

Steam Flow, lb./hr.	Available Pressure, psi	Velocity f.p.m.*
40,000	138	5,820
	135	5,150
45,000	149	6,380
	145	5,980

* Crane recommends 6,000 to 10,000 f.p.m. for 150 psi

STEAM PRESSURE LOSS IN 14″ LINE
RELOCATION OF HAMMER AND FORGE SHOP   -3-

STEAM FLOW IN 14″ LINE

Date	Steam Flow lb./hour	Steam Pressure, psi		
		Boiler House	*Tie-Plate Bldg.	No. 11 Engine
		Actual Conditions		
December 22, 19—ᵃ	66,000	150	—	144
February 19, 19—ᵇ	25,000	150	—	149
February 20, 19—ᵇ	27,500	150	—	162
		Calculated Conditions		
Present	27,500	150	—	149
Average	58,000	150	—	145
Maximum	70,000	150	—	142
Future				
Average	98,000	150	138	137
Maximum	115,000	150	135	133
Average	98,000	160	149	148
Maximum	115,000	160	145	143

* 8″ Gate valve at south end of Tie-Plate Building

Data from:

   (a) Indicator card taken on No. 11 engine by Steam Efficiency Dept.

   (b) Flow meter and pressure charts at boiler house.

Engineering Department
Pittsburgh Works

The conclusion (which could have been placed at the end rather than at the beginning) is an excellent example of brevity. The discussion of the problem itself deals only with essential information. The writer first gives the present facilities, and then moves to assumptions upon which he bases his calculations. These bring supporting evidence to bolster his conclusion.

The next report (pages 171–175),[2] "Soldered and Mechanical Connections for Electrical Wiring," is classed as an informal report chiefly because of its limited scope. It has many of the parts of a formal report, for it includes a cover sheet, a statement of conclusions and an appendix, illustrating again that reports must be adapted to the circumstances giving rise to them, rather than being arranged and written according to set rules.

Although the problem is a minor one, it is analyzed thoroughly. Major heads and subheads indicate the progress of the writer's thought about his investigation, and the appendix re-enforces the treatment of the subject.

PROGRESS REPORTS

The report on page 176 [3] is illustrative of one of the commonest types of reports—the progress report. Such reports are sometimes requested as the work on a problem proceeds; sometimes the scientific personnel are asked to make such reports at regular intervals, usually from month to month.

One of the special values of such reports is that they become an instrument for supervision. The administrator in charge of a scientific laboratory can read over the reports which are periodically turned in and make a reasonably good estimate of the efficiency, intelligence, and ambition of the men and women who are working for him. Under these circumstances, you can see the advantages of being able to write such reports well and being able to read them quickly yet thoroughly.

It is usually a standard measure to limit reports of this sort to a minimum of words. Since the entire project will be the subject of a full report later, it is the part of wisdom to keep the periodic report brief.

Mr. Hall's report on page 176 shows the work he has done, and also indicates the project he is going to undertake in the coming month.

[2] Reproduced by permission of the Aluminum Company of America.
[3] Reproduced through the courtesy of the Firestone Tire and Rubber Co.

MECHANICAL AND SOLDERED JOINTS

IN

ALUMINUM ELECTRICAL CONDUCTORS

Jan. 26, 19—

Chemical Metallurgy Division

ALUMINUM COMPANY OF AMERICA
Aluminum Research Laboratories   No. 183–6–10
Chemical Metallurgy Division
New Kensington, Pa.   Jan. 26, 19—

SOLDERED AND MECHANICAL CONNECTIONS FOR
ELECTRICAL WIRING

Outdoor exposures have been in progress for about 6 years to evaluate conventional methods of termination, when used on aluminum electrical conductor wire. Included were No. 8 aluminum wire (E.C. grade) and its electrical equivalent No. 10 copper wire. Three types of joints were used: (1) soldered Western Union, (2) wire soldered to 35-ampere copper lugs, and (3) wire mechanically joined to cadmium plated brass wedge type terminals. Sets of joints connected in series were exposed in searchlight circuits (13 amperes at either 110 or 220 volts A.C.) in the industrial atmosphere at New Kensington, Pa.: (1) on roof of these Laboratories (3 years), and (2) in plant at river bank (5¾ years).

MATERIAL:

A list of the various types of joints included in this investigation is shown in Table I. The connections in the copper wire employ the conventional 50–50 lead-tin solder and rosin flux; the aluminum wires were soldered with No. 800* solder and No. 61 flux.*

PROCEDURE:

Either four or five specimens of each type of joint listed in Table I were exposed at two different locations to the industrial atmosphere at New Kensington. One test rack was located on the laboratory roof, and the other was located on the river bank at the New Kensington Works. Both test racks were wired in series in existing floodlight circuits, operating at about 13 amperes.

Electrical resistances of each individual joint were measured prior to exposure and at various intervals during the test. The potential drop method employing a type K–2 potentiometer and a sensitive galvanometer was used to determine the resistances of these electrical connections. Current through the test specimen was supplied by a lead storage battery.

* Current recommendation for this type of application would be Alcoa No. 800 solder and Alcoa No. 64 flux.

–1–

One set of joints was removed from the rack at the plant after two years and five months. A metallographic examination of cross sections of joints of one of each type specimen revealed that all were in good condition. No significant corrosion was observed. A similar set of specimens was removed from this same test rack after 5¾ years of exposure. The results of this examination are presented in this report. Although the joints on the test rack on the laboratory roof had been measured periodically to determine changes in electrical resistance, none of these connections has been removed for a metallographic examination.

DISCUSSION:

Electrical Performance

All of the original resistances fell within the range of 395–483 microhms. Close agreement was found for the resistances of duplicate specimens of any given type. It is apparent from these graphs that: (1) irrespective of the type of joint, the electrical resistances were in the neighborhood of 400 to 500 microhms, and (2) exposure to the industrial atmosphere at New Kensington for 5¾ years caused no significant changes in the electrical resistance of these joints.

Resistance to Corrosion

The Western Union joints in both the copper and aluminum wires are in good condition. Several voids can be seen in the soldered copper joint and slight porosity is evident in the aluminum joint. No appreciable corrosion has occurred in either case.

When aluminum wire specimens were exposed without any protection, the solder showed some corrosion in the fillet only and the aluminum wire showed some corrosion immediately adjacent to the solder. No corrosion, however, developed within the joint with the copper lug and there was no apparent change in the electrical efficiency of these joints. Duplicate joints using rubber insulated aluminum wire and electrician's tape over the soldered joint did not reveal any corrosion of the wire or solder.

The mechanical connections made with cadmium plated brass terminals produced moderate corrosion on the aluminum wires adjacent to the brass terminals. This was evidently galvanic corrosion which developed after the cadmium coating had weathered from the freely exposed surfaces of the brass. The mechanical connections apparently formed a weathertight joint since there was not any evidence of corrosion of aluminum within the joint and no change in electrical resistance of the termination. Of the two aluminum specimens (bare or insulated) the depth of attack was slightly greater on the aluminum

–2–

wire that had been covered with rubber insulation, possibly because moisture in the crevice of this type of joint would tend to dry more slowly than when the wire was bare. It is likely that the attack of the aluminum adjacent to these mechanical joints could have been prevented by the use of a wrapping of electrician's tape. The cross-sectional views of the mechanical joints on the copper wire reveal that they are in good condition.

Both aluminum wire and copper wire displayed their expected high resistance to atmospheric weathering at areas away from the joints. The uninsulated wires were darkened by the accumulation of industrial dirt, but corrosion was very shallow. On the aluminum wire some galvanic action took place adjacent to the copper or brass terminals, but this attack did not have any noticeable effect on the electrical resistance of the joint.

CONCLUSIONS:

From these tests of 5¾ years' duration in an industrial atmosphere, the following conclusions have been drawn.

(1) Aluminum conductor wire (E.C.) revealed a high inherent resistance to corrosion and performed satisfactorily when terminated by conventional methods: (1) soldered Western Union joints, (2) soldered copper lugs, or (3) mechanical type cadmium plated brass terminals.

(2) Some galvanic attack developed in the aluminum wire immediately adjacent to soldered copper lug or cadmium plated brass mechanical terminals, but the corrosion being "outside" the joints did not affect the electrical resistance. It was shown that such corrosion could be prevented by covering the joint with electrician's tape.

(3) Since most electrical terminations are not freely exposed to the weather and are generally protected by tape when out in the weather, the good electrical performance during almost six years' exposure outdoors of the aluminum conductors and terminations indicates the adequacy of aluminum conductors and the adaptability of conventional methods of termination for general electrical applications.

A. B. McKee
A. B. McKee

Approved: *C. J. Walton*

ABM:smp

TABLE I

SOLDERED AND MECHANICAL CONNECTIONS FOR ELECTRICAL WIRING

S. No.	Joint	Wire	Solder	Flux	Insulated	Joint Taped
63947	Soldered Western Union	#10 Copper(1)	50-50 Lead-Tin	Rosin	No	No
48		#8 Aluminum	No. 800(2)	No. 61(2)	No	No
51	Soldered 35 ampere Copper Lugs	#8 Aluminum	No. 800	No. 61	No	No
54	"	#10 Copper	50-50 Lead-Tin	Rosin	No	No
55	"	#8 Aluminum	No. 800	No. 61	Rubber	Yes
58	"	#10 Copper	50-50 Lead-Tin	Rosin	"	"
59	Mechanical Type	#8 Aluminum	None	None	No	No
60	Cadmium Plated	#10 Copper	None	None	No	No
61	Brass Terminals	#8 Aluminum	None	None	Rubber	No
62		#10 Copper	None	None	Rubber	No

(1) All copper wire used in this investigation was tin-coated. This tin-coating prevents corrosion of the wire by the sulfur in rubber insulation and also facilitates the soldering operation.

(2) The current recommendation for this type of application would be Alcoa No. 804 solder and Alcoa No. 64 flux.

STRESS RELAXATION OF SPECIAL POLYMERS FOR
HIGH TEMPERATURE USE

Problem No. 1052
G. L. Hall
July 6, 19--

Object:

To determine the stress relaxation rate of butyl, silicone and Viton rubber stocks.

Summary of Results and Conclusions:

Silicone and Viton A stocks had very good stress retention in a 10,000-minute test at 120°C. Viton A-HV had lower stress retention, and butyl rubber the lowest retention of stress among the high-temperature elastomers tested.

Experimental Details and Data:

The measurements were made in the stress relaxation apparatus under the standard test conditions for continuous stress relaxation (1). The tests were conducted at 120°C at a continuous elongation of 50 percent. The silicone rubber stocks gave a very small stress decay in the standard one-day test, and the time was extended to 10,000 minutes.

The stress relaxation data are listed below as the percentage losses of the original stress. The original stress of each vulcanizate strip was measured one-half minute after the strip had been elongated 50% in the 120°C apparatus.

Resin-cured butyl (stock No. 4492) (60-min. cure @ 320°F)	65%
Cohrlastic M-777U (stock No. 3603)	20%
Silastic 916U (stock No. 7861)	27.5%
Silicone SE-555U (stock No. 735)	25%
Viton A (stock No. 7868)	25%
Viton A-HV (stock No. 7890)	46.5%

Thus, the Viton A and silicone rubber stocks lost about one-fourth of the original stress, and the Cohrlastic M-777U was best among the three silicone rubbers which were tested. Viton A-HV lost 46.5 percent of the original stress, almost twice as much as Viton A. Resin-cured butyl rubber showed the highest stress relaxation, losing 65% of the original stress.

However, resin-cured butyl was much superior to Hevea and SBR vulcanizates, which had been tested previously (2) and found to lose 100 percent of the original stress under these test conditions.

Major Objective for Next Month:

To modify the stress relaxation apparatus for operation at high temperatures - up to 275°F.

References:

1. Tobolsky, A. V., I. B. Prettyman, and J. H. Dillon, J. Appl. Phys., 15, 380-395 (1944).

2. Hall, G. L., Conant, F. S., and Rigby, J D., Firestone Research Report, Problem No. 983, Report No. 6, April 6, 1954, page 6.

Reference to Original Data:

Original Data Sheets Nos. 1-3, Problem No. 1052, dated June 6 and 24, 19--.

FORM REPORTS

Sometimes informal reports require nothing more than adding figures or remarks to questions asked on printed sheets. Such reports, however, now and then require careful technical consideration. Recommendations and conclusions are rarely offered, and there is no necessity for such things as cover sheets, letters of transmittal, or appendixes.

These reports, usually called "form reports," do pose certain problems to the person who is required to make the form out. He must canvass the entire problem, asking himself, "What must such a form report tell me?" If the form report is merely an inspection report, like that on page 178,[4] the person responsible for making out the form must know the apparatus well enough to make certain that he includes all items that might be pertinent. If the inspection report were to deal with such a product as a refrigerator which has just come off the assembly line, then totally different kinds of information would be needed on the report—the state of the door seal, for instance, and the quality of the painting.

In such a report as this the aim is to secure the needed information with a minimum of written matter. The employee should remember when making out forms of this type that the least possible "bookwork" is a desirable feature.

The report on page 179 requires a far greater degree of technical education and ability than the preceding example.

The form report [5] on pages 180–182 requires much greater technical skill and knowledge than the preceding one. Completion of such a report requires considerable mathematical manipulation, following the formulae given on the second and third pages of the form. The aim of the report is to give the location of the center of gravity, and after this has been determined, to arrive at the value of the car's moment of inertia.

The growth of union activity in modern corporations has made necessary the type of form shown on page 183. Representatives of the union and management often need to talk over matters pertaining to the labor situation within the company and to discuss grievances of workers. The union officials, usually members of an incentive group, must be paid for their time. As a rule, this payment is made by the corporation concerned rather than by the union. Under

[4] By permission of the Aluminum Company of America.
[5] Reproduced through the courtesy of General Motors Proving Ground.

ALUMINUM COMPANY OF AMERICA
CLEVELAND WORKS

CRANE INSPECTION REPORT

Location _Bldg. 8 Heat treat Dept._ Date _12-22-52_
Crane No. _4 Ton Euclid Crane_ Inspected by _Joe Vostruck_

Indicate items checked and condition of those items as O.K., Need Attention, Worn-out, Burned-out, Etc. Use Remarks section and reverse side for fuller explanation and recommendations, and list of parts needed.

Motor Parts	Armature	Commutator	Field	Brushes	B.Holders	Bearing	Grease Oil	Rotor	Stator	Gear Pinion
Bridge Motor				OK	dirty	OK	OK	OK	OK	fair
Hoist Motor				OK	dirty	OK	OK	OK	OK	fair
Rack Motor				OK	OK	OK	OK	OK	OK	fair

Controller Parts	Brushes	B.Holders	Finger	Contacts	Levers	Resistance	Bolts	Wiring
Bridge Controller			fair	fair		OK	OK	OK
Hoist Controller			fair	fair		OK	OK	OK
Rack Controller			OK	OK		OK	OK	OK

Knife Switches		Bridge Track Wheels	OK	End Trucks		OK
Limit Switches	OK	Trolley Track Wheels	OK	Gear Guard		OK
Safety Switches	OK	Bridge Axle Bushing	worn	Cage		
Fuse Clips	OK	Trolley Axle Bushing	worn	Bolts and Rivets		loose
Relays		Traverse Bushing	worn	Railings		OK
Electric Brake	OK	Bearing (Not Motor)	worn	Walks		OK
Mechanical Brake	OK	Drums	OK	Bumpers		OK
Foot Brake		Drum Gear	fair	General Wiring		OK
Main Collector	OK	Drum Pinion	worn	Leaders		
Trolley Coll.Shoes	need change	Bridge Gear	worn	Grease Cups		
Conductor Rails		Trolley Travel Gear	worn	Crane Alignment		OK
Trolley Wires	OK	Intermediate Gear	worn	Top Blocks		OK
Cables	worn	Traverse Shaft	worn			
Bottom Blocks	OK	Main Hoist Shaft	worn			

REMARKS _Splined coupling and splined motor extension shaft are worn, also top cover bolts in Trolley carriage gear case are loose (thread needs retapping) / change steel cable 125' 3/8"_

these circumstances, a report must be submitted of the time spent in conference.

The technical man who may be in a supervisory position in a large plant is often asked to fill out forms pertaining to industrial accidents. All forward-looking corporations now keep careful records of accidents in an attempt to prevent recurrences. The report shown on page 184 gives an idea of how carefully these records must be made out.

Form 638-3   CARSON ELECTRIC CORPORATION
                       ANDERVILLE, LOUISIANA

DATE: August 1, 19—

FROM: E. H. Robbins   PLACE OF   Apex Trans-
              Field Engineer   EXAMINATION: mission Co.
To: Engineering Dept.   Newark 2, N. J
              East End Works

                                           DATE OF   July 27, 19—
                                           EXAMINATION:

APPARATUS: Transformer   PURCHASED ON: June 22, 19—
STYLE #   DRAWING #
634299   42A649   DATE OF FAILURE: July 25, 19—

COMPLAINT: Transformer caught on fire on July 25, 19—.

CONDITION AT TIME   All insulation badly charred. Some copper melted
OF EXAMINATION: down. Oil almost completely evaporated. Steel case
                    warped.

CAUSE OF FAILURE: High voltage connection (drawing, item 27) became
                    detached and fell on low voltage connection (drawing,
                    item 3) causing 66 kv to flow through winding designed
                    to carry 660 volts.

OPERATION BY
ENGINEER: Examination made.

CONCLUSIONS: The cause of failure lies with the Apex Transmission
                    Company who installed the transformer. The holding
                    bolts on the high voltage side were not turned down
                    sufficiently to hold the connection in place, nor were
                    the necessary lock washers used.

MATERIAL NEEDED: None.

CHARGES: None.

                                   E. H. Robbins
                                   E. H. Robbins

EHR:cs

GENERAL MOTORS PROVING GROUND

CENTER OF GRAVITY LOCATION
AND MOMENT OF INERTIA

CAR NO. _____

CAR _____

MODEL _____   YEAR _____

ENGINE

DISPLACEMENT _____ CU IN.

COMPRESSION RATIO: SPEC _____ OBS _____

IGNITION TIMING _____ °BTC

HORSEPOWER _____ @ _____ RPM

TORQUE _____ @ _____ RPM

CARBURETOR _____ BBL   EXHAUST _____

FUEL _____

CHASSIS

BODY STYLE _____

TRANSMISSION _____

AXLE RATIO _____ :1

N/V _____

TIRES _____

SIZE _____

PRESSURE: FRONT _____ REAR _____

TEST WEIGHT-POUNDS: _____

DISTRIBUTION:

LF _____ + RF _____ =

LR _____ + RR _____ =

TOTAL _____ + _____ =

WHEELBASE _____ INCHES

TREAD: FRONT _____ INCHES

REAR _____ INCHES

DATE _____

ODOMETER _____

CENTER OF GRAVITY LOCATION

_____ INCHES ABOVE GROUND

_____ INCHES BEHIND CENTERLINE OF FRONT WHEEL

_____ INCH TO _____ OF CENTERLINE OF CAR

MOMENT OF INERTIA

ABOUT TRANSVERSE HORIZONTAL LINE THROUGH CENTER OF GRAVITY

_____ LB FT²

PG-475

MOMENT OF INERTIA
CALCULATION

Car_____ Model_____ Year_____

Date_____   Odometer_____

BASIC FORMULA - LONG SWING: $I = K W_1 L_1 (T_{1c}^2 - T_1^2) + W(B_1 - H) (K T_{1c}^2 - B_1 + H) - A(B_1 - H)^2$

$$I = 20028 \left(\underset{T_{1c}^2}{15.736} - \underset{T_1^2}{\quad} \right) + \left(\underset{W}{15.736} - \quad \right) (0.81466 \times \underset{T_{1c}^2}{15.736} + \underset{H}{\quad}) - \left(\underset{A}{15.736} - \underset{H}{\quad} \right)^2$$

$I = \underline{\hspace{4cm}}$

$I = \underline{\hspace{4cm}}$

$I = \underline{\hspace{4cm}}$ Pound-Feet Squared

BASIC FORMULA - SHORT SWING: $I = K W_s L_s (T_{sc}^2 - T_s^2) + W(B_s - H) (K T_{sc}^2 - B_s + H) - A(B_s - H)^2$

$$I = 10176 \left(\underset{T_{sc}^2}{8.234} - \underset{T_s^2}{\quad} \right) + \left(\underset{W}{8.234} - \quad \right) (0.81466 \times \underset{T_{sc}^2}{8.234} + \underset{H}{\quad}) - \left(\underset{A}{8.234} - \underset{H}{\quad} \right)^2$$

$I = \underline{\hspace{4cm}}$

$I = \underline{\hspace{4cm}}$

$I = \underline{\hspace{4cm}}$ Pound-Feet Squared

NOTE: Since the above calculations are to find the moment of inertia of the car about its own center
of gravity, the two results should be equal.

PG-474 Rev 1-55

Car No._____

CENTER OF GRAVITY LOCATION CALCULATIONS

Car _____ Model _____ Year _____ Date _____

$$H = \frac{20028(\,T^2_{lc} - T^2_{1}\,) - 10176(\,T^2_{sc} - T^2_{s}\,) + (12.819 \times \underline{\quad} \, T^2_{lc} \quad -6.708 \times \underline{\quad} \, T^2_{sc}\,) - (\underline{\quad}) + \underline{\quad}\,)179.82}{0.81466 \times (\, W \, T^2_{lc} - T^2_{sc}\,) - (\, W \,) + A \quad 15.004}$$

H= _____

H= _____

H= _____

H= _____ = _____ Feet, or (X12) = _____ Inches

H= _____ Inches Above Ground

Y= Lateral Location of C of G = $\dfrac{(LF - RF)FT + (LR - RR)RT}{2W}$ = _____

Y= _____ = _____

Y= _____ Inch to (Left Right) of CL of Car

X= Longitudinal Location of C of G

X= $\dfrac{\text{Wheelbase (LR + RR)}}{\text{Total Weight}}$ = _____ = _____ =

X= _____ Inches Behind CL of Front Wheels

UNION CALCIUM COMPANY
MILWAUKEE, WISCONSIN

**UNION-MANAGEMENT CONFERENCE
TIME REPORT**

PAYMENT APPROVED   x

PAYMENT NOT APPROVED _____

FOR TIME SPENT IN CONFERENCE

ON   Grievance of H. C. Heaslip, Transportation Div.

BY   William Alvah Kennedy
            (name of union representative)

TITLE   Shop Steward, Transportation Division
            (title of union representative)

WITH   G. William McKee
            (name of management representative)

TITLE   Associate Manager, Industrial Relations Dept.
            (title of management representative)

I CERTIFY THAT THE TIME HERE REPORTED HAS
BEEN USED SOLELY FOR UNION-MANAGEMENT
MEETINGS, IN ACCORDANCE WITH AGREEMENT
#S–23

SIGNED   *William Alvah Kennedy*
            UNION REPRESENTATIVE

APPROVED   *A. H. Blackstone*
            TIME STUDY DEPARTMENT

FOR ACCOUNTING DEPT.

UNION   USWA

HOURLY   x

SALARY

STARTING TIME
9:00 AM

STOPPING TIME
11:30 AM

ELAPSED TIME
2.5 hours

NAME
William Alvah Kennedy

DEPARTMENT
Transportation

FOR PAY ENDING
August 23, 19—

APPROVED:
L. N. Asch
Paymaster

DATE OF MEETING
8/15/—

Memoranda Reports

Formal reports are furthest removed from memoranda reports. In this latter type, the technical man finds it most simple and direct to express by means of a letter the body of information which he wishes to communicate, perhaps to members of his own company, or to interested persons outside his organization. Since this textbook has already taken up in some detail the common forms of interoffice memoranda (see pages 78–81) and has given a good deal of atten-

METHANOL CORPORATION
SIOUX CITY, IOWA

ACCIDENT REPORT

DATE ___7/25/—___

NAME OF EMPLOYEE	John T. Charles DIVISION Refrigeration
PLACE OF OCCURRENCE	At employee's bench, FOREMAN Section Kr, Refrigerator Aisle Arthur S. Sibling
DESCRIPTION OF ACCIDENT	Employee was bracing refrigerator unit, Style 3844058, with steel blocks. One of these blocks (weight 11 pounds) fell from the bench and struck him on the instep of the right foot, fracturing two small bones.

WAS EMPLOYEE WORKING AT HIS REGULAR JOB?   YES   No   (IF NOT, STATE REASONS)
                                                                       x

MACHINE INVOLVED IN ACCIDENT   None   IDENTIFICATION OF   PART OF MACHINE
                                                            MACHINE   CAUSING INJURY

WERE MECHANICAL SAFEGUARDS PRESENT?   YES   No
                                                                   x

WERE MECHANICAL SAFEGUARDS IN USE?   YES   No
                                                                x

RECOMMENDATIONS TO PREVENT RECURRENCE

(SUPERVISOR'S RECOMMENDATION)   It is recommended that a strip of wood, two inches high and one inch wide, be screwed firmly across the entire width of the outer edge of the bench. The strip will be too narrow to allow the worker to place the blocks on it.

(SAFETY ENGINEER'S RECOMMENDATION)   The foreman's recommendation should help to prevent another such accident. It is also suggested that the employee be forbidden to have more than one block on the bench at one time.

(EMPLOYEE'S RECOMMENDATION)   A tin sheet should be placed below and about two inches out from the edge of the bench. If a block should then fall, it would be caught by the sheet which should be bent in such a way as to cause the block to fall under the bench.

PERSONAL DATA ON EMPLOYEE

AGE	SINGLE	MARRIED	DIVORCED	WIDOWED	MALE	FEMALE	NATIONALITY
38		x			x		American

OCCUPATIONAL DATA

LABOR GRADE	WORK SCHEDULE	DAYS PER WEEK	JOB #	PAY RATE
8	7:00 AM–4:00 PM	5	322	$2.25

EXTRA HOURS WORKED IN THE THREE DAYS PRIOR TO ACCIDENT   5½

WAGE PAYMENT PLAN WHEN INJURED	DAY WORK	INCENTIVE	SALARY	AVERAGE WEEKLY WAGE
		yes		$90.00

JONES & LAUGHLIN STEEL CORPORATION

Pittsburgh Works

October 22, 19—

TO:　　　A. L. Sanders, Assistant Vice President, Main Office Bldg.

FROM:　　E. H. Bell, Production Superintendent

SUBJECT:

Furnace Cooling Water Piping

Booster Pump to Furnaces ·

Study:

Is present furnace cooling water piping from the proposed booster pumps to the proposed slab reheating furnaces adequate for the increase in cooling water supply?

Recommendation:

It is suggested that the cooling water piping to the slab reheating furnaces be increased to the diameters shown in the accompanying Sketch A.

Present Equipment:

Cooling water to the slab reheating furnaces is now supplied by a 4000 gpm pump at 50 psi. The present diameter of the cooling water piping is 12 in. throughout its entire length.

Proposed Equipment:

It is proposed that the 4000 gpm pump be replaced by a new 6500 gpm pump with 80 psi discharge. The pump should be such that by replacing the impeller at some future date it will pump 7200 gpm at 80 psi.

The proposed piping is based on a flow of 7500 gpm so as to be adequate for a future pump capacity of 7200 gpm. With a flow of 6500 gpm, the pressure drop through the suggested line sizes (See Sketch A) will be approximately 7.0 psi.

Operations During Changeover:

The present cooling water piping can be removed and the new lines installed without interfering with furnace operations. The 6 in. emergency lines to each furnace can be used during the installation.

CC:

L. C. Heldt, Maintenance Superintendent, 243 Main Office Bldg.
R. V. Goss, Foreman, Slab Reheating Furnaces

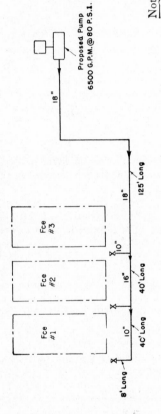

Engr. Dept

22 Oct. 1948

JONES & LAUGHLIN STEEL CORPORATION
Pittsburgh Works

STRIP MILL

Slab Reheating Furnace Cooling Water Piping

Booster Pump to Furnaces

Note: The above are approx. straight pipe lengths.

SKETCH A

S.V.

tion to the form of the business letter in Chapter 2, we may assume a fairly complete knowledge of this type of letter.

The material treated in the memorandum usually deals, as was indicated on page 165, with matters of minor importance, or perhaps with individual phases of larger projects. Reports giving information about subjects of comparatively slight value are almost always capable of being condensed into a one or two page letter.

As in other reports, it is advisable to separate the material by descriptive headings in even so short a report as a memorandum must be. Observe the report on pages 185–186 [6] to see what the writer has done to clarify his material.

The material of this report has been thoroughly condensed by the writer. Because of the self-explanatory heads, even a quick glance will reveal to the Assistant Vice President the purpose, the basic recommendation, and the details pertaining to the study. The carbon copy notations, which appear at the end of this report, take the place of the distribution list of the informal report used by this company and illustrated on page 167.

The following memorandum report, written within the E. I. du Pont de Nemours and Company organization, gives information to a special group of employees—those charged with communication activities, such as the writing of advertising copy, technical and semi-technical articles, and material for employee magazines. The subject deals with the protection of the company's trade-marks.

E. I. DU PONT DE NEMOURS & COMPANY, INCORPORATED
WILMINGTON, DELAWARE

August 4, 19—

TO: All Plant Managers

FROM: Public Relations Department

Subject: Trade-Marks

In view of the enactment of the Lanham Act, every reasonable precaution should be taken to ensure the protection of du Pont registered trade-marks in all literature, including employee publications.

Trade-marks have a very real value. If a trade-mark is not properly used and protected, there is danger of its being forfeited.

[6] Reproduced by permission of the Jones and Laughlin Steel Corporation.

Rules for Protection of Trade-Marks

A. Always use the du Pont oval trade-mark with the words "<u>Reg</u>. U. <u>S</u>. Pat. <u>Off</u>." beneath in small letters. This is done by capitalizing the initial letter and enclosing the word in quotation marks. Moreover, the oval should always stand alone and <u>nothing</u> should impinge upon it.

B. Another rule is that the trade-mark must be made quite distinctive. This is done by capitalizing the initial letter and enclosing the word in quotation marks. Sometimes, the quotation marks are omitted, in which case each letter of the trade-mark should be capitalized.

C. Another rule, and one easily overlooked, is that the public must be provided with a suitable generic name for the product in question. For example, when a trade-mark is used for the <u>first</u> time in a given story, it must be used as an adjective modifying a suitable generic term such as "Acele" cellulose acetate rayon, "Duco" lacquer, "Żelan" durable repellent finish. (It should be pointed out in this connection that it is not sufficient or proper to use the trade-mark in opposition with the generic expression, e.g., "Acele," a cellulose acetate rayon.)

D. According to the Legal Department, the above general rule holds only for the first time the trade-mark is used in any given story. Thereafter, in that particular story, the trade-mark may be used alone. If, however, several separate stories on the same product are used in any given publication the rule outlined above should be followed, since each is a separate and distinct story.

E. One exception is found in the case where a suitable chemical name is given first, followed by a statement to the effect that the product in question is sold under such and such a designated trade-mark. For example, the following is permissible.

> The du Pont Company has developed a line of surface active agents, technically known as fatty alcohol sulfates, which are sold under the trade-mark of "Duponol."

(Incidentally, the Legal Department says we should use the expression <u>trade-mark</u> rather than <u>trade-name</u>, since the latter applies more accurately to our corporate name or its abbreviation—du Pont.)

F. The du Pont Products Index should be consulted whenever there is any question of the proper trade-mark designation. You are referred to pages 3 through 16 in the Products Index for the discussion of this subject as well as a listing of the major trade-marks owned by E. I. du Pont de Nemours & Co., Inc., and its subsidiaries.

Allan Perry
Community Relations Division

The technical man will also be asked to make occasional memorandum-type reports of small individual problems that occur in the course of the day's business. A customer may perhaps complain about the quality of the material which he is receiving. As a result, the official of the company who is concerned with such matters will ask for a scientific analysis of the material in question. A memorandum report, such as the one reproduced on page 190,[7] will then suffice for the answer to the question.

A concluding example of the memorandum report is that on page 191.[8] In this a salesman reports to the home office about materials and processes which are being developed by another concern and which seem to offer possibilities for the sale of the company's product.

Sales engineers and technicians are often asked to make such investigations as these; they often make such informal reports on their own responsibility. As a result of the information which has been forwarded by Mr. Waters, the home office will probably indicate its interest in the projects under development by Messrs. Small and Briggs.

Thinking About Report Problems

In order to summarize the steps which may be taken in the preparation of a report, the following procedure may be set down.

1. *Formulating the problem clearly.* Usually the authorization will determine the problem, but the writer must limit it and state it as explicitly as possible. He must exclude everything that does not advance his main purpose.
2. *Surveying the problem.* This will consist of looking over what has been done and is being done on the problem. The writer will then determine what he must do and, most important of all, how he will do it. Once the writer has determined the method of attack on the problem, he has gone a long way toward solving his difficulties.
3. *Gathering data on the problem.* From the formulation and survey of the problem, the writer will know generally what type of information he is seeking. He may secure this from company files, from books and periodicals, from laboratory work and the observation of processes. He may question individuals who have worked in the same field. As a result of the formulation and survey of

[7] By permission of the Jones and Laughlin Steel Corporation.
[8] Reproduced by permission of the Aluminum Company of America.

JONES & LAUGHLIN STEEL CORPORATION
PITTSBURGH, PENNSYLVANIA

COMPLAINT ON MASTERCRAFT SPRING WIRE ·

TO: E. H. Bell, Production Superintendent

FROM: R. Nolan, Testing Laboratory

DATE: Jan. 23, 19—

1.   Subject concern claims it has encountered some 10-1/2 gage
Mastercraft Spring Wire which seems to have both hard and soft spots
in the same coil. Some sample springs have been submitted for our
examination. No claim has been made, but customer has asked that we
take caution. No shipping references are available.

2.   Examination:

Sample	Size	Tensile (psi)	% R/A	Etch
1	.129″	204,000	45.0	Sound
2	"	204,000	46.0	"
3	"	203,500	46.0	"
4	"	193/204,000	22.0/46.0	"

Chemical Analysis:

Samples	C	Mn	P	S	Si
Nos. 1, 2, & 3	.67	.89	.027	.020	.21
4	.65	1.04	.032	.024	.25

Microexamination:

Samples Nos. 1, 2 and 3—Satisfactory patented and drawn
structures.

Sample No. 4—Martensitic areas observed on surface are
excessive.

3.   Comments:

The nonuniformity encountered by customer, substantiated by
our examination, is believed due to the martensitic formation observed on
the surface of one of the samples submitted for our examination. This
unusual grain structure is believed due to a fin on the hot rolled rod that
either cooled extremely fast after the patenting operation or caused
excessive temperature in drafting the wire. Customer can be assured that
every effort is being made to correct this condition.

```
                            SALESMAN'S MEMORANDUM 7         DATE   5/19/-
   FROM      R. G. WATERS              TO      MR. THOMAS C. JONES
             CHICAGO OFFICE                    CHICAGO OFFICE

   RE -      APEX HARDWARE CO.                 CHICAGO                    ILLINOIS
                           (CUSTOMER)           (TOWN)                     (STATE)
   PRODUCT OR {                         PARTIES  { Mr. R. M. Small, Dev. Engr.
   INDUSTRY      Aluminum Sheet        INTERVIEWED { Mr. A. R. Briggs, Project Engr.
```

Confirmed results of tests made on experimental samples of aluminum sheet submitted for making initial run of aluminum lock sets.

Mr. Small has also been developing a line of aluminum drawer handles and cabinet handles fabricated from sheet.

We are also testing a clear protective coating made by the A.B.C. Company.

R. G. WATERS

RGW/eh

CC: Mr. W. T. Mitman, Pgh.
     Mr. M. G. Roth, Pgh.
     Messrs. P. C. Althen & C. Braglic, NH

the problem and the gathering of data, the writer will be able to make a tentative outline with its necessary subdivisions.

4. *Classifying data on the problem.* Once the writer has secured all necessary data, he must group them in their proper relationships. His classification will be determined by the subdivisions he has made of the problem as he has surveyed it. Classification will put each fact in its proper place within the outline.

5. *Evaluating data applicable to the problem.* Interpretation of those facts which have been left after classification must be done by logical process, largely by inductive reasoning, although the application of general principles to specific cases also has a part in this. The writer has now reached the recommendation and conclusion stage of the report, and he must view his details in the light of his problem to ascertain their meaning.

6. *Stating recommendations and conclusions.* These results of the writer's thought on his gathered, classified, and evaluated data should usually be arranged in climactic order of importance.

Conclusion

In this chapter, we have illustrated the informal and the memorandum types of reports. We have indicated the form and organization of these types. We have stressed the advisability of headings and subheadings for even short memorandum reports. To the technical man the nomenclature applied to the types of reports is least important. Instead, the clarity and logic of his presentation are paramount.

Discussion Questions

1. What is the advantage of numbering short reports?
2. What kinds of material do the informal memorandum reports usually deal with?
3. Give a half-dozen actual examples of possible subjects for memoranda reports.
4. What special value may a progress report have for a supervisor?
5. Why is it more difficult to make out the form of the form report than to make the report itself?
6. Why are the mathematical formulae added to the report on page 142?
7. Why would it be necessary to have a report on an employee's grievance?
8. What use is commonly made of accident reports?
9. Why is it so important to formulate the problem of any kind of report clearly?
10. How does the use of a card notation system make it easier to classify data on any problem?

6

The Technical and the Semitechnical Article

Purpose of This Chapter

This chapter is intended to help those students and practicing technical people who may wish to write articles dealing with their special fields of interest and information. Although the person intending to write such an article must necessarily have a central idea which is to be developed, he still has the difficult task of putting down this idea in clear-cut prose. He must phrase well; he must know the ways of gaining and holding attention; he must know how to emphasize the important ideas and subordinate the unimportant; he must gain the reader's interest and attention early in his article. In short, he must present his thesis in such a way that people will want to read it.

Values in Publication

Although the rate of pay one receives from technical journals is either very low or non-existent, the technically trained man will nevertheless often wish to write an article because of the indirect values which may be gained. As in the learned professions, publication of worthwhile writings will enhance the standing of the author within his professional field. It is usually only through article writing that a technical man achieves a reputation for excellence within his special area. Through his articles, the writer may often secure a number of indirect returns. He may be called in to act as a consultant. He may be invited to give papers before the technically trained personnel of other companies.

A second value in publishing articles is that the writer's understanding of his work broadens as a result of the investigations he has made and the reading he has done to produce his article. He becomes better informed and technically more proficient as a result of doing the research necessary for the composition of a technical or semitechnical article. It has often been said that there is no better way to learn a subject thoroughly than to write a book about it, and the same result may be expected from the production of articles, although to a lesser extent.

The third advantage accruing to the technically trained man who also writes is the clarification of his thought. If one is to explain a process, a piece of apparatus, or a theory, these must first be clear in one's own mind. All of us have at least a hazy idea of how an atomic reactor operates, for instance, but can we give a clear, concise explanation of this operation? Probably not, but if first we study the process intensively in the library and in the laboratory, express the parts of the operation in an outline, and then develop that outline in sentences, paragraphs, and finally in the completed article, we come to a much clearer understanding of the sequences in the operation of the reactor. When we finish our explanation, we are forced to admit to ourselves that part of our earlier uncertainty about the reactor was due to a muddled understanding of its operation. We now understand because we have written to make others understand.

A technically trained person who writes accurately and ably for publication is of value to the company in whose plant he works. It receives publicity through his connection with the company, and in addition, the publication of articles indicates to potential customers that the company employs men of outstanding ability and that, consequently, the customers may expect good performance from apparatus designed by such people. The company affiliation of the writer who contributes to technological and scientific journals is almost always added to the by-line under which he writes; hence both he and the company share in the publicity and its consequent benefits.

Another value of the technical and the semitechnical article is the stimulation of the reader into thought which may branch out from the article and help that reader to solve some problem of his own. The solution of a problem in pure science may be brought about by the application of data which once solved a portion of the writer's problem about some industrial process; perhaps the technical or semitechnical article which he has just read may open a path for the engineer to find an answer to a practical problem. If scientists generally, and those of America in particular, had not read the articles on nuclear fission written by Fermi, Hahn and Strassman, and Lise Meitner, nuclear fission, the transmutation of the elements, atomic-powered submarines, and the hope for the eventual cure of cancer might still be merely dim visions.

The Technical Article

FINDING AND LIMITING THE SUBJECT

In preparing to write, one must first determine what subject he is going to use for his work. Although the material which the technical man writes about usually grows naturally out of his professional field, he often errs by beginning on a subject that cannot be handled within the space usually given to an article.

Let us consider the case of a person who has specialized in the field of rectification, the changing of alternating into direct current. He either wants to or is required to write an article dealing with his specialty. First he tries "rectification" as the subject for his article, but after he sits down to think about it he realizes that his material is of such a nature that it would require a dozen books to express it completely.

Knowing that he must bring his subject into a much smaller compass, he begins to search for a topic which would be suitable for treatment within an article. As he leafs through the *Proceedings* of the Institute of Electrical and Electronic Engineers, he starts to examine the subjects which other people have used for their problem. He sees that the good article is one which treats a very small phase of a subject with such certainty that a reader can clearly see the process of thought which runs throughout the writing. The prospective writer finds that he will probably have to make two or three attempts to bring his material into focus, for he discovers shortly that he knows a great deal more about the material than he had previously thought. If he does not do so, he will find himself stating only generalities which will be known to anyone working in the field.

Perhaps, as a final choice of subject, he will take up so small a phase of rectification as "Selenium Rectifiers in Small Power Installations." Such a subject is narrow enough to allow of fairly complete coverage in a single article; more important, if the article is well written and if the technically trained man is thoroughly acquainted with his subject, the article will give the reader information he formerly did not have. Like the specialist in rectification, every technical writer will find that he must narrow his subject by going through this limiting process.

READING BACKGROUND

Of great importance to the writer who is interested in securing a subject for a technical or semitechnical article are the ideas which he may gain by intelligent and thoughtful reading of the work of others. Perhaps the author of an article has had as his aim something only slightly connected with the investigations of the person who is reading it, yet the two interests touch here and there. Dr. Jonas, for instance, may have been carrying on an investigation on electrical resistors and writing an article about them; he may have carried out one of his experiments with some material which was not at all suitable for resistor use because it melts at a temperature so low as to make it valueless, yet Mr. Hendricks, who has been searching for something to break the circuit on an oven when the temperature rises too high, may, as a result of reading this article, find that what was worthless to the writer is exactly the thing for which he has been searching.

Today, most large corporations have their own libraries to which the employees may go to learn of the newest scientific developments within their fields. If, as a result of his work, a physicist has decided that he is going to write on the development of hot channels in an atomic reactor, one of his first steps should be to go to the library and make a thorough search of the literature, and then read what has already been written on this subject. It is wasteful to make experiments, to organize material, to draw conclusions, and then finally to write an article which merely repeats what someone else has already published months before.

You may ask, "How am I to find out what has been done? I haven't the time to read through all the technical magazines." The answer is that you can check quickly those sources that will give you the information you want, particularly the indexes and the volumes of abstracts. You will find *Applied Science and Technology Index*, as well as *Engineering Index* and the *Rand Index* of technical reports, most helpful. *Chemical Abstracts, Biological Abstracts,* and *Nuclear Science Abstracts* list articles in the fields indicated and give the contents of each. The indexes list, by general field and author, as well as by title, all the periodical material printed within the dates called for on their covers. Current articles must be sought for in the monthly or quarterly issues of the journals themselves, since both *Applied Science and Technology Index* and *Engineering Index* are printed as of the previous year. When the engineer or scientist has finished looking up in the indexes the particular subject in which he is interested, he can feel certain of what has been written on this subject; and if articles connected with the subject on which he wishes to write have appeared, he can then secure copies of the journals in which they have been printed.

Another answer to the question of how to find the time to read the technical magazines in one's field lies in the improvement of reading skills. Scientists and engineers all too often read at a rate that is far slower than it need be. Few technically trained people have mastered the skills of skimming—that is, running over material rapidly until they find that section of the written work in which they have a special interest. Although it is not in the purview of this text to deal with reading skills in themselves, every technically trained person ought to make an effort to enhance his skills until he is reasonably efficient in reading. To this end, we may suggest some of the following books and pamphlets as possibilities for aid in improving one's reading.

J. F. Sherbourne, *Toward Reading Comprehension* (D. C. Heath & Co.)

S. U. Wedeen, *College Remedial Reader* (G. P. Putnam's Sons)

J. H. Wise and others, *The Meaning in Reading* (Harcourt, Brace and World, Inc.)

Zetler and Crouch, *Successful Communication in Science and Industry* (McGraw-Hill Book Co., Inc.)

Everyone who wishes to become well known as a writer on technical or semitechnical subjects must read, not only for information or for learning whether his subject already has been fully explored by other writers, but also to discover how other writers have approached similar problems and how they have presented their material. This is a part of article writing which many scientists and engineers, as well as other technically trained people, often slight, for their laboratory and shop training make them want to plunge directly into physical experimentation and observation. The bibliographical exploration has its place, however, and is often quite as important as any other part of the process of getting ready to write.

Collecting Information

NOTES ON LABORATORY PROCEDURES

After the preliminary investigation of the literature has been made (it should be remembered that some investigations may not require any reading), the writer will then proceed to collect his data. Sometimes he will do this by lengthy experiments in the laboratory; sometimes he will view shop procedures and report on them; sometimes he may mathematically develop some question which will provide a solution to a problem. Every student knows how painstaking and exact such work must be if the results are to be valid. Actually, it is to this painstaking and exact work that a great deal of his earlier training has been directed.

One of the important aids when one is gathering information leading to the writing of the technical article is the data book or the notebook. If the technically trained man wants to write about laboratory experimentation, he must have detailed information concerning material used, the explanations of procedures, time values, and type of equipment.

If an engineer is getting ready to note down data about laboratory tests which he has made on a vacuum pump using different quantities of oil, his data book may look something like this:

```
Purpose: To determine speed of operation of 20-inch oil dif-
         fusion pump using different quantities of oil

Material: 2, 3, 4, and 5 quart measures of Goodwood high-
          vacuum oil, label #VB-6244

Power input: 5.5 kw

Line voltage: 235 volts

Apparatus: 1 McLeod gage, serial #62421
           1 Pirani gage, serial #55-6
           1 Bausch leak valve, serial #435

Procedure:
```

Time elapsed in seconds	Microns of vacuum McLeod	Pirani	Volume of oil in quarts
0	400	450	2
5	85	90	
10	65	25	
15	25	25	
20	20	25	
25	19	25	
30	20	25	
40	20	25	
50	20	25	
60	20	25	

Time elapsed in seconds	Microns of vacuum McLeod	Pirani	Volume of oil in quarts
0	250	300	3
5	25	35	
10	15	8	
15	8	6	
20	6	7	
25	5	6	
30	5	6	
40	5	6	
50	5	6	
60	5	6	
0	400	420	4
5	50	25	
10	5	1	
15	2	2	
20	2	1	
25	1	1	
30	1	1	
40	1	0.003	
50	1	0.003	
60	0+	0.003	
0	400	410	5
5	4	5	
10	1	0.1	
15	0+	0.0005	
20	0+	0.0005	
25	0+	0.0005	
30	0+	0.0005	
40	0+	0.0005	
50	0+	0.0005	
60	0+	0.0005	

The next page which the writer might use would continue with the experiment, using different volumes of oil if the engineer felt that it was worthwhile to continue the experimentation beyond the 5 quart level. Perhaps the investigator might also plot the results of his experiment on a curve. When using a data book, one should develop certain habits, such as the setting down of pertinent information with accuracy. Usually one can say that in general the data book should show:

1. The purpose of the experiment
2. The materials and apparatus used (with proper identifications so that these can later be found and the experiment rerun, using the same apparatus and perhaps the same material)

3. The procedure of the experiment
4. The results found by the experiment
5. The conclusions which the investigator came to as a result of observing the experiment. (These conclusions are usually noted only after the entire experiment has been run to completion.)
6. Recommendations which grow out of the conclusions

THE PROPER USE OF THE LIBRARY

As has been said, frequently the technically trained man who is preparing an article must use material he has read. This will almost always be found in the various technical, semitechnical, and trade journals that deal with his field. However, to learn what other workers in his area have written and to get a survey of this material, he must know how to make efficient use of the library.

The first guide to the library is its card catalogue. Such a catalogue lists on cards, three inches by five inches, all books and bound periodicals which are in that particular library. In most large libraries there are generally special rooms or a series of rooms set aside for books and magazines which deal entirely with technological subjects. These books and the bound numbers of technological magazines are classified according to one of two systems: the Dewey Decimal System or the Library of Congress System. The Dewey Decimal System classifies books as follows:

000–099 General Works; Encyclopedias
100–199 Philosophy and Psychology
200–299 Religion and Mythology
300–399 Sociology, Education, Economics
400–499 Philology
500–599 Natural Science
      510 Mathematics
      520 Astronomy
      530 Physics
      540 Chemistry
      550 Geology
      560 Paleontology
      570 Biology
      580 Botany
      590 Zoology
600–699 Useful Arts
700–799 Fine Arts
800–899 Literature
900–999 History

The entire field of knowledge is divided into nine major divisions, with a preceding division labeled "General Works." Each of the major divisions is subdivided further into ten subdivisions. In the illustration above, notice the subdivision of "Natural Science." Besides the nine subdivisions listed, books labeled 500–510 would deal with general works on natural science. Books labeled 210–299 would, consequently, list general works on religion and mythology. Each of the ten subdivisions of each department of knowledge is divided further into ten subdivisions of its own.

The alternate system, the Library of Congress System, divides all knowledge into 20 fields. A letter is used to designate each field. The classification goes like this:

A. General Works
B. Philosophy—Religion
C. History—Auxiliary Sciences
D. Foreign History and Topography
E.–F. American History
G. Geography—Anthropology
H. Social Sciences
J. Political Science
K. Law
L. Education
M. Music
N. Fine Arts
P. Languages and Literature
Q. Science
R. Medicine
S. Agriculture—Plant and Animal Industry
T. Technology
U. Military Science
V. Naval Science
Z. Bibliography, Library Science

This scheme is put to use in Fig. 5, showing a card which classifies a book according to the Library of Congress system under the heading of "Technology." Notice of the organization responsible for producing this publication is listed in heavy, black type at the top of the card. Notation is made of the title of the book, followed by the name of the editor, the place of publication, and the publisher. The date of publication is given as "1961."

The card also gives information about the book. The "x" means that there is an introductory section of ten pages. Following this is the length of the book proper, 393 pages, and an indication that it is

illustrated and has diagrams in it. The height of the book is indicated
in centimeters.

TL
787
S9   **Symposium on Psychophysiological Aspects of Space Flight,**
          Brooks Air Force Base, Tex., 1960.
            Psychophysiological aspects of space flight. Edited by
          Bernard E. Flaherty. New York, Columbia University
          Press, 1961.

            x, 393 p. illus., diagrs. 24 cm.

            Includes bibliographies.

            1. Space vehicles — Congresses. 2. Space flight — Physiological
          effect — Congresses. 3. Space flight — Psychological aspects — Con-
          gresses. 4. Human engineering—Congresses.   I. Flaherty, Bernard
          E., ed. II. Title.

          TL787.S94 1960   612.0144   60–15809

          Library of Congress   [30]

Fig. 5. Library of Congress subject card.

Below this is a description of the material to be found within the
book. The Library of Congress call number appears at the bottom
left-hand side. You will notice that the call number is not exactly
the same as the call number used in any particular library; in other
words, the "4" is omitted because this particular library does not have
so many books as to require the "4." The "T" is the indication of a
technological publication. The item "612.0144" is the book's code
number in the Dewey Decimal System. The item "60–15809" is the
means by which the card is ordered from the Library of Congress. At
the bottom center, the characters in brackets stand for qualities of the
card itself. They are used only by librarians ordering the cards.

Let us now look at an author card. The one shown in Fig. 6 indicates
that this book, too, is concerned with technology. Notice that the
author's name given on the line at the top appears in the following
order: last name, first name, and the date of birth. The title of the
book, *Victory Over Space*, follows and a note is made of the name of
the translator. Descriptive material then indicates that this is the
first American edition and this is followed by the place of publication,
the name of the publishing house, and the date of publication.

Following this is the material which somewhat describes the book,

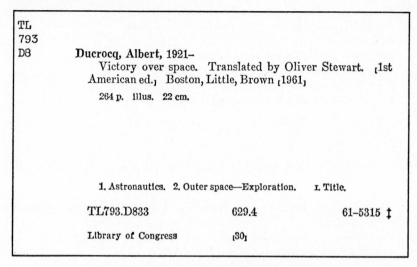

TL
793
D8   Ducrocq, Albert, 1921–
                 Victory over space. Translated by Oliver Stewart. [1st
              American ed.] Boston, Little, Brown [1961]
                 264 p. illus. 22 cm.

              1. Astronautics. 2. Outer space—Exploration.   I. Title.

              TL793.D833   629.4   61–5315 ‡

              Library of Congress   [30]

Fig. 6. Library of Congress author card.

and which tells us that it has 264 pages, is illustrated, and is 22 centimeters high. The material toward the bottom of the card states the major fields covered in the book—astronautics and the exploration of outer space. The Library of Congress call number appears at the left-hand bottom of the card and the Dewey Decimal call number is in the center.

A subject card may be created from an author card simply by typing in the subject, usually in red or black capitals, above the author's name. Otherwise, the two cards are essentially the same.

If the research worker does not know the name of the author of a book but does know the book's title, he may find the author's name by consulting a title card. If he wants to find a book under a general subject he can then consult the subject card. Cross-referenced cards direct the writer to related fields. He will often find that following these leads will supply him with further sources.

Useful Reference Books

Indexes are an important source of information for the technical man. They follow an alphabetical arrangement: some by author, title, and subject; some by author and subject; some by subject only. The most important indexes and volumes of abstracts are listed below.

Engineering Index
Applied Science and Technology Index
Rand Index
Readers' Guide to Periodical Literature
Readers' Guide Supplement (1907–1919)
Poole's Index to Periodical Literature (1802–1907)
International Index to Periodicals (1907–   )
Chemical Abstracts
Biological Abstracts
Nuclear Science Abstracts

For exhaustive definitions of words, the researcher should consult the following:

New English Dictionary on Historical Principles (*Oxford English Dictionary*)
Dictionary of American English on Historical Principles
Dictionary of Slang, ed. by Eric Partridge

The following biographical dictionaries are helpful:

American Men of Science
Dictionary of American Biography
Dictionary of National Biography
Living Authors
Authors Today and Yesterday
Who's Who
Who's Who in America
Who's Who in Engineering

Good sources for all sorts of information are the *World Almanac* and the *Information Please Almanac*. The alert writer will buy one of these almanacs for his home library. Each is an important factual source for articles of various kinds.

Making a Bibliography

If the investigator knows his library and its system of classification of books and the general sources of information, he is in a position to find books and other materials dealing with his subject. The process is known as making a bibliography. Suggestions for such books may be obtained from encyclopedias and general reference works and the various periodical indexes. Special books having to do with his subject will also be suggested by subject headings referring to his topic. These, of course, will be found in the card catalogue.

Other books will be suggested in the footnotes and bibliographies within sources he already knows. The list of books and articles thus obtained is known as the *preliminary bibliography.*

Each item in this bibliography should be set down on a separate card. If more than one item is on a card, the writer will have difficulty in alphabetizing his bibliography. He should put the following information for each complete book on a card 4 inches by 6 inches, or 3 inches by 5 inches.

```
                                    Library Call No.

   Slosson, E. E. Creative Chemistry. New York: Garden City
       Press, 5th ed., 1940
```

The library call number helps the writer to get the book from the library at any time. The title of the book is always underlined, to indicate italicization. The place of publication, the publisher, and the date are all items needing to be set down in the final bibliography.

A bibliography card for a magazine article should follow this order: The author's surname comes first, followed by his first name and middle initial, or just his initials; the title of the article is placed in quotation marks; the title of the magazine is underlined (to indicate italicization); the volume number, followed by the issue number (if any), is given; the date (in parentheses) when the magazine was published is indicated; and the pages (in Arabic numerals) where the article is to be found are noted. This example will illustrate:

```
                                    Library Call No.

   Dever, Frederick S. "Causes and Prevention of Welding
       Defects." Iron Age. 159,16 (April 17, 1947) 50-53.
```

An article in an encyclopedia may be indicated as follows:

```
                                    Library Call No.

   Close, C. F. and Winterbotham, H. St. J.  "Surveying."
       Encyclopaedia Britannica, 14th ed., 21, 609-618.
```

It is often helpful to place on the preliminary bibliography cards notes about the book or article itself. One should record, for instance, what chapters of a book are most helpful, whether the book is to be read entirely or only partially, or what paragraphs in a magazine article are most applicable to the specific topic.

If a number of articles have been edited by one man and bound in one volume, the following entry should be used:

```
                                        Library Call No.

    Clyne, R. W. (ed.). Engineering Opportunities.  New York:
    D. Appleton-Century Co., Inc., 1939.
```

If a book has been edited by someone other than the original author, it is recorded as in this example:

```
                                        Library Call No.

    Bacon, Francis.  The New Atlantis.  Ed. by G. C. Moore
    Smith.  Cambridge University Press, 1900.
```

If a book has been revised, the following entry is proper:

```
                                        Library Call No.

Montgomery, Franz and Becklund, Luther N. Essays in Science
and Engineering.  Revised ed. New York, Farrar & Rinehart,
Inc., 1938.
```

If a book belongs to a series, the form below is used:

```
                                        Library Call No.

Lobell, F. L. and Horton, R. E. Human Factors in Flight.
(Book 2, Columbia University, Teachers College, Aviation
Education Research Group.) New York, The Macmillan
Company, 1942.
```

Bulletins and pamphlets may be indicated as shown below.

Out of all the books gathered for the preliminary bibliography, the investigator might use only a few. Whatever books, magazine articles, and periodicals he uses for his piece of writing constitute the items which will have to be cited in his *final bibliography*, to be appended to his article or other writing. These items should be arranged alphabetically by authors, last name first. The following information should usually be cited:

Haldane, J. B. S. Science and Everyday Life. New York: The Macmillan Company, 1940.

Muller, H. J. Science and Criticism. New Haven: Yale University Press, 1943.

Northrop, F. S. C. Science and First Principles. New York: The Macmillan Company, 1931.

Sinnott, E. W. "Science and the Whole Man." Vital Speeches. 14 (Dec. 1, 1947) 111-177.

If no author is cited, it is best to alphabetize by the agency which is responsible for the publication, such as the American Institute of Chemical Engineers or U. S. Bureau of Standards. In all cases, the form for the final bibliography which is used by the best periodicals in any field should be followed.

Taking Notes

To be able to organize information most effectively, the technical man should take careful notes. A card system is the best way to re-enforce his memory on what he has read. To be equipped for note taking, he must have a stack of cards either 3 by 5 inches or 4 by 6 inches. The notes which he will take on these cards may be divided into three general categories: (1) a summary of the entire article or book; (2) an outline of the article or book, or parts thereof; and (3) direct quotation from the article or book. An example of each type is shown.

Summary Card

File classification head	**LAVA FLOWS** James G. Moore Donald H. Richter "Lava Tree Molds of the Sep- tember 1961 Eruption, Kilauea Volcano, Hawaii" Geological Society of America <u>Bulletin,</u> Sept., 1962. Vol. 73, No. 9, 1153-1158
Summary of article	Tree molds were formed during the eruption to the east of the volcano. These were produced when lava flowing through the forest became chilled against large trees and later drained away. Where the lava ponded temporarily, tree molds more than 14 feet high were formed.

Outline Card

File classification head	**FACTORS IN PLANT GROWTH** N. C. W. Beadle "Soil Phosphates and the Delimi- tation of Plant Communities in Eastern Australia" 281-288, <u>Ecology,</u> Vol. 43, No.2, Spring, 1962

Outline of complete article	1. Soil phosphate level delimits plant growth
	   1.1 rain forest
	   1.2 wet sclerophyll forests
	   1.3 xeromorphic low forests
	
	2. Soil phosphate controls fixation of nitrogen.

Quotation Card

*File
classi-
fication
head*

MARSHALL PLAN

> Albert R. Baron, pp. 21-34
> "Investment Decisions in
> Foreign Countries: Austria"
> The Engineering Economist,
> Vol. 7, No. 3, Spring, 1962

*Page
reference
for notes*

P. 27. "Except for essential food imports, Marshall
Plan goods were investment goods and were
used to rebuild Austrian industrial plants
and enterprises in all sectors of the
economy."

In order that all note cards may be sifted and the remainder put in logical order after the note-taking process is finished, each card is given a heading which will recall its contents to the writer. All cards are filed under the headings assigned them. At the top right-hand side of the card the writer should note the name of the author, the title of his article or book, the magazine in which the article appeared as well as its volume and number (Vol. 73, No. 9), its date of issue, and the pages which the article covers. Since it may be necessary for him to credit particular authors in his footnotes,[1] he needs the material just cited for such reference. Each notation on the cards is preceded on its left by the page number where the information was found.

Organization of Material

Once the technical man has gathered enough information on the problem about which he wishes to write, he should begin the organization of this material. If the experimental procedure has been a long one, he may find it convenient to copy his data on cards which then can be arranged in their logical order among the note cards from his reading. Before this organization can be carried out, it will be necessary for him to formulate an outline of the entire project. When he has made his outline (which will be done from the file classification heads on his note cards), his material will then be so organized that he may begin to write.

[1] For footnoting techniques, see pages 222–223.

To make the organization of a technical article concrete, we cite Professor Enrico Fermi's article, "Nuclear Disintegrations," which appeared in *Electrical Engineering* when atomic physics was relatively new.

Nuclear Disintegrations [2]

By Enrico Fermi

The fission of uranium, in which the uranium nucleus splits into two fragments of comparable size, achieved during 1939 by bombardment of uranium with neutrons, has stimulated great activity in this field of research and may lead to further research of fundamental and far-reaching importance.

Historical approach

Recent scientific discovery

1. Much of the information available at present on the structure of atomic nuclei has been gathered by a successful application of the technique of the so-called nuclear bombardments. This technique, initiated by Lord Rutherford about 20 years ago, consists in hurling against the nucleus a projectile (originally this was one of the alpha particles spontaneously emitted by radioactive substances) and in observing the changes in the nuclear structure produced by the impact. In the last years this technique has received new impetus due, on the one hand, to the development of artificial sources of high-energy projectiles (high voltage apparatuses and cyclotrons) and, on the other hand, to the discovery of the neutron.

Definition

2. Several hundreds of different artificial nuclear disintegrations have now been investigated. Their study has led to the development of the so-called nuclear chemistry in which, instead of changes of aggregations of atoms to form different molecules, as in chemistry, changes in the aggregation of neutrons and protons to form different nuclei are observed. This nuclear chemistry obeys rather simple rules, and the different types of nuclear reactions can be summarized as in the following paragraphs.

Technical description

3. Nuclei have been bombarded so far mostly with the following types of projectiles: alpha particles, protons, deuterons, and neutrons. Whenever one of these particles strikes the nucleus it is incorporated into the nuclear structure, and another particle may be emitted which belongs to one of the same four types. In a few instances nuclear reactions have been produced by hard gamma rays or by high-energy

[2] By permission of *Electrical Engineering,* the magazine of the American Institute of Electrical Engineers.

electrons. We have further to add the many cases of radio-activity, both natural and artificial, in which an unstable nucleus spontaneously emits an alpha particle, or an electron (negative or positive). The residual nucleus that remains after the reaction is always different from the one before the impact. In general, however, the changes in atomic weight, or atomic number, are not very large. Indeed, the greatest changes in atomic number occur when an alpha particle is either absorbed or emitted in the process. Since the electric charge of the alpha particle is of two units, this produces a displacement in the atomic number of two places only.

4. In many cases in which a chemical identification of the reaction products of nuclear bombardment has been possible, it has been found consistently that the reaction products are either isotopes of the original element bombarded, or they differ from it in atomic number by only a few units. There was, therefore, a great sensation among nuclear physicists *Recent* last year when Hahn and Strassman announced that by bom- *scientific* bardment of uranium (atomic number 92) with neutrons, *discovery* they had found definite evidence of the formation of some radioactive isotopes of barium (atomic number 56). Such a change by 36 units in the atomic number had never been considered possible before; subsequent investigation has shown that it corresponds to a nuclear reaction of an entirely new kind, in which the uranium nucleus splits into two fragments of comparable size.

5. This discovery of Hahn and Strassman has opened a very interesting new field of investigation. It is well known that all the heaviest elements of the periodic system are to some extent unstable, as is shown by their natural radioac-tivity. The physical reason for this instability is the electro-static repulsion between the positively charged constituents of the nucleus. These repulsions are approximately propor-tional to the square of the nuclear charge and, therefore, increase considerably with increasing atomic number. Insta-bility sets in when the electrostatic destructive forces over-come what we may call the cohesive forces of the nucleus.

6. The theory of nuclear forces is not yet developed so far as to enable us to calculate exactly at what value of atomic number instability sets in. Probably, however, this limit is *Statement* not far beyond 92, the atomic number of uranium. The *of thesis* discovery of Hahn and Strassman shows, indeed, that in the case of uranium the relatively unimportant perturbation of the nuclear structure due to the capture of a neutron is

already sometimes sufficient for breaking into pieces the nucleus, giving rise to the so-called fission process.

Analogy

7. A pictorial image of the process has been suggested by Bohr, who compared this process with what happens when a liquid drop divides into two smaller droplets as a consequence of a very strong oscillation in which it changes from the original spherical form into an elongated shape. In the case of uranium, however, as soon as the two fragments are separated and the cohesive forces cease to attract them, the strong repulsion due to both fragments being positively charged, pushes them apart, impressing

*Scientific
facts*

on them a relatively enormous kinetic energy. In fact, the amount of energy released in the fission process is approximately ten times greater than any amount of energy released in atomic disintegrations, it being of the order of 200 million electron volts. (An electron volt is defined as the amount of energy gained by an electron in passing from a point of low potential to a point one volt higher in potential.) Although the discovery of this process is only one year old, a great many investigations have been carried out in laboratories all over the world, so that a general description of the main features of the phenomenon is now possible, in which, however, many important details are still missing.

*Scientific
method*

8. The fission process can be produced by bombardment with fast neutrons having energy above one million electron volts, and by slow neutrons, having energy corresponding to thermal agitation equivalent to a small fraction of an electron volt. Neutrons of intermediate energy are rather inefficient as agents for producing fission. It has been pointed out, especially by Bohr, that this fact might possibly be interpreted on the assumption that the fast-neutron and the slow-neutron process are due to two different isotopes of uranium. Probably the fast-neutron process is due to isotope 238, which

*Scientific
interpre-
tation*

represents more than 99 per cent of natural uranium, whereas the slow-neutron process might be attributed to a much rarer isotope of weight 235, which is known to be present in an amount somewhat less than 1 per cent and is the parent substance of the actinium radioactive family. No direct experimental information on this point, which is of considerable importance both from the theoretical and the practical point of view, is at present available.

*Scientific
facts*

9. Each fragment into which uranium splits in the fission process weighs approximately one-half of the original nucleus. Apparently, however, the fission does not always occur

in exactly the same way, and there are certain limits between which the weight of the fragments can vary. Since each fragment gives rise to several artificially radioactive nuclei, it is clear that the fission process will produce a large variety of new radioactive elements. An extensive chemical investigation of these elements has been carried out in several laboratories and has already led to the identification of more than 20 such elements, but the list is probably still far from being complete.

Experimentation

10. When uranium undergoes fission some neutrons are emitted. It has not been decided so far whether these neutrons are emitted in the very act of fission, or a very short time after the process. The two fragments into which uranium splits get away with a very high internal excitation. The excitation energy might be so large as to produce the spontaneous emission of neutrons from the two fragments. The largest part of this emission of neutrons certainly occurs within an exceedingly short time after the fission; the emission of a small number of neutrons, however, lasts for some seconds after the fission process. This delayed emission of neutrons is probably a secondary process of some beta disintegration.

Scientific facts

11. The emission of neutrons is not only an interesting feature of the phenomenon, but might perhaps be of far-reaching importance, as it opens at least one possibility of exploiting the fission of uranium for the production of nuclear reactions on a large scale.

Scientific interpretation

12. Let us assume for a moment that in every fission process two neutrons are emitted (actually experiment shows that probably the average number of neutrons emitted is somewhat larger, between two and three). If this were so, every neutron that enters the uranium nucleus and produces fission would give rise to two neutrons with the net gain of one. If we assume that these two neutrons again produce each one a fission we get at the end four neutrons from the original one. Any one of these four neutrons might again produce a fission, multiplying the number of neutrons once more by two, and so forth, until the number of neutrons might in principle be multiplied by an arbitrarily large factor, thus giving rise to a self-perpetuating nuclear reaction—the so-called chain reaction. In order that the chain reaction might occur, it is obviously necessary not only to have more than one neutron produced for every neutron that is absorbed in the process of fission, but also to be able to utilize for pro-

Hypothesis

ducing new fissions a large fraction of the neutrons produced; otherwise the loss might be larger than the gain.

13. Assuming, as before, that two neutrons are produced in every fission, it is evident that for the chain reaction to take place more than one-half of the neutrons produced must be used in new fission processes. There is now, on the one hand, some loss of neutrons that diffuse outside of the reacting mass before they have a chance to react. This loss can be made, at least in principle, arbitrarily small, by increasing the amount of the reacting material. On the other hand, some of the neutrons are lost for the reaction because they are absorbed by uranium itself in a second process, which does not lead to fission but to the formation of a heavy radioactive isotope of uranium. Some absorption is finally due to those substances that must be present in order to slow down the neutrons, so as to increase their aptitude to react with uranium. Whether these absorptions are, or are not, sufficiently large to prevent the chain reaction, cannot be answered at present. The experiments require the use of very large amounts of both uranium and "slowing-down" materials and are, therefore, very expensive. The problem seems to me, however, worth the effort that its solution will cost. There is indeed a chance that research on these lines *Future* might open entirely new technical opportunities, whose *possibilities* range at present can only be guessed. The large release of energy by the reaction, whose development, by the way, could be easily controlled by simple mechanical devices, is indeed probably only one and very likely not the most important aspect of the problem. Far more important might eventually prove the production of radioactive materials and of neutrons in practically unlimited amounts, for medical, biological, and physical investigations. In conclusion, although there is only a chance of success, the stake appears large enough to justify some gambling.

In outlining [3] this article, Professor Fermi might have proceeded as follows:

I. Introduction
   A. Methods of securing data on atomic nuclei
      1. By alpha particles of radioactive substance
      2. By high energy projectiles
      3. By the neutron

[3] For outlining procedures, see pages 267–270.

B. Nuclear reaction
   1. Definition
   2. Types of nuclear bombardment
      a. Result in isotopes or small changes in weight
      b. Result in larger changes (Hahn and Strassman experiment)

II. Body
   A. Thesis: instability of uranium atom
      1. Doubt of point where destructive forces have upper hand
      2. Effect of capture of neutron (Bohr's analogy)
      3. Energy release from capture of neutron
   B. Methods of producing fission
      1. Slow neutrons
      2. Fast neutrons
   C. Description of fission process
      1. Fission of uranium
      2. General results
   D. Fission effects on uranium

III. Conclusion
   A. Cost of experiments
   B. Possible future developments

Point of View

Once the outline had been made up in detail, Professor Fermi's next problem would be to determine the point of view. Since his article was to be technical, he would realize that he should follow the impersonal attitude throughout, if possible. This impersonal attitude is the one commonly used in technical writing. It avoids the personal pronoun; it strives to attain the impartiality and impersonality of science itself. Professor Fermi does *not* say, "*I have not been able to decide* whether these neutrons are emitted in the very act of fission. . . ." Instead, he phrases the statement, "*It has not been decided* so far whether these neutrons are emitted in the very act of fission. . . ." Such a point of view eliminates the personal element; the reader is never conscious that Professor Fermi is speaking instead, he feels that it is a scientist speaking. He is convinced that the data have been considered objectively, and no matter what the personal opinions of the writer may have been, it has been the data which have dictated the conclusions to which the writer came. This is the point of view followed in almost all reputable technical articles.

Introductory Devices

With his material, outline, and point of view determined, Professor Fermi was confronted with the problem of how to begin. For anyone who is unaccustomed to writing, this is a difficult step. He will wish to present his material in the most attractive and the most interesting way possible. Should he begin immediately by stating what the main theme of his article is to be? Should he instead try to put his readers in a receptive mood by appealing to their interests? The technical author knows his material thoroughly; his first problem is how to introduce it.

Here certain rhetorical devices will help him. Although devices are used throughout any article, they are of paramount importance in the introduction. Their interest and attention-getting values here allow the writer to present his material in such a way as to ensure that he will have the reader's attention for the important statement of thesis which often follows.

The devices that are commonly used to open a technical article are listed below. These are also applicable to the semitechnical article, but the writer will see that some are likely to be of greater value to one form than the other. (Devices contained in articles reproduced in this chapter are shown by marginal notations.)

1. Historical approach
2. Specific instance (recent scientific discoveries, etc.)
3. Startling statement
4. Appeal to fundamental interests of the reader
5. Short narrative passage
6. Quotation and literary references
7. Definition
8. Descriptive opening
9. Analogy
10. Anecdote or joke
11. Gradual narrowing
12. Comparison or contrast
13. Negative detail
14. Direct statement of thesis
15. Concrete examples
16. Reference to specific occasion

Professor Fermi began by using two of these devices. Once he had chosen them, he could start to write, with good prospects that what he had to say would not only give his readers new information, but would also interest them. In "Nuclear Disintegrations," he opens his discussion of atomic energy by using an impersonal point of view and the two devices, historical approach and recent scientific descovery. He points out how, about twenty years ago, Lord Rutherford perfected the technique of bombarding the nucleus of the atom, and how recent discoveries (the cyclotron and other high-voltage apparatus) have forwarded atomic research. Any technical man may, if he wishes, begin his article by using the same devices. His material may be entirely different—he may perhaps write about new compression ratios, the mathematical formulae by which the slant of a type of flying wing is determined, or a new unit process in chemical engineering—but he may still apply to his problem any of the devices listed.

If Professor Fermi had not used the historical approach and the recent scientific discovery as devices to begin his article, he might have used almost any other of the methods (although it is more than probable that neither the anecdote nor the joke would be appropriate). For instance, he might have begun with a startling statement—"The end of the civilized world is now in view"—and in the light of events, no one could argue that his statement would not be scientifically true. He might have appealed to the fundamental interests of engineers by saying, "Power in unlimited amounts, power that is nearly free, is almost within our hands." The other devices which have been listed would, of course, take other forms, but almost any one could be used. The narrative opening might have told of the conversation of two men of 1990 as they talk about the explosion of the great atomic power plant at the South Pole, or how this new power has propelled a strato-liner across the Atlantic in an hour; the quotation device might have given the lines from Tennyson's "Locksley Hall,"

"For I dipt into the future, far as human eye could see,
    Saw the Vision of the world, and all the wonder that would be;"

and the author could have then pictured in a paragraph what he feels atomic power may do for us in the days to come.

GETTING READER INTEREST

The thoughtful technical writer will realize that he must direct what he writes to the interests of his readers; these interests will determine, to some extent, the sort of devices he may use. Within the first ten lines the writer must convince the reader that the rest of the article has something of importance for him.

Since Professor Fermi is writing for an audience composed almost exclusively of engineers, he does not need as much of an attention-getting device as if he were addressing the general public. The engineer may reasonably be expected to have an interest in the material itself; hence the historical introduction given in paragraph one is sufficient to secure the attention of the group.

In the second paragraph (which continues the introduction) Professor Fermi uses the device of definition to give his readers an exact idea of the science of nuclear chemistry. In paragraph three he depends on description to tell his readers what takes place during atomic bombardment by various projectiles. In the fourth paragraph he returns to a recent scientific discovery (that of Hahn and Strassman).

SUMMARY OF THE INTRODUCTION

Since the introduction of the technical or semitechnical article is difficult to write, rhetorical devices will help the beginning writer over the first hurdle. When he uses them, he must constantly keep his reader in mind by choosing the device, or devices, which will make the strongest appeal. With the introduction completed, the writer has taken the first step toward the body of the article, which is primarily centered on an analysis of his purpose.

The Body of the Article

Since Professor Fermi's material was practically unknown even to technical people in 1940, it had to be introduced by the necessary background. Hence it is not until paragraph 6 that we find the body of the article begun by the statement of the main thesis. Such a statement of thesis is very often used to open the body of a technical article rather than to act as an introductory device or as the final statement in the whole introduction.

The body of a technical or semitechnical article may generally be defined as an extended analysis of the author's purpose. It is in this section that he must consider all pertinent divisions of his problem and assign to them their proper places within the framework of his article. The author can do this only by the use of a logical outline in which he must take care to include all the material necessary to make his essential points, but must be equally careful to omit irrelevant matter. All of us have read articles which seem to proceed logically up to a certain point and then deflect from their normal course into a path which leads to a conclusion at variance with the major idea.

DEVICES FOR KEEPING READER INTEREST

In the body of the article, as in the introduction, the writer can be helped by learning a number of devices and then determining which ones will be most applicable to his purpose. Some of these devices are the same as those used in the introduction, but they can be employed within the body as well. Following is a list secured from a study of a large number of technical and semitechnical articles:

1. Definition
2. Rhetorical question
3. Quotation
4. Humor
5. Specific instance
6. Contrast and comparison
7. Narrative
8. Analogy
9. Negative details
10. Description
11. Startling statement
12. Charts, maps, and graphs
13. Statistics and tabulations
14. Repetition for emphasis
15. Vital facts
16. Citation of authority

LOGICAL SCHEMES FOR ANALYSIS OF THESIS

Several logical schemes of development govern the use of these devices within the body of the article. Again the writer must consider his audience to be sure which of these will be most effective; he must also make his choice of these schemes with his material in mind, for what may be a suitable way of discussing a laboratory research problem may not be at all useful in explaining a manufacturing sequence. The standard schemes of development follow:

1. Chronology
2. Cause and effect
3. Mathematical development
4. Relationships of the parts to the whole
5. Reduction to an absurdity
6. Climactic development
7. Statement of probabilities

The technical man must treat the body of his material in the light of these schemes and with the devices which he feels will be most satisfactory. Thus, if he were writing a paper on a new system of roller conveyors, he would be most likely to use a chronological development—pointing out how, in time sequence, the material to be carried moves from one place in the manufacturing cycle to another—and he would quite possibly use the devices of contrast and comparison to show how much superior the new system of conveying is, and perhaps statistics and graphs to indicate the greater rapidity of movement and the cheaper manufacturing costs. More often a writer will combine two or more of these methods of logical development to attain his desired effect, just as he may combine the devices he wishes to use.

Cause and effect is one of the most useful of the logical schemes for the presentation of material. The chemical engineer constantly uses it in his statements of reactions; the power engineer in his computations of the Btu's to be secured from a ton of coal of a certain standard. It may be defined as that sort of statement which says that if one event occurs, a second always results. It may be observed from this that the relationship is a temporal one; that there is an interval of time between the cause and the ensuing effect. If an engineer who is writing a technical paper about the passage of high-voltage currents through various materials uses this logical scheme, he may adopt as his cause the actual discharge of electricity; he will then describe the results, which may take the form of fulgurites if the current has passed through sand.

Mathematical development is a type of logical scheme that is likely to be almost too appealing to the technical writer. Much of his training has been in mathematics; he handles it as a descriptive language.

In the technical article there can be no objection raised to mathematical treatment, but most magazines prefer that their writers explain the significance of the equation in words. In order to arrive at generalizations which may cover an entire field, the writer many times has to resort to the formulation of an equation, such as the one which follows:

The equation

$$C_e = \cfrac{1}{\cfrac{1}{U_e} + \cfrac{1}{1.65}}$$

may be used to calculate the winter heating load of a given room where U_e = over-all coefficient—Btu/hr times ft² times F

C_e = conductance coefficient—Btu/hr times ft² times F

Both the Ue and C_e values can be calculated from the above equation. The C_e value is a measure of the insulating quality of each room. Thus, the room with the highest C_e value will have the greatest heat loss.

In the example just given, the writer has explained the nomenclature as well as the use of the equation which he has given. A heating engineer will be able to determine the amount of heat required to warm the room to a predetermined figure by making a calculation of the C_e value and thus correcting the heat input according to the amount of heat lost. It is a standard practice in highly mathematical articles to include a nomenclature column which indicates the values assigned to the several symbols.

The scheme which uses the relationship of the parts to the whole is particularly applicable to the descriptive technical article. In such a scheme, the parts which make up the whole topic being discussed are arranged in the light of their importance to the complete topic. If the industrial engineer wishes to describe a newly designed manufacturing cycle, he will give an evaluation of each part, such as conveyor belts, automatic handling devices, etc., and fix their importance to the entire procedure.

The scheme of reduction to an absurdity is useful when the writer is confronted with several choices of process, of which only one can be right. If he adopts the reduction method, he will not try to show which is right by direct proof, but will instead show that the others cannot be right. If, for instance, a mechanical engineer is trying to determine which of three sizes of steam line to use on an installation, he may arrive at the correct value by showing that one size will not give enough pressure at the outlets, and that the largest size would be capable of carrying more steam at greater pressure than is needed.

In "Nuclear Disintegrations," the reader will see that Professor Fermi has used the scheme of climactic development. He has given the background of the problem and has analyzed it thoroughly in order to lead up to the climactic, "the large release of energy by the reaction . . . is indeed probably only one . . . important aspect of the problem." Since his material was not yet completely investigated, Professor Fermi also has used the scheme of statement of probabilities. "Far more important might eventually prove the production of radioactive materials . . ."; "This delayed emission of neutrons is probably a secondary process of some beta disintegration."

VISUAL AIDS

Under the general heading of visual aids come maps, charts, and graphs. These are particularly useful to the technical writer, for through them he may be able to introduce proof of his thesis, and since the proof often would require many pages of written work, he can save time for his reader by presenting it in the more compact form of graphs. Again, however, he must constantly be aware of his audience, for if the reader should be unable to follow a particular visual aid, the writer must give the information in another way.

FOOTNOTING

Often a writer can save a great deal of space through the introduction of footnotes which make a reference to other publications. To substantiate an explanation of some point in the body, he refers to another work in which the problem has been investigated. Such notes also add the authority of other and perhaps better-known writers in the field.

Most footnotes when they appear in printed form are found at the bottom of the page, although in a short article they often appear at the end of the article. They usually include the following information:

Name of author
Name of article or book referred to
Place of publication ⎱ ⎰ Usually omitted when the footnote refers
Name of publisher ⎰ ⎱ to an article
Date of publication
Pages on which the suggested material is to be found.

Not all magazines follow the same method of placing footnotes, but the technical man can write for a style book to whatever publication he thinks may be interested in his material. The style book will tell him exactly how the notes are to be given. The G.P.O. Style Manual, Washington, D. C., U. S. Government Printing Office, 1945, will be found valuable.

A common method of placing the notes in a typed manuscript is as follows:

This system has already been worked out in detail. 1/ The easiest
1/ Carney, A. P. "Surveying the Boulder Dam Site." The American
Surveyor, 27 (January, 1947) 276-289.
of all methods that have been used previously in geological . .

In this method the footnote follows the end of the line in which the superior number is used.

The older method of placing footnotes is to add them at the bottom of the typed page, separating them from the rest of the manuscript by a line about 1½ inches long. Whatever method is used, the footnotes should be single spaced, just as the manuscript itself should always be double or triple spaced.

Often the writer will use footnotes which are purely explanatory in type. These notes are related to the body of the text, but the writer feels that placing them in the text proper would interrupt the smooth flow of thought, so he calls attention to them by a superior number and places the desired explanation in a footnote. Most footnotes, however, are presented as evidence that will buttress the conclusions to which the author has come, in that they call upon authorities who have written on the same general subject and whose opinions are respected.

The Conclusion

The conclusion, like the introduction and the body, also makes use of devices. Occasionally an article which uses the climactic scheme of development comes to its conclusion immediately at the end of the analysis. There need be no restressing of points or summary paragraphs under these circumstances. Most articles, however, require some type of device with which to conclude. The most popular methods of closing an article follow.

1. Restressing of main points (or summary)
2. Restatement of thesis
3. Apt anecdote
4. Humor
5. Rhetorical question
6. Quotation
7. Enunciation of future possibilities

The conclusion of an article is of great importance, for it is usually the part to which every reader gives most attention and which he remembers better than any other part. A lame ending to an otherwise excellent paper may negate all its preceding good qualities. It produces the same effect as does a speaker who can find no better way to close than to say, "Well, I guess that's all."

Professor Fermi makes use of the type of conclusion which stresses the possibilities of future development. He suggests the infinite uses to which radioactive materials may be put; he points out the great power possibilities inherent in the atom. Since his main logical scheme of presentation within the body of the article was the climactic, he naturally has a shorter conclusion than is often found in scientific articles.

If an article concerns itself with a new means of shop layout which will allow small motors to be manufactured on an assembly-line, mass-production basis, the author might in his conclusion restress the main points he has made in the body; he might draw certain conclusions from his previously stated material, or he might indicate what further possibilities lie in assembly-line production for other pieces of apparatus.

The beginning writer should be warned against making his conclusion too lengthy. Rarely if ever should it exceed 5 per cent of the total wording of the paper.

Two Well-Written Articles

EXAMPLE OF THE TECHNICAL ARTICLE

There are so many technical articles written for scientific journals that it is possible to include only a few examples in this textbook. One which takes up a problem that has undoubtedly interested almost all of us at one time or another is that of J. J. Gilman's "Fracture in Solids." As a metallurgist for the General Electric Research Laboratory in Schenectady, Dr. Gilman has been interested to determine why things break. His article is limited quite narrowly in scope, and he is therefore able to take up the mechanics of the fracturing of solids in an intensive way. He examines the basic causes of fractures and then goes into detail concerning the causes of fractures which occur as a result of the metal "tiring."

All of us have no doubt wondered why an ornamental piece of glass upon which flower pots were placed should hold their burden for years and then, without any warning, suddenly snap in two and deposit the plants on the floor. Dr. Gilman makes an adequate explanation of even so puzzling a phenomenon as this.

Fracture in Solids [4]

Examples of fractures

Every solid material, from the frailest eggshell china to the toughest steel, has its breaking point. It resists stress up to that point, perhaps yielding and stretching somewhat, and then suddenly it is broken by fracture. Fracture can be catastrophic: a cable snaps, whipping dangerously into its surroundings; a mile-long length of pipeline splits like a sausage skin; a pressurized aircraft fuselage bursts in flight. But fracture can also serve a useful purpose: it is easier to split things than to saw them, whether they are logs, granite or diamond. At times the event seems all out of proportion to its cause; the diamond cutter places his chisel and taps smartly with his hammer, a sharp cracking sound is heard and the solid, hard diamond cleaves into two pieces along an almost perfectly flat surface.

What happens in the instant of fracture? The speed and finality of the process seem to have discouraged investigation of it in the past. A great deal more is known about other responses of materials to stress, such as elasticity and plastic flow. For the engineer, fracture was simply the calamity to be avoided by means of careful design. The fracturing of entire ship hulls during World War II, however, brought the subject under concerted investigation at a number of research centers. It is now possible to describe the mechanisms of fracture at the atomic level and to begin the definition of their general laws.

Statement of thesis in question form, followed by examples and general statement of thesis

The key to an understanding of fracture was provided some 35 years ago by a British engineer, Alan A. Griffith. He postulated that most solid materials contain small, often invisible cracks and that these cracks are extremely efficient levers for prying atoms apart. He calculated the amount of leverage that a crack exerts, and confirmed his calculations in a series of elegant experiments. On glass globes of a standard size and thickness he incised scratches of various measured lengths and converted these scratches into cracks by gentle tapping. Then, having coated the inner surface of a globe with a thin film to make it airtight, he gradually increased the pressure inside until it burst. The pressure required to burst each globe decreased with increasing crack length in a precise way. Griffith was thus able to show that a crack, like the arm of a lever, multiplies an applied force by an amount that increases with the crack length. A crack, moreover, focuses the stress onto the atomic bonds at the vertex of the crack. This concentration of stress is handsomely demonstrated by the double-refraction patterns observed in some plastics subjected to stress and viewed with polarized light. With applied stress being multiplied by a leverage factor, the

History of previous investigations

concentrated stress soon reaches a high enough value to break atomic bonds and thus produce fracture.

Detail to show different types

The crack that starts a fracture may be visible to the naked eye, or it may originate in a surface scratch, or a minute fissure between crystal grains or a defect in the atomic lattice of a crystal grain of a kind that allows it to flow plastically. Since materials in common use have such imperfections, fracture is incipient in all of them. This explains why the strength of ordinary materials is so much less than the theoretical ideal suggested by strength of their inter-atomic bonds. A tumbler made of ideal glass, only a 64th of an inch thick and lying on its side, could support the weight of a 200-pound man. Made of ordinary glass, the tumbler walls would have to be 16 times thicker

Example contrasts actual with ideal material

(that is, a quarter of an inch thick) to sustain the same stress. The ideal material would withstand a stress of about a million pounds per square inch; the real material fractures under a stress of about 2,000 pounds per square inch.

The characteristics of ideal materials are now being approximately mated in crystals prepared by modern techniques. Many early perfect crystals have been obtained in the form of fine fibers or "whiskers," but some, such as germanium and silicon, have been made in substantial sizes, as thick as a thumb. These crystals approach the ideal in strength because of the perfection of their atomic structure. As can be seen under the microscope, they

Explanation of causes of of strengths

have remarkably smooth surfaces. Internally, their atoms are arranged in a perfectly orderly, repetitive array. When such a structure is subjected to external force, the internal stress is distributed uniformly to all of the bonds in the lattice. No crack is present to concentrate the stress in a small area, and a crack cannot form until all of the bonds are stretched nearly to the breaking point.

Even though most metallic crystals, and some nonmetallic crystals may have no cracks initially, they often contain defects called dislocations which allow them to flow plastically. This makes these crystals vulnerable to crack formation through a simple mechanism. Crystals deform plastically by the sliding of one part of a crystal

Use of analogy

over the rest; rather like the sliding of the cards in a deck over one another. If the sliding occurs freely, the result is just a change in the shape of a crystal. However, if the sliding is blocked by a hard particle inside a crystal, or at the boundary between crystals, then a high concentration of stress collects at the place where the sliding is blocked. The atomic bonds at this location, now under great stress, stretch beyond their limit and rupture, forming a tiny crack.

Once a crack is well started it takes very little force to carry it through to a complete fracture. Since the force depends on the length of the crack, a specific case must be examined in order to state how much force is involved. For example, consider a plate of steel that is six inches wide and a quarter of an inch thick. Suppose that it has a two-inch crack running into one side. Then the force required to make the crack run the remaining four inches would be only about 400 pounds. Without the aid of the crack it would require a force of 500,000 pounds to pull the plate apart if it were made of the best commercially available steel, and a force of about 10 million pounds if it were made of ideal steel. It is a large leverage effect like this that makes it possible for a relatively small force to crack an entire ship in two.

Example: to further general thesis

Although plastic flow can be detrimental to the strength of a material if it is blocked and thus leads to crack formation, it can also be beneficial. By relieving the stress concentration at the tip of a crack, plastic flow can greatly increase the force required to make a crack run. But this benefit is dependent upon temperature: as the temperature decreases, the tendency to flow also decreases. When plastic flow is inhibited, unrelieved stress builds up at the vertex of the crack and more readily stretches the atomic bonds there to the breaking point. Thus as resistance to flow increases, resistance to cracking decreases, but the material becomes highly susceptible to it at low temperatures. This temperature effect caused most of the trouble with wartime ships. In southerly waters there was no problem, but during the winter in northern waters the hulls often cracked under shocks from heavy seas. Sometimes a crack ran instantly through the plates of a ship; at other times a crack remained dormant and caused serious damage later.

Value of plastic flow

Effects of temperature on strength of material

Fracture usually occurs so rapidly that the unaided eye cannot observe it. A skilled glazier, however, can make a crack creep slowly through a piece of glass by applying just the right force. If he increases the force only slightly, the crack quickly accelerates to a high velocity. During

*Description of
apparatus and
process for
measuring
speed of
cracking*

the cleaving of a diamond, five million to 50 million atomic bonds may be ruptured in a millionth of a second. One way of measuring the high velocities at which cracks can travel is to photograph them with a high-speed motion-picture camera; the distance the crack travels in the interval between pictures gives its velocity. A second method is to make the crack itself trip timing devices. The test material is painted or plated with a grid of very thin metallic strips, each of which is part of the circuit of an electronic stop watch. As the lengthening crack successively breaks the metallic strips, interrupting the stop-watch circuits, the velocity of the cracks is recorded.

*Description of
theory explain-
ing speed of
cracking*

Cracks have been clocked at velocities approaching that of sound: about 15,000 feet per second in solids such as glass and steel. The speed of sound is, in fact, the theoretical limit of the speed at which a crack can run, for this is the maximum speed at which the applied force can be transmitted to the crack. The velocities at which sound travels and an applied force is transmitted in a material are both limited by the elasticity of the interatomic bonds—not, as might be expected, by the magnitude of the force or the loudness of the sound. If a crack is already moving at the speed of sound, its velocity cannot be increased by a sudden increase in the applied force, because the increase in the force, transmitted at the same maximum speed, cannot overtake the crack. The crack thus never "learns" that the force has been increased, and so it cannot be driven faster than sound.

*Explanation of
process: crack-
ing of glass
after it has
"tired"*

"Sudden" and seemingly inexplicable fractures are often the culmination of long series of discrete steps. A sheet of glass, for example, may support a load for a long time without apparent damage and then break without warning. In many such instances corrosion abets the fracture mechanism. The load does not exert sufficient stress to fracture the glass outright, but only exerts enough to open the invisible cracks in its surface. Then atmospheric water-vapor lays a thin film of moisture on the glass. The smooth surface resists penetration, but as the water reacts with silicon-oxygen bonds within a crack, it breaks those bonds and forms reaction products that have a larger volume than the glass. The reaction products act as a wedge, spreading the crack-faces apart. This stretches the bonds at the vertex of the crack further, encouraging the next reaction event to occur. Hence the process is both self-sustaining and self-accelerating. In time the combined effect of applied stress and increasing crack-leverage allows propagation of the crack without the aid of the wedging effect of the chemical reaction. The crack, which has been advancing a few atom-diameters at a time, now surges forward at a speed approaching that of sound, and complete fracture is the result. The same sequence of events underlies the so-called static fatigue fractures that occur in other materials.

From such understanding of what makes cracks start in materials and move through them it may soon be possible to develop materials with greater resistance to fracture. This will be a rich return on a few years of fundamental research.

Enunciation of future possiblities

As in Professor Fermi's article, this discussion of the phemonenon of cracking begins by using a specific device to catch the reader's interest and attention. The writer begins by contrasting the frailest eggshell china with the toughest steel and points out that all things break. His examples are vividly presented; he also goes into the advantages that may come from cracking. Early in the article (in fact, in the second paragraph), Dr. Gilman states his major point and tells us that he is going to describe the mechanisms of fracture at the atomic level and thus explain why things crack and how they crack. After going into the history of earlier investigations on this subject, the writer then presents us with more theory and with a wealth of examples to illustrate the generalities which he states.

The conclusion of the article enunciates the possibility of future developments: that we may be able to produce materials which will resist fracture much more strongly and thus will be better building materials.

EXAMPLE OF THE SEMITECHNICAL ARTICLE

In the following article, "Cosmic Listening Post," and its two accompanying illustrations (pages 230–231), the author gives his readers a story of a new radio telescope. Since our age is a space-minded one, such an article is likely to secure the interest of his readers because of its subject material. The writing is simple in vocabulary and yet does what the semitechnical article must do: it gives the reader information he did not previously have in a form which he can understand easily.[5]

[5] By permission of *Steelways*.

Appeal to audience interest through a startling statement

This fall a team of space scientists will gather at the rim of a steel-lined limestone valley near Arecibo, Puerto Rico, to begin a long awaited conversation with the universe. It promises to be a strange one, for the men will be either listening to unanswerable signals or talking to themselves over the world's largest and most powerful radio-radar telescope.

Description of apparatus

This giant instrument combines the basic functions of radio and radar telescopes. A radio telescope tunes in on the natural radiations of space, while a radar telescope bounces signals off distant objects and catches them on their way back.

Vital facts

The main task of the Arecibo telescope will be to probe the earth's ionosphere, a blanket of electrically charged air beginning about 25 miles up. The electric and magnetic properties of the ionosphere are known to affect global and space communications systems as well as missiles and satellites passing through. Data gathered at Arecibo should widen scientific understanding of this mysterious region.

Fragment of thesis: use for radar telescope

A major tool of the Department of Defense's Ionospheric Research Facility at Arecibo, the big ear will also be used to investigate other unanswered questions about our universe.

Fragment of thesis: use for radar telescope

One of its first experiments will seek to determine whether or not stars in other solar systems emit radio signals like those of the sun. If signals are received, they may help to explain the physical laws that govern the phenomenon.

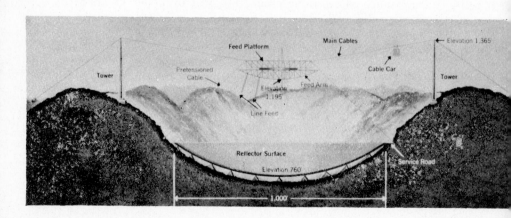

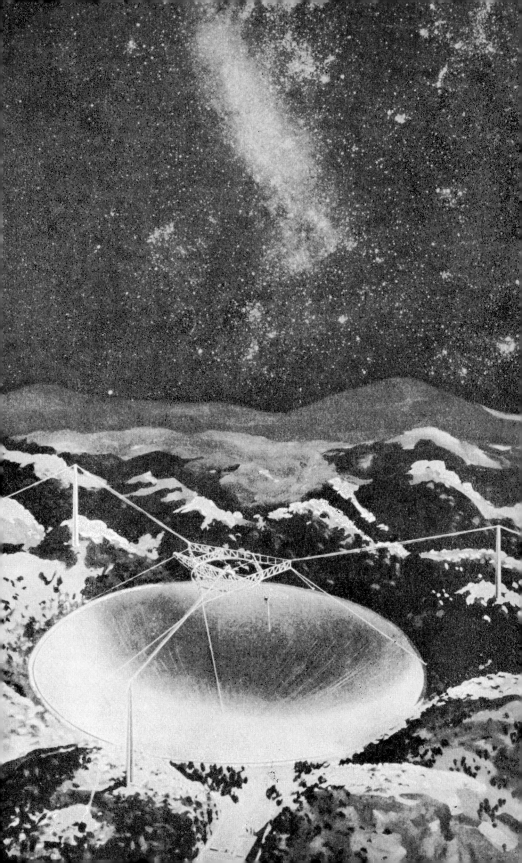

Fragment of thesis: use for radar telescope

The moon will be in for a lot of attention also. High on the list of the Arecibo assignments is a bombardment of the moon with radar signals. Correlating the roughness of radar echoes with optical details will yield a topographical map of the moon of possible use by lunar travelers of tomorrow.

Use of the question to maintain interest

There are other enigmas the Arecibo Observatory may help to unlock. Is there life on Mars, for instance? What are the main features of Jupiter's atmosphere and surface? Do the thick green clouds of Venus conceal continents and oceans? What cosmic dangers are awaiting the astronauts?

Vital facts

This kind of cosmic lock-picking calls for a big key. The new reflector will be about 1,000 feet in diameter, four times the size of the largest now in use at Jodrell Bank in England and 400 feet wider than the giant ear scheduled to begin its operations at Sugar Grove, W. Va., in 1964.

Vital facts

Funded by the Advanced Research Projects Agency under the general direction of the U. S. Air Force's Cambridge Research Center, which Cornell University serving as major contractor, the project will cost about $6 million. Its unique design accounts for the comparatively low price tag.

Vital facts

Electronic telescopes have been traditionally built with movable reflectors and fixed feeder mechanisms, through which signals are sent and received. The Arecibo planners reversed this practice. They set the reflector in a natural bowl, formed by a ring of mountains, and suspended a movable feeder mechanism above it.

Description of apparatus

The fixed reflector has more limited scope than movable reflectors, but this disadvantage is offset by the fact that no massive supporting towers and structural framing are needed. It can be made of strong, inexpensive materials, and the size is almost unlimited. (A movable reflector the size of the one at Arecibo might cost 20 times as much.)

Description of apparatus

The reflector design calls for millions of square feet of galvanized steel mesh held just above the valley floor by a spherical sling of steel cables. The 450-ton structural steel platform on which the feeder mechanism moves will be suspended from 14,000 feet of spun cable attached to the lip of the reflector and to three reinforced concrete towers located on the hills above.

Today these hills are untamed. Pocking their slopes are ancient caves decorated with crude drawings scrawled long before Columbus discovered the island. Within a year this site will be a link between the past and the future—a steel link that will bring man closer to the infinite than he has ever been before.

Historical reference
Enunciation of future possibilities

From reading this article you have probably noticed how closely the writer keeps to the special interests which his readers have: the interest in the space age and its mechanisms.

The reader's imagination is caught up by the question, "Is there life on Mars?" The reference to the other planets and to such things as cosmic dangers and astronauts continues to hold the reader's interest as do the notations about missiles and satellites.

The writer of "Cosmic Listening Post" has spent much time in detailing his ideas in readable fashion for the benefit of his audience. In addition, the cutaway presentation of the radar telescope helps the reader to understand its method of construction. The writer has remembered one of the major rules of illustrations—that they must in every case add to the reader's understanding of the points he is trying to make. You will also notice that there are not too many items on the illustration: that the picture is concerned with the major parts of the radar telescope and does not go into excessive detail. When illustrating, bear in mind that too many items in one illustration tend to clutter up the figure.

Making the Unfamiliar Understandable

The writer's problem in most semitechnical articles is to make unfamiliar material clear to readers not trained in the fields which the articles represent. "Logical Approaches to Problems of Space Flight," by Commander G. W. Hoover, attempts to do this in the article which is reprinted below. As you read the article, check the devices which are set down in the margin of each page.

Logical Approaches to Problems of Space Flight

Introduction

The American Astronautical Society has by its own charter placed itself in a unique and challenging position. By implication, the members have decided to contribute their joint capabilities toward solving the problems of Space Travel through the development of the astronautical sciences. A commendable objective—but an extremely difficult task.

Appeal to fundamental interests of the reader

Use of
analogy for
explanation

First of all when we refer to space travel we are talking about a man-machine system. Such a system divides itself into a "brain" and a "muscle."

The "brain" can be divided into sensors, computation, display, and mechanism amplifiers, displays, and controls.

Definition

In addition to the above we have the problems of: (1) communication, (2) aero-medicine, (3) geophysical and astrophysical.

Major Requirements

Gradual
narrowing

Now that the problem is divided into specific areas we can establish the requirements for each. This is not an easy task but is absolutely essential if we are to determine the proper direction in which to look for the completely adequate answer. In the brain portion one primary question to be answered is simply, "What is it the pilot needs to have displayed?"

There are actually two major requirements. These are position in space; and position astrophysical. The first is observed normally with respect to a vertical plane and the second with respect to a horizontal plane. The first is primarily orientation, the second situation display.

Definition

Each of the two areas must be further divided into three types of display: (1) Orientation, which tells the man what he is doing; (2) Director, which tells the man what he should be doing; (3) Quantitative, which tells the man how he is doing.

Statement
of thesis

In order to determine the details of these three types of display, it is necessary to make a complete analysis of the information requirements. To determine these requirements the operators must be interrogated to establish the fundamental information necessary to accomplish the task at hand. Not an interrogation of the individual's opinion, but rather an assessment of the essential information required with which the task can be accomplished without interpolation or mental computation. For example, during an orbit interception the pilot must have range information. Engineers realizing this would provide a means for determining range and then proceed to present it in miles and yards. However, when prospective space pilots are asked the question, "Why do you want range information," they answer by stating they need range data in order to know when to reduce thrust, when to reverse thrust, and when to stop thrust. When

denotes time, not distance. In other words, fundamentally, range must be indicated as a director type of presentation in order to eliminate the necessity of the pilot remembering at which range to reduce, reverse, and stop thrust. When the questioning reaches a point where the operator states that without X data he cannot carry out the task, then X data is the fundamental information requirement.

By using the visual world as our yardstick it is relatively simple to determine what it is in the visual world that causes us to react as we do throughout various phases of flight. If we resort to invention we can only compare one idea with another, both of which may be fundamentally wrong. On the other hand, if we use the visual world as one of the elements of our comparison, which we know incidentally is adequate, we at least can establish an equally adequate display. This comparison then is made against a natural, rather than a man-made model. If we can create a synthetic display comparable (not a duplicate) to the visual world, then we know axiomatically that the display will be adequate. Having once established this we can then proceed to bring about innovations to take care of the deficiencies in the visual world which are apparent during the special modes of space flight. *Specific instance*

Such an approach to determining a display is merely resorting to the concept of "doing what comes naturally." We have no difficulty in walking in clear weather nor in driving a car in clear weather. By the same token we fly well in clear weather. This then should be the display for which we must create a correlate. The proof here for a display is by axiom rather than evolution because if it is true that we orient ourselves by our perception of the visual world, it follows that our display must be adequate if it reproduces the same cues which are apparent in the visual world. *Quotation* *Logic*

If conventional methods of conducting research and development in this field are carried out the answers may be forthcoming, but not for a long time, and not without a tremendous expenditure of money. There are many reasons why conventional approaches to the problems of research and development are inadequate but perhaps the most predominant is the influence of inhibited thinking. *Concrete examples*

Perhaps the most important cause of inhibited thinking, however, is due to the methodology employed in carrying out most research and development. Too much reliance is placed on intuition and invention. Too often the expert opinion is really not much more than personal opinion, or *Negative details*

where a group is involved, a consensus of opinion. Because
an engineer or scientist has worked in a particular field for
a long time does not in itself qualify him to stand unques-
tioned. Too often decisions are made as a result of past
experience which may have been excellent for previous

Quotations   circumstances but will not hold up under new requirements.
Such opinions are not always backed up by facts. The expression, "Don't confuse me with the facts, I've already made
up my mind," is not always made in jest.

Programs and projects are started too often without mak-
Startling   ing a complete statement of the problem, which results in
statement   only a partial solution which is justified by calling it a
compromise.

An approach which permits inhibited thinking can only
Startling   lead to short term answers with little or no future, ideas
statement   resulting in inventions requiring lengthy development and
test programs, opinions often leading to blind alleys, and
small improvements at a very large cost.

Approaches to Problem

Literary   Actually we have had the right approach with us since
reference   1620 when Sir Francis Bacon in his *Novum Organum* made
the following statement:

"It is idle to expect any great advancement in science
Quotation   from the super-inducing and ingrafting of new things upon
old. We must begin anew from the very foundation, unless
we would revolve forever in a circle with mean and con-
temptible progress."

In other words, we must stop modifying modifications.
Restate-   We must stop accepting compromises or partial solutions.
ment of   We must think uninhibitedly and seek an adequate solution
thesis   by stating the problem in its fundamental terms. In order
to think in this manner we must treat each problem as a
completely new one and start by wiping the slate clear.

Such an approach calls for the user to seek not a partial
solution, but rather an ultimate solution. Many engineers
today consider such tactics as dreaming. Engineers seem to
Humor   prefer to be what they call objective in their thinking, practical, with their heads not in the clouds, but with their feet
solidly on the ground. This is certainly a very healthy attitude, providing their feet don't get stuck too deeply in the
mud.

From the information requirements and the display requirements we can determine that the following sensors are necessary: (1) inertia, (2) force, (3) heat, (4) quantity, (5) geometry, (6) electromagnetic radiation.

Concrete examples

All of the equations related to the flight of any space craft can be solved by using these six sensors with respect to time. Navigation is a function of velocity which is a function of acceleration. Fuel management is a function of fuel available with respect to time. Position, obstacles, and weather are some of the information requiring the use of some form of electromagnetic radiation. Here again these sensors are fundamental because they represent the basic parameters relevant to the motion of any craft in space. They are all variables in the equations of navigation and orientation and therefore all modes of flight.

Specific details

Since information requirements cannot be determined, these are replaced by operational or functional requirements. In other words, what is the machine required to do? Following this we must determine the environmental requirements, —in what environment must the machine operate? Next we determine the structural or configuration requirements. In this instance we establish what general shape or design the machine must conform to in order to meet the operational and environmental requirements. And finally we must determine the material requirements in order to meet the previous requirements. In other words, what must the materials be?

Rhetorical questions

Concluding Remarks

What I am suggesting is not an easy thing to do because it necessitates divorcing from your minds everything you have learned except the fundamental laws of physics during the determination of the requirements. The worst pitfall during this process is falling in love with new possibilities which will arise and thus discounting the seeking out of the fundamental.

Restatement of thesis

What I have suggested here may be quite confusing but I assure you that, based on experience, such an approach will work. When the fundamental requirements of any problem are established, the solution to the problem becomes apparent. If you will take the time to state the problem at hand in its fundamental terms, if you will stop inventing and seek a completely adequate solution, if you will look at the total problem and work as a team; then you will be thinking

Logic

uninhibitedly and progress will be made not in small increments, but in a continuous series of major breakthroughs.

Restate-   In simple words: state the problem completely before you
ment   try to solve it and space travel will become a reality rather
of thesis   than a discussion.

This article appeals to readers because of its subject matter and
the clarity with which the writer has expressed himself. His use of
analogy and definition is very effective and his restressing his thesis
brings his point home to the reader.

The advice which the author gives the reader in his final sentence
is advice that is applicable to all problems rather than to space travel
alone.

Summary

This chapter aims to show you what values lie in publication and
how publishing can help you to become more successful. It has considered technical and semitechnical articles. In order to emphasize
the necessity of wide reading, the use of the library and the various
reference books that can be found there have been emphasized, and
the methods of setting down information secured from laboratory
procedures have been noted. Examples of technical and semitechnical
articles have been presented, with side headings showing the general
method which has been used in the writing of these articles. Attention has been given to the various parts of the article and the methods
by which these parts have been developed.

Discussion Questions

1. Indicate four values of being able to write articles which will be read
   by others in your own field.
2. Why is it necessary in article writing to go to such trouble to limit
   the subject?
3. What special values are there in reading widely in the general area
   in which you wish to write?
4. How do the indexes help you to find what has been written in your
   field?
5. Why is it important to learn to read well?
6. What special value is there in using cards to make your notes?
7. Discuss the comparative values of the Library of Congress System and
   the Dewey Decimal System.
8. Why do you need to make a bibliography as a preliminary to the
   writing of an article?

9. Why is outlining so valuable when you are writing a technical or semi-technical article?
10. What is the essential difference between a technical and a semitechnical article?
11. Why should one adhere to a particular point of view when writing an article?
12. Name some devices for keeping reader interest in the body of an article.
13. What is the special value of footnotes?

7

Illustrating the Report and the Article

Aim of This Chapter

Before beginning a discussion of the techniques of illustrating the article and the report, it should be made clear that the aim of the material to follow is *not* to attempt to teach the elements of engineering graphics. It is presumed that you possess already, or will secure, the necessary skills in drafting. Instead, we shall try to give you some of the information which the technical writer will need so that he can decide on the kind of illustration that will be most effective for his subject matter.

The Audience for Illustrations

Just as you must consider your possible audience when you are writing a report or an article, so too you must bear that audience in mind when you are drawing any sort of illustration. If, for example, you are producing a drawing of an assembly which will be considered only by a sheetmetal worker, you will not want to cross-hatch the drawing or smudge it to show some of the surfaces in a different tone from others. Instead, you will want to give the workman an exact communication of what you want to have built, and will not be concerned with the beauty of the finished drawing. In the first place, the professional appearance of your drawing will not get you a better finished job, even though it may gladden the heart of the sheet metal worker. Secondly, it will take you a great deal of time to put in these finishing touches. But if you intend to submit an article for publication in a technical magazine, you will be expected to follow the standards for illustration which that magazine sets. Before you decide

240

on what you will attempt in illustration, look over some previous issues of the magazine and see what its requirements for illustrations may be.

Much the same sort of judgment must be exercised when you are considering the illustration for a report. Let us assume that the report is going to a small group of people, all of whom are familiar with the various pieces of equipment you have used. Under these circumstances, you should use simplified drawings of the apparatus you are dealing with, rather than drawing them out in detail. If you have a water pump as part of the equipment under consideration, you need not draw it in detail, but in a simplified form. If the report is to have wide circulation, you will probably find it of value to take greater pains with the illustrations. Many of your readers may be unacquainted with the equipment; further, it is expected that the art work for a report which will have wide circulation will be of high quality.

You should also give thought to exactly what sort of illustrations you need. It is apparent that if you can describe something in a few words, there is no need for a drawing or a picture of it. Yet if you omit a drawing which can clarify your text, you are injuring the effect of your report. Properly used, visual aids can plant your message lastingly in the minds of your readers. They help tell your story in such a way that the mental pictures left stimulate the readers to take action on your report or article.

Definitions of Illustrative Devices

The illustrative devices used in the report and the article are usually of three general types: figures, tables, and exhibits. Figures include drawings, photographs, curves, and graphs. It is best to title them "Figure 1," "Figure 2," and so on, carrying the numbers throughout the entire report or article.

Tables include such items as tabulated information and calculated data. They are usually numbered in Roman, as "Table I," "Table II." As with figures, the numbers should be carried in sequence throughout the entire body of work.

Exhibits include material not coming under either of the categories of figures or tables. Sample or original data sheets are usually considered exhibits, as are copies of correspondence, safety, maintenance or operating instructions and procedures, and nomenclature defining symbols you have used. Exhibits are labeled "Exhibit A," "Exhibit B," etc.

Functions of Illustration

In general, illustrations in the report or the article have three major functions. The first thing that they must do is clarify the written material. If a complicated description of where and how a specific fitting is mounted on an engine can be reduced to a minimum of words by a picture or a drawing, it is good judgment to make use of the illustration. If a schematic diagram will make it easier for your reader to understand a process, by all means draw one.

Closely allied to clarifying the textual matter that you are presenting is the second aim of the illustration: the abbreviation of description. Suppose that you have so simple a piece of apparatus as an ordinary wire coat hanger of the type the cleaner gives you. If you are required to write a description of this article, it will probably take you about 125 words at a minimum. But a simple drawing makes all its elements obvious; you need write nothing if you have an adequate illustration.

The third aim of the illustration is to add interest to your writing and attract a reader's eye toward the page. As the reader leafs through your report or the manuscript of your article, the pictures, charts, and graphs may either catch his interest so that he starts reading right away, or they may so repel him by their complexity or dullness that he puts the material aside, "to read later," which usually amounts to the same thing as dropping it into a wastebasket.

The key to effective figures, tables, and exhibits is simplicity. Do not try to present too much information or too many variables in one figure or table, and avoid heavy grid lines for graphs, for they will obscure or detract from the important element, the curve itself. Figure 7, intended as a light-hearted satire on the tendency to try to give more information than a graph will carry, will probably bring this point home to you more forcibly than any number of words can possibly do.

When you are using any sort of illustration, always be sure that your titles and headings give all the essential identifying information in as few words as clarity permits. In addition, be sure that your nomenclature is consistent. Decide in advance what you want to call everything that you are going to discuss, and then use these descriptive words or phrases every time you have occasion to mention a given article. Nothing is more calculated to exasperate a reader than to make him try to determine whether the small tank on one page is the same thing as the reservoir on the next page, and then have the

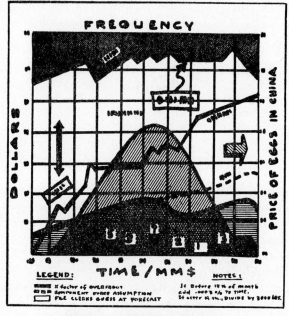

Fig. 7. The overloaded graph: Hide-and-Seek among the variables. (Reproduced by permission of E. I. du Pont de Nemours and Co.)

illustration confuse him even further by a reference to a "receiving vessel."

Consider the three functions of illustrations, referred to on page 242, as they apply to the details of tables. A table is a device to present numerical information that either cannot be presented on a curve or will be more effective in tabular form. The rule is to put the units of measurement in the column heads rather than to place them horizontally. Such an arrangement makes the values easier for the reader to compare and easier for the stenographer to type, for the values will of course appear in the columns. Examine the following table: it violates the rule, to its considerable disadvantage.

COMPARISON OF TURBOJET ENGINES

	J30	J34
Diameter	19 in.	28 in.
Weight	705 lb	1184 lb
Thrust	1550 lb	3400 lb
SFC	1.18 (lb/hr)/lb	1.04 (lb/hr)/lb

If you now set this same table up,[1] following the rule just given—keeping the units of measurement in the column heads—the result will have this appearance:

COMPARISON OF TURBOJET ENGINES

	Diameter (in.)	Weight (lb)	Thrust (lb)	SFC (lb/hr)/lb
J30	19	705	1550	1.18
J34	28	1184	3400	1.04

Your recasting of the table has led to several advantages. First, you avoided repeating the units of measurement after each value by moving them into the column heads. Next, you put the values to be compared into columns, making the table much easier to follow. Last, you could easily list more engines if you needed to without requiring much additional space.

Notice that the preferable table has a minimum of ruling. Eliminating the boxed-in look saves time in making up the table, presents a more attractive picture to the reader, and makes the table easier to read.

Curves and Bar Charts

Unless you need to give exact values, tabular data can often be presented as curves or bar charts, which are much easier to understand than tables, for they give a pictorial image rather than an entirely intellectual one to the reader.

There are two general types of curves: trend curves and performance curves. The former shows trends and is often used to carry information of a general nature. For example, if you were charged with the responsibility of predicting sales for the next year by a division of your company, you would probably want to give this information through the use of a trend curve, which is far simpler than a performance curve. If, however, you were responsible for presenting the amount of fuel used by a sodium metal reactor in a given period, you would probably want to use a performance curve, for you would be able to give exact figures, and the performance curve will do this. Figures 8 and 9 show representative examples of these types of curves.

[1] Reproduced by permission of the Westinghouse Electric Corp.

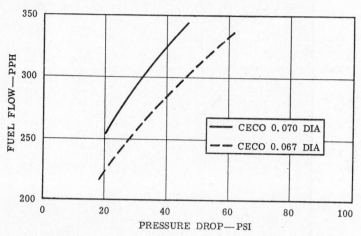

Fig. 8. Typical trend curve. (Reproduced by permission of Westinghouse Electric Corp.)

The bar graph or bar chart is the most dramatic of these devices, for it pictorializes quantities. Assume that you want to show the value of pitchblende shipped from the Congo to the United States for the five years specified in Fig. 10. Each bar will then represent one year. In this form the bar chart makes a relatively simple statement, but it may be adapted to a greater complexity of data.

Cross-hatching is often of value in bar charts, for by this device you will be able to show such relationships as the percentage of crude pitchblende as compared to the refined. Figure 11 employs this technique.

If you want to show more than two items on a bar chart, you have only to use different shadings for the different items. The chart of Fig. 12 illustrates this, although you should be warned that it is possible to encumber your bar chart with too many items and consequently diminish its total impact.

Closely related to the bar chart is the circle graph. This has come into very wide use to represent amounts of money spent or received. It also has a strong pictorial impact. The only possibility of your erring in its use is that you may want to represent too small amounts. Try to lump together those items which do not occupy an appreciable amount of the circumference of the circle. If it is essential to represent some small items on such a circle graph, you will have to enlarge the figure. Figure 13 is a circle graph showing the income of a college for a year.

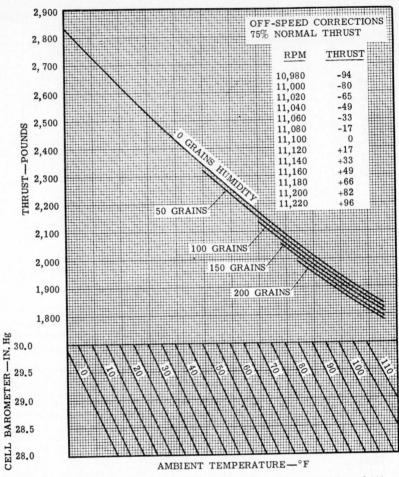

Fig. 9. Typical performance curve. (Reproduced by permission of Westinghouse Electric Corp.)

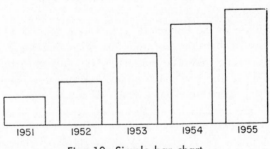

Fig. 10. Simple bar chart.

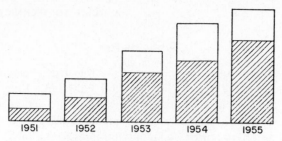

Fig. 11. Shaded bar chart.

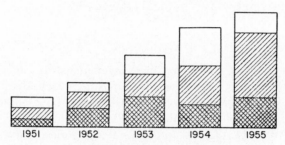

Fig. 12. Varied cross-hatching.

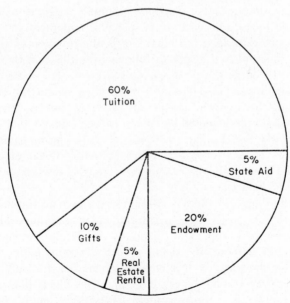

Fig. 13. Circle graph.

Types of Art

All illustrations used in the report or the article can be divided into two general categories—line art and halftones. Line art is any illustration that can be printed without the use of a screened negative. (Screened negatives are made by photographing the illustration through a fine screen, often as fine as 133 lines to the inch. The result is that the illustration is converted into thousands of small dots which supply the gradations in tone. The larger the dots in a given area, the darker that area will be, as Fig. 14 shows.)

LINE ART

Line art, too, may be given many gradations. It can range from simple lines to very elaborate renderings in which shading sheets, stippling, line shading, or textured board may be used to simulate tones. An example of typical line art is Fig. 15.

Line art can be divided into several categories: curves (for the discussion of these, see pages 244–245), schematics, exploded views, spot illustrations, and other illustrations which do not require a "photographic" appearance.

Schematic diagrams are used to eliminate a great many words which would have to be written if a piece of apparatus and its operation were to be described. In other words, the function of a schematic diagram is to simplify the text. It follows from this that the schematic itself ought to be as simple as possible. If you had a cross-sectional drawing which you needed to convert into a schematic, you would eliminate all the unnecessary details, such as bosses, to make the schematic as simple as possible. When calling out on your schematic, you should use the standard symbols, to make misinterpretation difficult. Figure 16 is a schematic representation of the interconnections between the drive coils, the control box, and the driving power source of a magnetic loop tracer.

Schematic diagrams such as the one just shown are often simplified with a variation of the schematic—the block diagram. The aim in such a diagram is to represent pictorially the different elements of the apparatus, but without any detail. Block diagrams allow of the use of names for the parts better than do schematics, for only the major elements appear in the block diagram. The block diagram reproduced in Fig. 17 is a representation of the total components of the

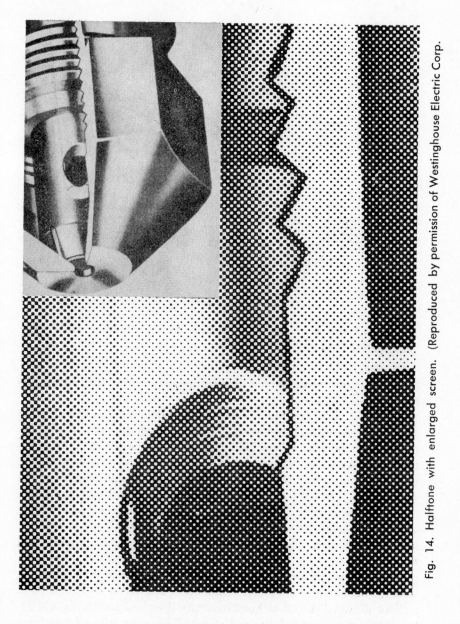

Fig. 14. Halftone with enlarged screen. (Reproduced by permission of Westinghouse Electric Corp.

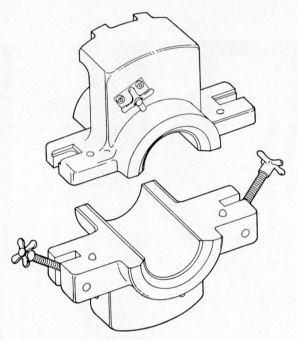

Fig. 15. Example of line art. (Reproduced by permission of Westing-house Electric Corp.)

magnetic loop tracer whose driving power source was illustrated schematically before.

Exploded views are very commonly found in such publications as customers' manuals, advertising brochures, and the like, where the reader must be able to see hidden parts of the apparatus. Although cut-away views can often be used to advantage to achieve this end, if the apparatus has parts within other parts, the cut-away does not show all the elements in the full detail that an exploded view will.

If it is necessary to show the process of assembling or disassembling a rather intricate piece of apparatus, the exploded view is the one likely to be chosen. The items are numbered, and a legend below tells the name of the piece and how it is to be fitted into the other components of the apparatus. Calling-out would encumber the drawing with too many names. Figure 18 shows the value of the exploded view.

Spot illustrations, often humorous, are designed merely to add interest to a report or an article. Considerable judgment and tact must be used in preparing these; only too often the artist producing them

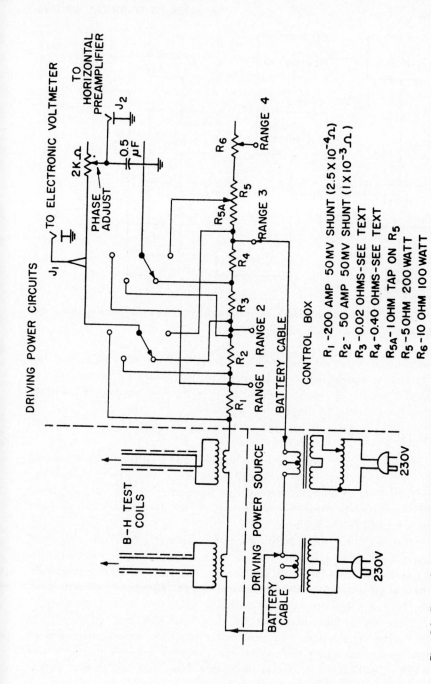

Fig. 16. Example of schematic diagram. (Reproduced by permission of the Research Center of The Burroughs Corp.)

251

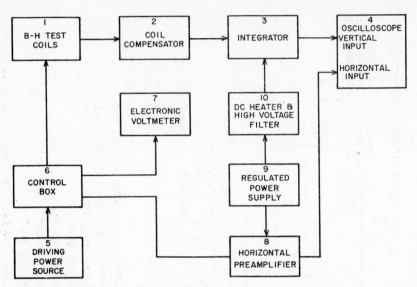

Fig. 17. Example of block diagram. (Reproduced by permission of the Research Center of The Burroughs Corp.)

finds himself carried away with a clever but salacious idea, and his illustration repels many of his readers because of its poor taste. A good example of the spot illustration is the one on page 243, illustrating the danger of overloading a graph.

HALFTONE ART

Halftones are printed reproductions of continuous-tone photographs, wash drawings, airbrush retouchings, etc. To preserve the full range of continuous tone values appearing on the original illustration, a screened negative must be made for the printer's use. Figure 19 is typical of the halftone.

The basis for most halftones is the photograph. You will often have occasion to take pictures, or have them taken, of pieces of apparatus you have been working on so that you can later incorporate these illustrations into an article or a report. However, you will need to observe a few precautions with the taking of these pictures.

First, try to take more pictures than you think you will need. As you write your report, you may find a need for a particular view of the apparatus under discussion. If you took enough pictures, you will probably have it; if you took only those that you at first anticipated using, you probably will not.

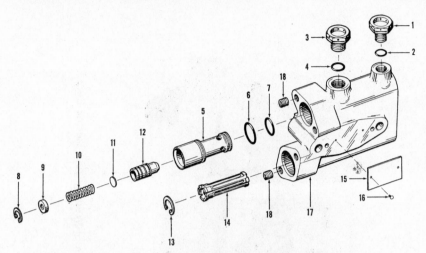

Fig. 18. Example of exploded view. (Reproduced by permission of West-inghouse Electric Corp.)

Second, try to blank out, by one means or another, objects that are not pertinent. Sometimes, hanging a sheet behind the apparatus to block out the background and accentuate the things you want to bring out is a good procedure.

Third, photographs can often be greatly improved by airbrushing them. The tonal values can be brought out much better by this technique, and lines can be accentuated. The whole picture appears cleaner and neater after it has been retouched by airbrushing. The "before-and-after" effect is clearly visible in the contrast between the two parts of Fig. 20.

Another interesting and sometimes useful effect can be produced by airbrushing ordinary line art. If you need a cutaway view, you will have to use line art to produce it; but if the drawing is done with care and if the airbrushing technique is used on it, it will have practically the finished effect of a photograph. Machines which are not actually in existence can be drawn and airbrushed; apparatus which you have used, but which has since been modified, torn down, or shipped away can be accurately and elegantly reproduced by the use of the airbrush on line art.

Examine the two parts of Fig. 21 to see the effect of airbrushing line art. There is no doubt that the figure on the left is a good piece of line art, but that on the right produces an effect that is almost photographic.

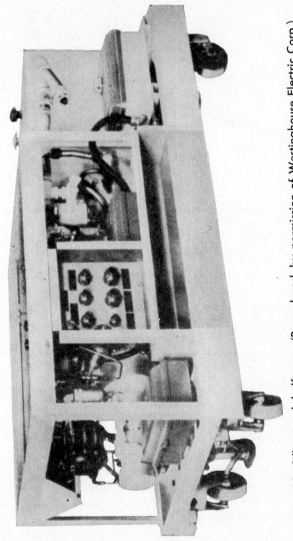

Fig. 19. Silhouetted halftone. (Reproduced by permission of Westinghouse Electric Corp.)

Before

After

Fig. 20. Pictorial quality of a halftone, before and after retouching. (Reproduced by permission of Westinghouse Electric Corp.)

Simplification of Illustrations for Instructions and Minor Reports

The practice of using functional, simplified drafting techniques is much more widespread than it was twenty years ago, when nearly all drawings were required to conform to set standards. Yet by no

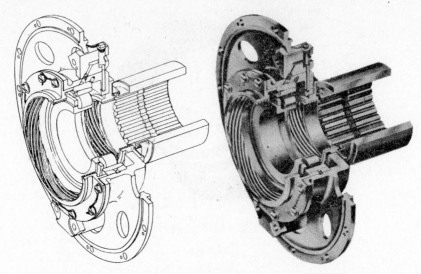

Fig. 21. Line art converted to halftone effect by airbrushing. (Reproduced by permission of Westinghouse Electric Corp.)

means do all companies follow simplified drafting practices, and you will first need to find out whether your company approves before putting into effect the technique which will be suggested. In your company, conventions in drafting may be stronger than efficiency; hence, you should find out what the standard practices are.

BY VERBAL DESCRIPTION

The guiding principle underlying this simplified practice is, "If it's easier to describe it, don't draw it." Of course, the use to which the drawing will be put, and the person who will use it must always be kept in mind. If you think a drawing is needed or would be helpful, by all means make one. Such a determination is a matter of judgment; it is impossible to set exact rules to determine whether or not a drawing will be needed.

Look at the drawing in Fig. 22; then examine the description to its right. You must ask yourself, "Will the person who is going to use this information be able to understand the simplified form?" If you decide that the drawing is superfluous, don't draw.

It is quite possible that an even greater simplification can be made here. The probability is that the bill of material for the entire apparatus will contain the simplified description given at the right.

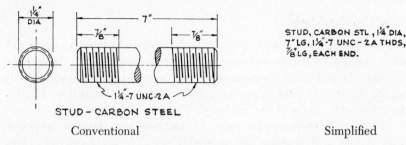

STUD, CARBON STL , 1¼˝ DIA,
7˝ LG, 1¼˝ -7 UNC - 2A THDS,
⅞˝ LG , EACH END.

STUD - CARBON STEEL

Conventional   Simplified

Fig. 22. Simplification of drawing by verbal description. (Reproduced by permission of the Campbell Soup Co.)

Under these circumstances, you need only to make a reference to the bill of material and the item number representing this stud.

Sometimes drawings can be reduced from two or three views of the same object to one if suitable description is used (Fig. 23). Again, of course, judgment must make the determination as to whether two views of this item are necessary, but it seems likely that the person who is to use this drawing can do quite as well with the simplified form on the right as with the unnecessarily complicated delineation on the left. If you were to total up the time spent in making the three views on the left, and then compare the time spent in making the simplified version on the right, you would see that there would be a great increase in efficiency.

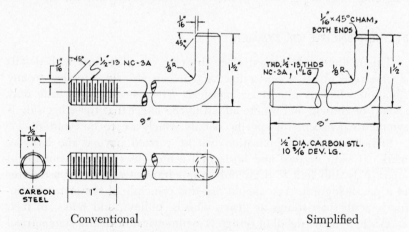

Conventional   Simplified

Fig. 23. Elimination of views by verbal description. (Reproduced by permission of the Campbell Soup Co.)

BY APPROVED SYMBOLS

Particularly in welding, piping, and in electrical work, there are many standard symbols with which every craftsman will be thoroughly familiar. If you think your drawing may contain symbols which will not be known, use them anyway, and set down a legend or key on the drawing to explain them verbally.

Most large corporations have an engineering standard practice book which will contain the approved symbols for electrical work, piping and welding. The brochure of the American Standards Association, "Graphical Symbols for Welding," gives all the approved symbols for welding. If you have not seen it, you may be interested in looking it up.

Single line piping is a recognized standard, yet many people double their work by drawing it as a double line. Sometimes, however, with piping two inches and over, and particularly in tight areas, there may be an advantage in using a double line. Gaining such an advantage, however, may encourage you to decide to extend the double line to the whole drawing. This is an inefficient practice.

Examine the two drawings below (Fig. 24). Is there anything on the elaborate drawing that would give a craftsman any more information than would be given by the simplified form? The spelled-out words accompanying the elaborate drawing do not insure any better work than the standard symbols and abbreviations. Further, the elaborate drawing is badly cluttered by the spelled-out words.

BY THE PRINCIPLE OF SYMMETRY

This method is best used when drawing complex parts with details symmetrical about a center line, and it can also be extended to any situation which is almost symmetrical. The more complex side only should be drawn, and a note added to the effect that the other side is symmetrical except for specific details which are to be omitted.

Sometimes the simplification can be carried beyond the halfway mark. If both vertical and horizontal center lines divide symmetrical areas, it is sufficient to draw only a quadrant of a circle or a quarter of a parallelogram. You should use this principle of symmetry particularly with such things as gears, wheels, pulleys, and tanks; in fact, everywhere if the detail of design is symmetrical or nearly symmetrical about the center line.

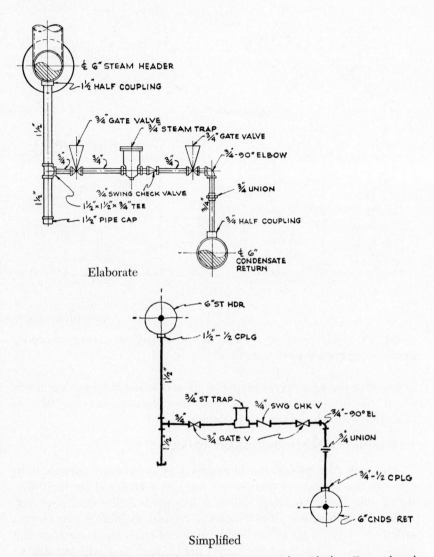

Elaborate

Simplified

Fig. 24. Simplification of drawing by approved symbols. (Reproduced by permission of the Campbell Soup Co.)

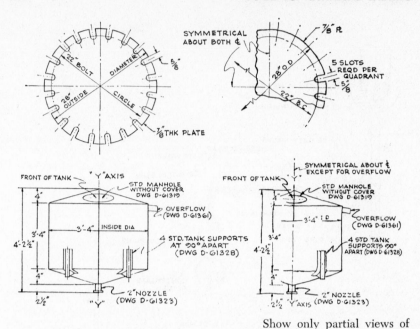

Show only partial views of
such symmetrical objects

Fig. 25. Simplification of drawing by use of symmetry. (Reproduced by permission of the Campbell Soup Co.)

Observe the four drawings of Fig. 25 and arrive at your conclusions about the accuracy of the message they convey and the relative efficiency with which they can be done.

BY ELIMINATION OF UNNECESSARY DETAILS

The first step toward the elimination of unnecessary details is to come to the realization that two or more of a kind call for the drawing of only *one*. This saving device will apply to batteries of anything, such as switchboards, drilled holes, electrical fixtures, doors, retorts, tanks, etc. Even if there are slight variations from one to another, the whole drawing need not be made, but instead you will be able to indicate on the second drawing that aside from a particular item, the second drawing is a facsimile of the first.

This principle applies not only to complete items, but also to their details. The detailing of a small area is all that is necessary if a continuous pattern exists. There is no need to draw in all the items in courses of brick or to show the entirety of a large piece of wire mesh.

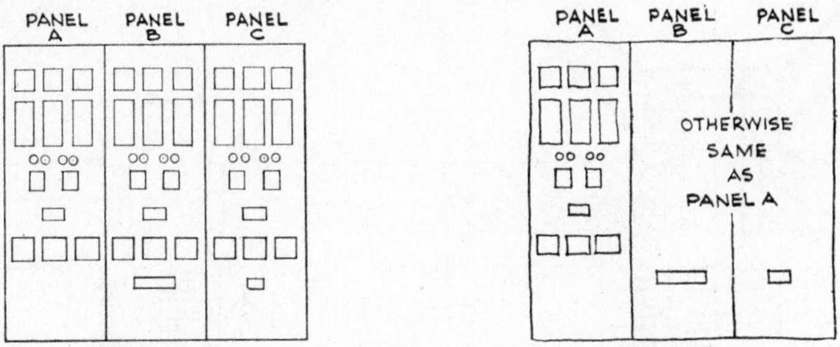

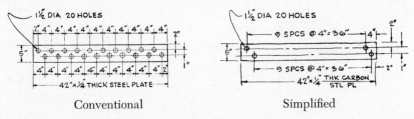

Conventional   Simplified

Fig. 26. Simplification of drawing by eliminating repetitive detail. (Reproduced by permission of the Campbell Soup Co.)

In the drawings of panels in Fig. 26, only a small difference exists among the three; consequently, a short note will suffice to point this up.

In the same way, the series of holes in the drawing of the steel plate at the left (Fig. 27) is quite unnecessary. This pattern can be done with much more speed and with complete detail and clarity by the drawing at the right.

A second step toward the elimination of unnecessary details can be taken in connection with assembly drawings. Since the purpose of an assembly drawing is to show how the various parts fit together and since its function is to show the relative position of each part, it is clear that it is necessary to show the parts in outline only and in the position they will occupy in the complete assembly. Compare the two drawings of Fig. 28. You will observe that the simplified form carries all the necessary information.

A third time-saving procedure is to eliminate artistic elaboration and excessive material indication. It is clear to every technically

Conventional   Simplified

Fig. 27. Simplification of drawing by generalizing for a series. (Reproduced by permission of the Campbell Soup Co.)

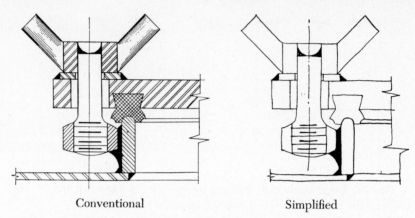

Conventional   Simplified

Fig. 28. Simplification of drawing by elimination of cross-hatching. (Reproduced by permission of the Campbell Soup Co.)

trained person that certain qualities and characteristics are clearly implied when an object is merely named or otherwise identified. For example, all screws have threads, and all threads have pitch, all coiled springs have turns, all round holes have circumferences and radii. The existence of windows implies glazing; the existence of brick or tile implies mortar. To pictorialize these implications will be a waste of your time.

Observe the tension spring at the left (Fig. 29), and consider how much time must have been taken to draw it. Then compare it with the simple outline at the right. The simplified form tells a craftsman everything he needs to know to produce the piece.

The basic purpose of cross-hatching is to indicate cut surfaces in sectional views and thereby aid clarity. It is, in other words, a symbol which carries an exact meaning. But it need not be spread over the entire surface under consideration; a mere indication will

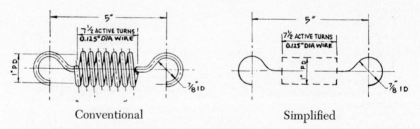

Conventional   Simplified

Fig. 29. Simplification of drawing by elimination of redundancy. (Reproduced by permission of the Campbell Soup Co.)

Conventional   Simplified

Fig. 30. Simplification of drawing by reducing cross-hatching and other conventions to the minimum. (Reproduced by permission of the Campbell Soup Co.)

do quite as well. The two drawings of Fig. 30 indicate the two techniques in cross-hatching, but it is clear that the elaborate drawing has merely wasted someone's time.

A final method for the elimination of unnecessary details is to make much scanter use of dotted lines. Drawing these lines is tedious and time-consuming, especially in respect to circles. Since the conventional purpose of the dotted line is to indicate a hidden surface, most of them can be eliminated by a note. For example, one way in which dotted lines are used needlessly is to indicate that metal has thickness (a fact reasonably well known), and yet it is an excellent instance of drawing something that adds nothing to the information that can be contained in a note such as "12 ga. (0.107″)." Again, this is exemplified by the two drawings of Fig. 31.

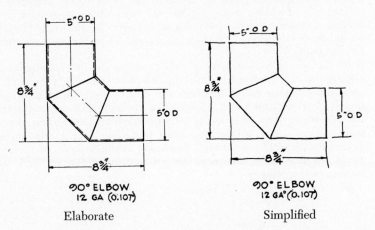

Elaborate   Simplified

Fig. 31. Simplification of drawing by elimination of the self-evident. (Reproduced by permission of the Campbell Soup Co.)

Summary

The audience for your material is a most important factor in your determining the scope of your illustrations. The three types of illustrative devices—figures, tables, and exhibits—have been defined and illustrated, and consideration has been given to the functions of illustrations. The two major types of art, line art and halftone, have been examined and subdivided, and the specific uses for each have been presented. Finally, instructions have been given for the use of functional, simplified drafting practices. If you follow the suggestions presented, you should have little trouble illustrating your own report or article.

Discussion Questions

1. Assume that your employer requires standard drawings rather than the more informal sort. Advance reasons which might back his stand on this.
2. State four distinct ways in which simplified drawings will be a saving of time and money.
3. Indicate four criticisms of the use of simplified drawings.
4. Discuss in detail (add actual cases) in which the use of a few words of explanation will improve the understanding of a drawing by someone required to work with it.
5. Discuss specific values in the uses of graphs to show quantitative values.
6. Discuss the specific values of airbrushing as an illustrative technique.
7. Discuss the general types of material that need to be amplified by making use of charts, maps, graphs, and illustrations in general.
8. Prepare a defense for the following statement: "All drawings intended for production personnel to work on should be in the most simplified form possible."
9. State the special values to be gained from the use of exploded views.
10. Discuss the most effective illustrative devices that might be used in an end-of-the-year report in which the company wishes to show such things as profits and losses, comparative production of apparatus from the preceding year, number of persons employed in various departments, comparative wages paid from preceding year to the present year, amounts paid out in stock dividends, amounts paid out to supervisory employees as compared to production employees, and total income of the company.

8

Language Essentials and Types of Technical Exposition

General Requirements of Technical Writing

Just as you do not go into the chemical laboratory and mix together various chemicals without having a hoped-for product in mind, neither do you undertake writing anything without having clearly in mind (and even better, on paper) the effect which that writing is to produce. You must then know how to bring this effect into your reader's mind.

A writer who has had little experience with his craft may err by choosing a subject that is too large for adequate treatment within the space he has allotted himself. The limitation of the subject is, therefore, important. Often, of course, the subject has been limited by the authorization granted to the writer to pursue a given investigation. But often, when you are going to write an article or make a speech, no such limitation exists, so you must be aware of the need for limitation.

A limitation and an organization of the subject can almost always be achieved by setting down an outline, preferably one written out in full sentences. Each of the sentences within the outline form may very well act as the lead sentence for a paragraph, a unit of thought. To write a good paragraph, you will need to concern yourself with this lead sentence (usually called a topic sentence), and with the details which follow it and help to explain the generalization which this topic sentence states. The rest of the paragraph must be governed by the elements of unity, coherence, and emphasis, but you will need to choose an appropriate method of development to bring about your

265

intended effect. You must, of course, use appropriate English, make an exact choice of words, and spell accurately. Almost always you will want to write on the formal level; technical communication rarely falls to the level of the colloquial or even the informal.

Since writing requires these qualities, the following section will examine them in detail. An outline of the material to be discussed follows:

1. The writer's aim
2. The analysis of the aim and the outline
3. The paragraph: its topic and subtopic sentences
4. The qualities of the paragraph—coherence, unity, and emphasis
5. The word
6. The sentence
7. Methods of technical exposition.

The Writer's Aim

In any piece of writing which the technical man has to compose— a business letter, a report, or an article—he must realize his aim clearly. Often this aim is formulated mentally; the letter writer, for instance, usually follows this procedure. There are times, however, when it is advantageous to set down the aim on paper. Many writers find that it is helpful to put on a separate sheet: "My aim in this paper is to . . . ," or "My aim in this article will be to . . . ," for the aim is the unifying factor of the writing.

LIMITING SUBJECTS

Once the general aim has been determined, the writer must be certain that he can treat the material in the space he has allotted himself. Suppose he has been asked to prepare a paper within his field of steam engineering. The first idea for a subject might be "Steam Engineering." The fault in this lies in its breadth; it is impossible to discuss the whole subject in a complete textbook, let alone in a paper of ordinary length. The engineer then begins to limit his subject; his next attempt may be "Transmission of Steam." After trying to outline this, he sees that here too the range of material is too great, and he finally comes to "A New Type of Steam Joint," a reasonably suitable subject for a paper of two or three thousand words.

After the aim has been made specific and the subject limited, the writer is ready to proceed to his next step: analysis of the aim. Whether this can be done easily or will involve a protracted labor period depends on how well he knows his problem and the data involved in that problem. Fortunately, the writer's education is the kind which makes him analyze constantly; and since he will be writing chiefly about those things which he knows intimately, he should not experience great trouble in dividing his aim into its logical parts.

Outline Forms

Outlines [1] may use Roman numerals to designate the main divisions of thought and capital letters to indicate subpoints under each main division. Further subdividing demands the use of Arabic numerals followed by small letters.

I. First main point
  A. First subdivision of main point
  B. Second subdivision of main point

II. Second main point
  A. First subdivision of main point
  B. Second subidivision of main point
    1. First subdivision of B
    2. Second subdivision of B
      a. First subdivision of 2
      b. Second subdivision of 2

If further subdivisions are called for, the writer should use Arabic numerals in parentheses, and for still further subdivisions, small letters in parentheses.

In addition to the method of outlining just given, another may be used. This is usually referred to as the decimal form, since it employs a system of points to set off the heads and subheads. If the outline form shown above were presented in decimal form it would be:

1. First main point
  1.1 First subdivision of main point
  1.2 Second subdivision of main point

2. Second main point
  2.1 First subdivision of main point
  2.2 Second subdivision of main point
    2.2.1 First subdivision of 2.2
    2.2.2 Second subdivision of 2.2
      2.2.2.1 First subdivision of 2.2.2
      2.2.2.2 Second subdivision of 2.2.2

[1] See pages 214–215 and 324–328 for additional material on outlining.

When a writer needs to outline an extremely long and involved matter, he may find that the decimal system will be preferable to the Roman numeral–letter–Arabic number method, for it is clear that he cannot run out of headings, since he merely needs to continue placing decimal points and numbers for any additional subdivisions that may be needed. Assume that two more subdivisions are needed for the heading marked 2.2.2.2 above. It will be set down as follows:

> 2.2.2.2.1 First subdivision of 2.2.2.2
> 2.2.2.2.2 Second subdivision of 2.2.2.2

Statements following major headings should be expressed in the same grammatical form wherever possible. For instance, if Roman numeral one is expressed by a complete sentence, material for all other Roman numerals should be expressed in sentences. If Roman numeral one is expressed by a phrase, then all other Roman numerals should use phrases. This practice has been kept throughout this book. Again, the same grammatical form is used for all subheads under each Roman numeral, although this form may differ from that used for the statements indicated by the Roman numerals. Some writers use complete sentences for Roman numerals and phrases for subpoints. It is necessary to phrase a group of subpoints under any heading in the same grammatical form. The most careful writers tend to use a complete sentence for each point because complete sentences are less likely to be misconstrued than phrases.

Since any unit cannot be divided into less than two parts, good outlining avoids such practice as I-A or A-1. If only one point follows a main head, make that point part of the main head. For example, consider the following statements:

> I. The young chemical engineer should read the journals in his field.
>   A. He should read particularly Chemical and Engineering News and The Chemist.

This should appear in an outline as:

> I. The young chemical engineer should read the journals in his field, such as Chemical and Engineering News and The Chemist.

Each part of the outline should be tested for logical and orderly arrangement. Does each Roman numeral develop the purpose of the whole composition? Is each Roman numeral in the most logical order, or does it need to be put somewhere else?

The following outline obviously needs revision:

  I. The sales engineer today must know more than the technical data pertaining to his own area of interest.

 II. The efficient engineer cultivates good human relations.
    A. He seeks to know the customers of his company.
    B. He aims to satisfy the customers' needs.
    C. He tries to anticipate the customers' needs.

III. He must have an understanding of the whole process of manufacture of his product.
    A. The sales engineer needs to follow this process through, step by step.
    B. He must ask questions of people who know the answers.

IV. He must follow developments in industries allied to his own.
    A. Be on the alert to master new processes.
    B. He should test the practice of his own company by the practice of other firms.
    C. Keep an open mind toward what others do.

 V. He should remember constantly that the more knowledge he has of other fields the more useful he will be as an engineer.

If you will read over the Roman numerals, you will discover that the most important point, that of cultivating good human relations, is mentioned as the first point under the purpose. A better arrangement, one which leads toward the most important point as a climax, would be to place this as IV, just before the concluding statement. Moreover, in II, point C should come before point B.

The statements following the Roman numerals are not in parallel. After the first citation of "sales engineer," future references to him should adopt "he." Since every subpoint under a Roman numeral is a complete sentence beginning with subject and predicate, the imperative to open a sentence should be avoided. The correct outline would read:

  I. The sales engineer today must know more than the technical data pertaining to his own area of interest.

 II. He must have an understanding of the whole process of manufacture of his product.
    A. He needs to follow through, step by step, this process.
    B. He must ask questions of people who know the answers.

III He must follow developments in industries allied to his own.
    A. He should be on the alert to master new processes.

    B. He should test the practice of his own company by the practice
       of other firms.

    C. He should keep an open mind toward what others do.

IV. He must cultivate good human relations.

    A. He must seek to know the customers of his company.

    B. He must try to anticipate the customers' needs.

    C. He must aim to satisfy the customers' needs.

 V. He should remember constantly that the more knowledge he has
of other fields the more useful he will be as an engineer.

The outline just given if presented by the decimal system would
appear as follows:

1. The sales engineer today must know more than the technical data
pertaining to his own area of interest.

2. He must have an understanding of the whole process of manufacture of his product.

    2.1 He needs to follow this process through, step by step.

    2.2 He must ask questions of people who know the answers.

3. He must follow developments in industries allied to his own.

    3.1 He should be on the alert to master new processes.

    3.2 He should test the practice of his own company by the practice
of other firms.

    3.3 He should keep an open mind toward what others do.

4. He must cultivate good human relations.

    4.1 He must seek to know the customers of his company.

    4.2 He must try to anticipate the customers' needs.

    4.3 He must aim to satisfy the customers' needs.

5. He should remember constantly that the more knowledge he has of
other fields the more useful he will be as an engineer.

The order of the main heads of an outline may be dictated by considerations of time, of space relationship, of cause-to-effect relationship, or by degree of relative importance. Whether the writer's aim
is carried out most efficiently by the order chosen is the chief test.
The good outline provides a foolproof blueprint of the writer's thought.

The Paragraph

With the outline complete, the next step is to write the whole
paper. The basic unit in this paper is the paragraph. Just as the
atom includes the electron, the proton, and the neutron, the main

thought of any piece of writing includes various smaller thoughts, which, added together, produce the effect for which the writer strives. The paragraph, being the most important subdivision of the aim of the writer, must be given careful consideration, for if the individual paragraphs are obscure or ill-developed, the entire objective of the writing is nullified.

The writer is often at a loss to begin. He realizes that he has something to say, but he is unable to find an appropriate sentence with which to start. If he will think of what he has to say, and his attitude concerning that material, he will be able to formulate his first topic sentence. It will, if well constructed, lead him naturally into the development of his first paragraph.

THE TOPIC SENTENCE

The expository paragraph is almost always prefaced by what is called a *topic sentence*. This statement usually expresses in general what the entire paragraph that depends on it says.

The setting up of industrial plants in residential districts is usually viewed with disfavor by the home owners of the neighborhood. The first of their complaints is the smoke nuisance which they feel certain will be created; the next ground for disapproval is the increase in local traffic, both automobile and pedestrian; lastly, the greatest objection is that real estate values will surely decrease.

The first sentence in this passage is the topic sentence. To a large extent it covers the details which follow. It is the most important statement in the paragraph, and all the other sentences evolve naturally from it.

Sometimes the topic sentence has other positions in the paragraph. Instead of being the first sentence, it may be the last. Under these circumstances, all other sentences lead toward the topic sentence, which then acts as a summary sentence as well as one which states the main point of view in the paragraph. Or the topic sentence may be the second, third, or fourth sentence. The preceding sentence or sentences will be merely introductory. By the time the reader gets to the actual topic sentence, he finds a definite statement of the purpose of the paragraph. The writer may put the topic sentence anywhere in the paragraph, in fact, and will often find it desirable to vary its position to avoid a mechanical and monotonous style.

There is a way of making sure that you actually have a topic sentence; there is a test that you can apply to it. First, see if there is something in the sentence that you will want to write about throughout all the rest of the paragraph.

You should usually be careful that the subject is not so large that it will take an elephant-sized paragraph to explain it thoroughly. In general, you should never write one paragraph of 500 words if you can divide it and write two of 250 words each; long paragraphs make hard work for the reader.

The second part of the test for the topic sentence is to determine if there is some attitude taken toward the material about which you are going to write. Is there a statement of like or dislike, a query, a statement of necessity, of approval or disapproval?

If you have both of these elements, you may be sure that you have a topic sentence. Consider this sentence:

There is no reason that industrial plants cannot be beautiful.

Here the writer is clearly going to discuss industrial plants; this is his material or subject. His attitude toward these plants is an esthetic one—that they can be beautiful.

You should be on your guard not to allow two subjects to become incorporated in the same topic sentence, for these will obligate you to treat both of them in the same paragraph, thus making you write a paragraph which is too long and which also runs the risk of becoming disunified. For example, if you had written, "There is no reason that industrial plants cannot be beautiful, and there are many outstanding examples of esthetically satisfying structures of this sort," you will have to show that industrial plants can be fine-looking, and you will also have to adduce a number of examples. If, however, you were to use the latter part of the sentence as a topic sentence for a following paragraph, you would be able to shorten your paragraphs and would also run no risk of disunity.

Suppose the technical man is asked to write upon the value of a wage-incentive system. His material is given him; he has to discuss this system of payment according to the amount of work performed. He must decide upon his own attitude. Assume that he favors such a production scheme. The topic sentence must then include the subject—the incentive system—and the attitude of approval which he takes toward it. The result will be something like this when he writes his topic sentence:

Forward-looking industrial corporations are moving toward the adoption of wage-incentive systems.

Here the attitude is not definitely stated in a few words; the reader instead apprehends it as a result of the entire statement.

Technical people who write a great deal do not not find it necessary to think consciously about the technique—the subject and the attitude —of good topic sentences. Instead, they find that these sentences are automatically formulated during the writing or dictation, if they have thoroughly learned their form. In the same way, most novelists write good topic sentences even though they do not stop to take conscious thought whether they have both subject and attitude expressed. The subconscious mind takes care of such matters—*but only after they have been thoroughly learned.*

PARAGRAPH SUBTOPICS

The next step in the construction of the paragraph is to determine the way in which it should be subdivided. If you were to take such a simple topic sentence as "I enjoy eating shellfish," you might arrange the outline of the paragraph in this way:

A. I enjoy eating shellfish.
   1. I enjoy them broiled.
   2. I like them deep-fried.
   3. I like them with Newburg sauce.

Items 1, 2, and 3 are subtopic sentences. Of themselves, they are not of sufficient importance to command an entire paragraph, but they are logical resolutions of the major or topic sentence, and they will help you to write your paragraph. They foreshadow the sorts of details you will need to use. Again, if a businessman says, "In recent months the progress of new industries in our town is encouraging," we look to the rest of the paragraph to tell us the details of that progress. The topic sentence, then, must:

1. Express the subject which one is to write about
2. Indicate the attitude to be taken toward that subject
3. Be narrow enough to allow of complete explanation in about one to three hundred words.

After the writer has gone through the process of choosing and limiting his aim, after he has analyzed it and outlined it and roughed out his topic and subtopic sentences, he must incorporate in his writing qualities of coherence, unity, and emphasis. These qualities are characteristic of all good paragraphs.

Exercises—The Paragraph

1. Show by limitation how a suitable subject for an article of about a thousand words may be derived from:
   a. Plastics
   b. Modern engineering methods
   c. Industrial incentive methods
   d. The civil engineer as a city builder
   e. Electric power in modern life
   f. Advantages of scientific courses in college
   g. America's great inventors
   h. Labor-saving devices in industry.
2. Outline one of the subjects above after you have limited it.
3. Write ten good topic sentences upon each of which a 200-word paragraph might be written.
4. Write five topic sentences with subtopics for each.
5. Outline the paragraph (with details for development) which might be written from one of the topics in question 4.

Discussion Questions—The Paragraph

1. Why may outlines not be divided as A-1, without having an A-2 to follow?
2. What are the disadvantages of having too large a subject upon which to write?
3. What point is served by actually writing down the subject to be considered?
4. What sort of process does subject limitation consist of?
5. Why is a climactic order often used in outlining?
6. Why do many careful writers use sentence outlines?
7. What test may be applied to be sure that a topic sentence covers all the requirements?
8. How can one determine when a subtopic sentence should be made a topic sentence for a paragraph?
9. What is the advantage in outlining a single paragraph?
10. Why should subjoints under one outline head be phrased in the same grammatical form?

Qualities of the Paragraph: Coherence

Coherence, although a paragraph essential, is not so much a grammatical function as it is the smooth flow of thought within the paragraph and within the entire body of written material. It is an effective verbal reflection of the complete connection of one thought with the following thought. Since coherence is a part of making communication clear, a writer must have some technique by which he may achieve it.

Most of us have this technique to some degree, although we have usually learned it from experience rather than through formal teaching. We have observed logical sequences in actual life; we automatically apply them to writing if our observation has been exact. It is necessary, however, that the writer be able to tell definitely if his work has coherence. He should be able to test it to see if one thought follows another in logical order.

Apply a test for coherence to the following paragraph:

Our public utilities are now subjected to much higher taxes than ever before, and many of them are having difficulty in showing sufficient return on their capital investments to pay the guaranteed dividends on preferred stock. The stockholders, suffering from a smaller return on their money than they have been accustomed to, are eager to lower taxes. One tax that is especially bad is the tax on articles imported into this country. The Swiss, for instance, can make watches more cheaply than we can, but the tax on these watches is so excessive that the selling price must be much higher than those of domestic manufacture.

If we examine this paragraph, we can see that the author intended to tell us about the high taxes on public utilities. Actually, he discusses the effects of these taxes, and logically shows how the stockholders wish the taxes to be lowered, as they are now receiving less return on their investments than formerly. Thus far, the process is clear and logical. It might be outlined this way, although the outline is necessarily incomplete:

I. Public utility taxation is now very high.
    A. The utilities have difficulty paying the stockholders.
        1. The stockholders are eager to lower taxes.

One can see how the writer passes from the fact that taxation is now very high to its natural effect. Since so much money is drained off by local, state, and national taxes, less remains for stockholders. The reader would expect, however, to be told what the taxes are and what effects these had on the earnings of public utilities. But at this point the writer's mind apparently went astray. He takes up, instead, import taxes on Swiss watches and shows how they raise costs. Since public utilities are not related to Swiss watches, the reader is thrown completely off the mental track.

Once the student is aware of the existence of coherence as a necessary part of any paragraph, he should be interested in the method by which it can be achieved. The logical mind is, of course, the greatest aid to coherence, but several methods by which that mind may work can be suggested.

BY TRANSITION

As the writer progresses from point to point of his explanation, he must notify the reader whenever he leaves one point for the next. He does this, and bridges the gap between points, by transition devices. One of the simplest of these is the repetition of the most important word which occurs in the latter part of a preceding sentence.

Mercury is peculiar in that it will form amalgams with a great many other metals. Of these amalgams, one of the most interesting is that of mercury and lead.

Here the transition between the sentences is gained by the repetition of the leading word, "amalgam." It takes the reader from the first main idea of the peculiarity of mercury in its formation of amalgams, to a second, more particularized, peculiarity in the formation of the mercury-lead amalgam. The same method may be used in moving from paragraph to paragraph.

Transition may also be accomplished by the repetition of the theme of a preceding paragraph in the opening sentence of the next paragraph.

The qualities of a plastic are partly determined by the type of chain connections between the atoms which make up the molecular structure of the particular plastic material being considered. To produce changes in these qualities, the chemist has only to vary the structure of the chain in one way or another. He may add some substance which can insinuate itself between the atoms of the plastic chain, thus making it more flexible. If he wishes, he can change the plastic from a tough, non-resilient solid to a liquid.

Such variations in molecular structure are not at all uncommon in high-polymer chemistry.

Here the theme of the preceding paragraph is repeated in the phrase "variations in molecular structure," and the reader's mind is led to the material to follow.

Another common transitional method is pronoun linkage. This consists of using a pronoun which refers to the persons, things, or ideas discussed in the preceding sentence or paragraph. An example of this follows:

Civil engineering is useful, not only to the surveyor, but to the contractor, the governmental authorities of the city, the motorist, the man about to build a home, and the ordinary taxpayer. All of these have a stake in the accuracy of the equations of civil engineering.

Here "all of these" refers to the individuals spoken of in the preceding sentence. The pronoun serves to refer the reader's mind to the matters just discussed and prepares him to move on to the next point.

When a process is being described by an author, a time-place sequence may often act as the transitional device, thus:

All manufacturing operations are carried out as the material moves along a series of roller conveyors. In the first step of the assembly, the television cases pass two workers who place the dials and push-buttons on the chassis. Next, one employee adds the controls and capacitors, after which another adds the tubes to the set.

In this paragraph the reader is led by a time-and-place transition from one operation to another. The first action occurs first in both time and place; as the television cases pass farther along the conveyor, the other actions follow in both time and space.

Cause-effect transition is always accompanied by either a time or a place sequence. In the nature of things, cause must always precede effect; consequently, the cause comes before the effect in time, and sometimes in place as well.

The reaction between sodium and water to produce the hydroxide is easily carried out. A small piece of pure sodium metal is placed in a beaker of distilled water. The reaction intensity is illustrated by the skipping of the metal on the water, and the emission of a train of hydrogen and water vapor. The hydroxide is formed in a water solution. By heating the beaker, the water can be evaporated to leave a residue of pure sodium hydroxide.

In this type of transition, the cause (the reaction of sodium and water) leads to the effect (the production of sodium hydroxide). The student will note that a time sequence is involved as well.

The mathematical sequence is a type of transition of particular value to technical people. It is used widely in technical article writing. Based on mathematical rules, it is usually followed by an explanation of the process in words.

$$\text{Per cent } K = \frac{I_r}{I_s} \times 100$$

where per cent K equals the least generator rating that will cause the relay to operate during a reverse current condition.

In this example the mathematical sequence is the governing factor for the explanation which follows the equation.

Another transition method is the employment by the writer of certain words which in themselves have a transition value. Such phrases as "on the other hand," "in spite of," "however," "nevertheless," and others are in themselves practically meaningless, yet they help to move the reader's attention from one point to another.

The transit is one of the most delicate of surveying instruments. It can, however, withstand hard usage without being damaged or thrown out of adjustment.

In this example, the reader's mind is led from the fact that the transit is a delicate instrument to the fact that it can withstand hard usage by the connective or transitional word "however." The writer should be warned that such transition words ought to occur within the sentence rather than at its beginning.

The transition schemes illustrated above will give you methods by which you may achieve the logical coherence that will hold your paragraph together.

BY DEDUCTIVE REASONING

Deductive reasoning is thought which moves from a generalization to a particularization. The generalization (called in logic the major premise) is followed by a specific application (in logic, the minor premise). The thought process then leads to a conclusion.

Major premise: All forms of precipitation consist, for the most part, of water.
Minor premise: Snow is a form of precipitation.
Conclusion: Snow consists largely of water.

Such a method of thought will produce coherence within a paragraph, for the elements of major premise, minor premise, and conclusion are organically one. The following paragraph might be written from the preceding syllogism:

The ancient Greeks wondered why the materials falling from the sky should change their form from winter to summer. The mild rains seemed to have no relation to the fierce snow storms that swept over the Peloponnesus in the winter. But very early, some shepherd observed that if he held the snow in his hand long enough, it took the same form as the summer rains. Both the rain and the snow were forms of precipitation, he knew, and now he could say that any precipitation from the sky normally is water.

But the writer who intends to use this method of thought should remember that the major premise must be completely true. If he begins with an untrue statement, his results will be invalid. Thus:

Anything with four legs is an animal.
This chair has four legs.
Therefore, this chair is an animal.

The writer has proceeded from this premise: since all animals have four legs, everything with four legs is an animal. The absurdity of such a premise can be seen at once.

BY INDUCTIVE REASONING

In inductive reasoning, we move from a particular series of instances to form a generalization. Let us assume that Mr. X owns two farms which are exactly alike, except that farm A is in the bottom of a deep valley while farm B is on a hillside. Mr. X finds that farm A can produce crops requiring a longer growing season than farm B. He arrives at this conclusion through observation of a particular case. If he wishes to take the thought process any further, he may observe that the only difference between the farms in the fall of the year is that farm A is blanketed with fog in the evening, while farm B is not. If this is the only variant between the farms, he may come to an even more general conclusion: fog keeps crops from being hurt by frost.

Such reasoning is clear, although the technical man must remember that he should not base a general conclusion upon only one piece of evidence. Parallel conditions should be set up; the hypothesis must be proved by a number of examples which show that parallel conclusions are reached.

Both the deductive and the inductive types of reasoning will produce coherence. Inductive reasoning does so because details which are not pertinent to the subject are omitted. Since the entire thesis of a piece of writing is equal to the sum of its parts, the writing is necessarily cohesive through its organic unity. In reverse order, the same is true of the deductive method. Both methods are logical; both may be tested by asking of any part of the outline, "Is this a part of the preceding head? Does it have an organic unity with that preceding head and with the entire thesis?"

Summarizing coherence, we may say that it is the clarity of thought within the paragraph. To achieve this clarity, we may use:

1. Transition
   a. by repetition of important words
   b. by repetition of the theme
   c. by pronoun linkage
   d. by time-place sequence
   e. by cause-effect sequence
   f. by mathematical sequence
   g. by transition words
2. Deductive reasoning
3. Inductive reasoning

Qualities of the Paragraph: Unity

By unity, we mean that a paragraph treats of one topic, and one only. It may, and probably will, need many details, but all of these must apply exclusively to the one topic under consideration. Lack of unity occurs when the writer, enticed from his main thought by some appealing side issue, allows the rest of the paragraph to be concerned with that issue rather than with the main idea with which he started. Errors in unity are almost always errors in coherence as well; they imply that the writer is not thinking straight.

Unity of material is the first requirement. By unity of this sort, we mean that the paragraph must treat only the material of the topic sentence (sometimes, this material is implied rather than stated explicitly).

Unity through knowledge of the effect wanted is another requirement. This means that everything in the paragraph, or group of paragraphs, must aid the purpose of the writer, a purpose he should have formulated clearly before he began to write. This purpose will determine the material he will use to detail his paragraph, as well as the treatment and interpretation of that material.

Unity through treatment of the material is the third requirement. This includes such things as style, mood, general attitude of the writer, and type of thought development used.

Once these requirements are clear, the student should be able to gain unity in the paragraph as a whole.

UNITY OF MATERIAL

In the following paragraphs the writer has failed to get unity of material:

We decided to visit the plant of the American Chemical Corporation at Uxbridge, Indiana, to observe their vulcanizing processes. There was a good deal of confusion getting started; the bus that had been chartered for the trip failed to appear, and Mr. McKinney, our instructor in Chemical Engineering, was upset. After calling the bus terminal, however, another was sent out and we started the trip at 9:45 a.m.

Once at the plant, we were interested to observe that the corporation used a mixture of synthetic and natural rubber in their process. This would have been impossible thirty-five years ago. The vulcanizing was carried out in huge molds heated by steam. A very unpleasant smell arose because of the large sulfur content of the rubber, but we were not delayed in making all necessary observations.

The material which appears in these two paragraphs should have as its main idea the observation of the vulcanizing process of the American Chemical Corporation. Actually, the reader is treated to only a short section on the vulcanizing; the writer has allowed irrelevant material to divert his attention. The incident of the delayed bus may have been important to the students who were assembled for the trip, but it has nothing whatever to do with the expressed topic.

A paragraph may often be unified by its structure. The topic sentence may be followed by subtopic sentences so closely related to the main topic that they will prevent the writer from straying from his material and thus violating both coherence and unity.

A common fault leading to violation of unity is that the material, although unified in the writer's mind, is not demonstrably unified in the written composition. The fault arises as a result of omitting an important statement which shows the connection between the parts of the paragraph. The writer is so well acquainted with his material that he errs in thinking his reader equally familiar with it. An example of this is shown:

The engineer must learn to write even more fluently and more exactly than the liberal arts student. Technical writing alone requires the precision that can come only after long hours of study, yet the engineer feels that his English courses are often a waste of time, in that they take away from the hours he might spend in the laboratory. The English teacher, he feels, asks too much for what he gives. Yet the instructor may ask him to report on the horsepower rating of an engine; his answer must be largely in words. Again, the instructor may ask the engineer, in the course of a class in thermodynamics, to give a summary of the several laws governing that study. Again the student must answer in words. Is not this sufficient to show him that his own language is the most important of his studies?

In the paragraph just cited, the reader feels upon the first appearance of the word "instructor" that it is the English instructor who is being spoken of. Yet later in the paragraph, it becomes apparent that the instructor must be a science teacher. As a result, the material must be reread in order to determine exactly where this change of person has taken place. The paragraph would have had all the necessary elements of unity if the writer had interpolated a sentence between, "The English teacher, he feels, asks too much for what he gives," and, "Yet the instructor may ask him. . . ." If the sentence had shown in some way that the instructor being spoken about in the latter part of the paragraph was a science instructor, the unification would have been accomplished.

In order to achieve unity of material in a paragraph, a report or in any piece of writing:

1. Choose a topic small enough so that all relevant material can be included.
2. Outline the topic thoroughly.
3. Examine each detail under the several subdivisions of the outline to be sure it is relevant.
4. Write a clear topic sentence.
5. Add all necessary explanatory material.

UNITY BY MEANS OF THE WANTED EFFECT

This type of unification is close to that of unity of material. The effect is partly dependent on the choice of the proper details. To secure unity through the wanted effect, the writer must have a consistent point of view. He must not suddenly change from an impersonal point of view to a personal, for this produces confusion in the reader's mind.

It was decided to visit the plant of the Owen Steel Corporation to determine their method of rolling sheet steel for tin cans and other light work. When you first enter the plant, one is struck by the light and airy appearance of the rolling mill. As a result of the excellent illumination, you can see the entire length of the mill without the use of artificial lighting. I noticed particularly the cleanliness of the mill floor; in opposition to the average steel mill, housekeeping is excellent, and you can see that the workers appreciate this.

Unity has been violated as far as material is concerned, but the writer also has changed his point of view. At first he began to use the impersonal approach so common in technical writing, then he shifted to the second person ("Whenever you first enter . . ."). After that he moved to the third person ("One is struck . . ."). In the last sentence he dropped back to first person ("I noticed particularly . . ."), and concluded the paragraph in the second person. Although the reader can determine more or less what the writer meant, he can do so only after an irritating examination.

In order to achieve unity through knowledge of the wanted effect:

1. Adopt an attitude before writing; do not change it.
2. Do not change the point of view within the paragraph.
3. Choose details suitable to the attitude taken toward the subject.

UNITY THROUGH TREATMENT OF THE MATERIAL

The technical man usually needs the impersonal point of view in his writing; he wants to attain objectivity. Most technical writing, for instance, has little place for such a device as the funny story. It would produce disunity were the writer, in the midst of a very serious discussion, to interject a joke which had no relation to his material. Although following the impersonal point of view all the way through his article or report is a part of unity through knowledge of the wanted effect, the writer should be aware of the nuances of style. He can learn these nuances only through reading and careful consideration. No book can teach style; it is a characteristic made up of the personality of the writer, his knowledge of grammatical construction, all his past experiences, and many individual differences. Each person expresses his individuality in his writing. For the writer to be sure that he has unity through treatment of the material, he must be literate—and he must be himself. In the following example, these principles are ignored:

Upon examination, the building was found to be in a dilapidated condition. Examination showed the main joists to be badly warped and eaten into by dry rot. So were the steps. These steps, instead of being covered by non-skid plates, were as slippy as a skinned eel. This was all the farther we examined the edifice.

In this short paragraph, the writer has a number of errors which produce disunity through unfortunate treatment of his material. He has failed to use pictorial details ("dilapidated condition" may imply that the windows were broken, that the building needed paint, or that the roof had weathered away); he has failed to subordinate material of little importance ("So were the steps.") and at the same time has produced a choppy sentence. His sudden attempt at humor ("a skinned eel") fails, and he admits a colloquial usage into what at first was apparently intended as a formal report. "Slippy" is colloquial, as is "all the farther." The reader feels that the paragraph is the work of a man who has little understanding of good, clear English.

In summary, although it is impossible to give complete rules for attaining unity through treatment of the material, a few cautions may aid the writer to criticize his own work:

1. Avoid the use of material which is not in "tone" with the major part of the work.
   a. Do not use slang in a formal discussion.
   b. Do not alternate passive voice with active voice.
   c. Avoid mixing colloquial expressions with formal expressions.
2. Avoid trying to get more than one effect in a paragraph.

Qualities of the Paragraph: Emphasis

The technical student ordinarily thinks of "effects" in paragraphs as limited to the liberal arts student who is taking a major in English language and literature. Yet he must remember that he, too, is writing for an effect, different from that of his liberal arts fellow, but an effect nevertheless. He must achieve this through unity and coherence in his paragraphs, and he must be aware of the need for emphasis where it will help his aim.

Emphasis is to a large extent a matter of the placement of the words within the sentences, and the placement of the sentences within the paragraphs. As a general rule, material at the beginning and at the end of the paragraph secures more attention than that placed in the middle. The topic sentence usually takes care of the first of these positions, for it determines what the paragraph is to be about, and it is customarily placed first, although this placement is by no means fixed.

The greatest emphasis is often secured by a climactic order of parts. In such a method the writer moves from the least important toward the most important statements in his paragraph, with his main point occurring near, or at, the end. The following example of a paragraph illustrates this method:

If a reporter was to stop a half-dozen men as they walked along the street, and ask them this question: "In what metal is an American banker

most interested?" the first answer that any of them would give would probably be "Gold." Silver would probably follow; then nickel and copper. But
they would all be wrong. The American banker is more interested in steel
than in any other metal in the world.

In this paragraph, the least important things are mentioned first:
the radio poll, the men on the street, and the several metals they
feel the American banker is most interested in. It is not until the last
sentence that the climax of the paragraph is reached; only then is the
point made which the writer wishes to emphasize.

A second useful method of emphasis is inverted order in the sentence. The English sentence usually proceeds from subject to verb
to object. When the order is reversed, the object is usually placed
first, to call greater attention to it. Such a method has the advantage
of keeping the writing in active voice, and it emphasizes the object
by placing it out of its natural order.

I used to work as an oiler on that turbine. (natural order)
That turbine I used to oil. (inverted order)

Inverted order is emphatic, but the writer must be warned away
from a too extensive use of it. Like many other means of securing
emphasis, it must not be overworked, or the reader will be bored
or (what is even worse) will no longer notice that the writer is
attempting to gain emphasis by the device.

There are also a number of mechanical means by which special
emphasis may be directed toward certain words or sentences within
the paragraph. One of the most useful of these is italicizing the
most important part of the sentence or paragraph.

Indeed, there is reason to believe that in the explosion of the atomic
bombs *temperatures perhaps as high as fifty million degrees Centigrade* may
have been obtained.

Such italicizing calls the reader's attention to the important point
the writer wishes to make.

In addition to italics, capitalization of important words, exclamation marks, and dashes add emphasis. All these devices should be
used sparingly and, except for italics, are rarely found in ordinary
technical writing. Now and then the sales letter may need such
methods, but otherwise they should be avoided.

Intensives are also occasional helps. Again they should not be
overused. Such words as "too," "very," "so" are intensives, but if
the engineer will remember the advice given by the late William

Allen White, he will limit their use. White was fond of intensives, and his attention being called to their overuse, he developed a scheme to cut down on them. After he had written his copy, he looked it over, and in every place he had put a "very," he took it out and substituted "damn." Since he was writing for a family newspaper, the proof-reader took out the "damns" and White's copy then went to press without the intensives.

Repetition may be used for emphasis. Often the student is told that to repeat the same word within three lines is to be avoided, but intentional repetition can be effectively used. It should be noted that when repetition is so used the material takes on a climactic quality, with each new element in the series contributing to the increasing intensity of the passage. In the following paragraph, the writer has successfully achieved the desired emphasis through repetition.

In the field of electronic research, our engineers are concentrating on control systems. It is the control system which starts the steel mill rolling, and stops it when the sheet is finished; it is the control system that determines the level of water in our great reservoirs; it is the control system that may some day steer our automobiles, warm our homes, and cook our morning coffee.

To achieve emphasis, then, the student should be aware of these methods:

1. Placement
   a. Climactic order
   b. Inverted sentence order
2. Mechanical devices
   a. Italics
   b. Capitals
   c. Exclamation marks
   d. Dashes
3. Intensives
4. Repetition

Qualities of the Paragraph: Summary

If the student understands coherence, unity, and emphasis, he will know how to produce a paragraph that expresses proper thought relationship, that is properly limited to one thought, and that places points of special importance where they belong. He will understand the use of the methods by which all the qualities of these three paragraph essentials are produced. When considering whether his paragraphs are unified, he will know that three types of unity are necessary: unity of material, unity by means of the wanted effect, and unity through proper treatment of the material. He will know how to use mechanical devices, repetition, intensives, and inverted order.

Discussion Questions—Qualities of the Paragraph

1. What is coherence?
2. What are the causes of incoherence?
3. Tell why the repetition of an important word from sentence to sentence helps secure coherence.
4. What possible danger do you see in using pronoun linkage to effect coherence?
5. Why does a mathematical sequence produce coherence?
6. What is most likely to cause disunification of material?
7. Why is a sufficiently small topic a requirement for unity?
8. Why should one adopt a different point of view when telling of a conversation with a classmate than when describing a piece of apparatus?
9. Why should one not use slang or colloquial expressions in most technical writing?
10. Why should inverted sentence order be seldom used?
11. What is the value in the occasional use of italics?
12. Why are intensives not to be used too frequently?
13. Where should material be placed in a paragraph to secure the greatest emphasis?
14. Why is the use of precise facts usually of greater value than the general statement?

Exercises—Qualities of the Paragraph

1. Rewrite the paragraph on utility taxation (page 275) so that it will have coherence.
2. Write sentences which will show the following transitional devices:
   a. Repetition of the important word
   b. Pronoun linkage
   c. Transition words.
3. Illustrate by outline the deductive and inductive methods of achieving coherence.
4. Write a paragraph using a cause-effect coherence device.
5. Write a paragraph showing a time-place coherence device.
6. Outline a paragraph unified by a structural device.
7. Assume that you are preparing to write a paragraph on city planning. You have decided to adopt a favorable point of view. Which of the following details will you use? Why?
   a. Homes of the poor must be torn down.
   b. Streets must be widened.

    c. Unsightly and unsafe dwellings will be razed.
    d. The city will present a more beautiful appearance.
    e. Costs of condemning the property will be high.
    f. The moral tone of the community will rise.
    g. Engineers will be given work.
    h. The property will be owned by the city rather than by private individuals.
8. Why do short, choppy sentences produce bad style?

Words

One has only to count the words defined on a page of an unabridged dictionary and then multiply by the number of pages to find out what a huge number of words our language has. No one person ever can or ever needs to know them all, however, for many of these words apply only to particular fields and are not in general use.

Often, the student who has applied himself strictly to science finds his vocabulary too limited for easy communication outside the range of the materials of science. The best way to improve a vocabulary which is too narrow is to read widely in fields other than your own,[2] and to make wise use of the dictionary. Listening sharply when others speak will also add to your store of words, although reading will probably give you more word meanings than any other single source.

It is not at all necessary to look up in the dictionary every word you do not know, for its context will often give you a fairly exact meaning for the unknown word. Assume, for example, that you do not know what the word "aphelion" means. But it occurs in a sentence in this way:

At perihelion, when the force of sunlight is strongest, the tail of the comet is driven away from the sun, but at aphelion, no such influence occurs.

From this sentence, you can deduce that, since the force of sunlight is strongest at perihelion, it is weakest at aphelion. From this you may conclude that perihelion is closest to the sun and aphelion is farthest from it.

Often, the word may actually be defined in one way or another in the sentence you read, or an indication of its opposite may be given, or the writer may have set down enough qualities of the word to enable you to make a pretty good guess about its meaning. You should not make entirely certain of the meaning of the word from

[2] See pages 433–441 for a selected reading list.

one contextual clue, however, but keep watch for it when it reappears. If the meaning you deduced from the first contextual clue seems appropriate the second time, you probably have an adequate idea of the meaning.

What a word means to an individual is determined by the associations it brings to his mind. Some words, particularly those classed under the heading of "concrete" nouns, are fairly similar in their meanings for almost everyone—the word *"davenport,"* for instance. There are variations in the images that even the concrete words bring up, however. "Rock" may mean a small stone to you, a huge boulder to someone else. The mere repetition of the word may bring up the image of someone moving a cradle to and fro. If none of us has had an experience with the actuality back of a word, the sound of it may be completely meaningless. What image is summoned up by "gradin," "prolepsis"?

WORDS OFTEN CONFUSED

The technical man, because of his interest in scientific and practical details, is likely to omit a study of the exact meaning of words foreign to his specific interests. They are, nevertheless, highly important to him for purposes of communication, and he should use them precisely. The similarities in sound of words that have very different meanings may lead him into errors. For this reason a list of words often confused is set below:

extinguish	stationery	caliber	ingenious
distinguish	stationary	caliper	ingenuous
tycoon	units	credible	content
typhoon	unites	creditable	contents
		credulous	
principal	duel	denote	imply
principle	dual	connote	infer
persecute	affusion	censor	lightning
prosecute	effusion	censer	lightening
marital	practical	celebrate	moral
martial	practicable	cerebrate	morale
eminent	cannon	aspects	receipt
imminent	canon	suspects	recipe
eminence	canyon		

personal	disinterested	guerilla	vise
personnel	uninterested	gorilla	vice
spontaneous	compliment	statute	effect
instantaneous	complement	statue	affect
formerly	accept	allusion	accelerate
formally	except	illusion	exhilarate
respectfully			
respectively			

It is impossible to make a complete list of words that may be confused with others; the only certain way of avoiding such errors is to make extensive use of the dictionary.

USE OF THE DICTIONARY

In order to be certain of the precise meaning of a word—its denotation—it is advisable to consult a good dictionary. Often, of course, it is possible to determine approximately the meaning of an unknown word from the context of the sentence, but to be certain it is best to look it up.

On page 291 is an example of typical listings in dictionaries.

Dictionaries vary a good deal. For thorough study of words, it is necessary to go to an unabridged dictionary, one which attempts to classify all the words in the language. For ordinary use, a college-level dictionary is sufficient, although many of the more obscure words are not listed in such a volume.

Dictionaries are used chiefly for three purposes.   The student goes to them mainly for (1) the exact definition, (2) the pronunciation, (3) the proper spelling of a word. Of these, the most difficult to find is the correct spelling. The student must be able to approximate the spelling before the dictionary can help him much. Words which begin with letters which have a sound similar to that of other letters ("j" and "g," "f" and "ph") often require the student to look up the word under several headings. The task then consists of simply looking through the words that are as close as possible to what the supposed spelling is.[3]

Under dictionary listings, the first thing the student finds is the proper spelling of the word, as "ohm." Next comes the pronunciation.   Here the dictionary uses a device known as diacritical mark-

[3] A consideration of spelling rules and a list of commonly misspelled words is to be found on pages 419–421.

Cyn·e·wulf (kin'i-woolf'), *n.* Anglo-Saxon poet; fl. 750 A.D.

cyn·ic (sin'ik), *n.* [L. *Cynicus;* see CYNICAL], **1.** [C-], a member of a sect of ancient Greek philosophers who held virtue to be the only good, and stressed independence from worldly needs and pleasures; they became critical of the rest of society and its material interests; hence, **2.** a cynical person. **3.** a person who believes that people are motivated in all their actions entirely by selfishness. *adj.* **1.** [C-], of or like the Cynics or their doctrines. **2.** cynical.

cyn·i·cal (sin'i-k'l), *adj.* [< L. *cynicus,* of the Cynics; Gr. *kynikos,* lit., canine, like a dog < *kyōn, kynos,* dog; IE. base *＊kuon-,* dog; hence akin to AS. *hund* (see HOUND, dog)], **1.** inclined to question the sincerity and goodness of people's motives and actions, or the value of living. **2.** morose, sarcastic, sneering, etc.
SYN.—**cynical** implies a contemptuous disbelief in human goodness and sincerity (he's *cynical* about recovering his lost watch); **misanthropic** suggests a deep-seated hatred or distrust of people in general (a *misanthropic* hermit); **pessimistic** implies an attitude, often habitual, of expecting the worst to happen (*pessimistic* about one's chances to win).—*ANT.* optimistic.

cyn·i·cism (sin'ə-siz'm), *n.* **1.** [C-], the philosophy of the Cynics. **2.** the attitude or beliefs of a cynic. **3.** a cynical expression or view.

cy·no·sure (si'nə-shoor', sin'ə-shoor'), *n.* [< Gr. *kynosoura,* dog's tail, constellation of Ursa Minor; cf. CYNICAL], **1.** [C-], the constellation Ursa Minor. **2.** [C-], the North Star, which is in this constellation. **3.** anything that guides or directs. **4.** any person or thing that is a center of attention or interest.

Cyn·thi·a (sin'thi-ə), [L.; Gr. *Kynthia,* epithet of Artemis, orig. fem. of *Kynthios,* lit., of or from *Kynthos,* Cynthus, mountain in Delos, celebrated as the birthplace of Apollo and Artemis], a feminine name: diminutive, *Cindy.* *n.* **1.** Artemis (or Diana), goddess of the moon; hence, **2.** the moon personified.

cy·per·a·ceous (si'pěr-ā'shəs, sip'ēr-ā'shəs), *adj.* [< Mod. L. *Cyperus,* sedge < Gr. *kypeiros;* + *-aceous*], of the sedge family of plants, which resemble the grasses but have solid stems and seeds in closed sheaths.

From *Webster's New World Dictionary* of the American Language, College Edition. Copyright 1962 by The World Publishing Co.

ings. These marks are used to show the pronunciation of words by indicating the sounds given to the vowels. These are capable of greater variation than are the consonants. At the bottom of every dictionary page, the reader may find examples of how the diacritical marks are used in words which almost everyone knows.

By transferring the sound from the example given to the word being looked up, the student can determine the proper pronunciation. The name of the part of speech then follows, usually abbreviated to "n." for noun, "adj." for adjective, and so on.

The next entry concerns etymology. The origin of the word is given, and if the word is taken from a foreign language, the language is indicated, as "L." for Latin, or "F." for French. If the origin is by way of French from Latin, this fact is also indicated. If the word is used particularly in a special branch of learning (as is "ohm" in electricity) that branch is usually mentioned. The definition of the word follows, and if there are several meanings for the same word, they are numbered. This in turn is followed by related words which have the same root as the original word.

Often words have several pronunciations. "Truculent," for instance, may be pronounced as "truck-u-lent," or "trook-u-lent." Often words vary in the British and the American pronunciation; in more recent dictionaries, the American pronunciation is given first.

CONNOTATION

Words also have the quality of connotation. This can be defined as the associations aroused in an individual by a word. "Instigate," for example, literally means to urge forward, yet because of the legal application—to instigate a riot, a plot, or a rebellion—it has come to have a sinister application. Words that tend to produce unpleasant associations must be used with the greatest care. In technical and scientific writing, however, the denotation of words is more important than their connotation.

SUMMARY

Words are one of the technical man's most effective tools for success in his profession, for research, even for daily living. His vocabulary should be large enough to allow him to express his thoughts adequately and to understand others completely. He must adapt his speech and writing to his circumstances. The dictionary is one of his greatest helps in attaining an accurate understanding of the meaning of words, their origins, and their spellings. The technical writer should be aware of the implied meanings—the connotations—of words, to avoid giving unintentional offense to the reader. Above all, he should use words with precision.

The Sentence

Grammarians and linguists have been searching for a long time for an adequate definition of a sentence. It is difficult for any one definition to please everyone; and since haggling over a definition is useless, perhaps it will be simplest to define a sentence as a piece of communication which carries sense. Thus, the word "No!" could be considered to be a full sentence, for it carries sense in itself.

Since we are accustomed to use sentences constantly in our everyday talk, we grow so used to this means of communication that we often give little thought to it. Yet when we write, we need to give careful attention to the structure of our sentences. The tones of our voices as we talk often carry to our listeners the intended sense of the sentence; sometimes the words and the construction of the sentence actually may belie the meaning which the sentence is really intended to carry. If you were to say, "That's a well-designed car if I ever saw one," the tone of your voice might carry the implication to your listener that the car was really very poorly designed.

Yet in writing we cannot change our tone, and so we must put our sentences together with much care in order that our intended effect and our intended meaning may be presented accurately. To begin, we should perhaps start thinking about standard types of sentences, not from a grammatical point precisely, but instead from the point of the patterns which the sentences tend to take.

English sentences are built around the subject-verb order. This is usually a statement of someone's acting or being. Thus, "He reads," or "I am" represent standard patterns of simple English sentences. In other words, the basic sentence pattern consists of someone or something and some expression of acting or being.

Sometimes the sentence structure continues on to something which may be defined as an object: that which receives or accepts the kind of action the verb indicates. If we were to continue the sentence, "He reads," with "a book," we would be then adding an object to the simpler form of the sentence. Since the verb "reads" is indicative of the action, "book" is the object which is receiving the action of the verb "reads." You may have noticed that in the sentence "He reads a book," one word was added which is neither subject, verb nor object: the word "a." This is the beginning of the variation of sentence patterns, the addition of modifying words. The word "a" is a modifier which is intended to tell us something about the book. It does tell us a little, although not very much; yet many modifiers do add considerably to our understanding of the finer points of the meaning a given sentence is intended to convey.

Let us continue with the addition of modifiers to see what effect these will have on the basic sentence pattern. First, you may wish to add the word "red." The sentence now reads, "He reads a red book." The modifier tells us something about the book; it is its color, and thus the sentence begins to produce a more distinct picture of the book than we formerly had.

In addition to single-word modifiers, we often use phrases to modify and to add clarity to the meaning of our sentences. "In the morning he reads a red book" gives us more information about the total value of the sentence than we had before. This information is conveyed in the phrase "In the morning," and it gives us the time of the action.

In addition to single words and phrases which may act as modifiers of parts of the sentences, we may have clauses which in themselves contain a subject and verb and possibly an object, as well as numerous modifiers, all of which may modify some word of the primary basic sentence pattern. In such a sentence as "He saw the lathe which had formerly been in section L-2 in its new location in S-5," the sense of the basic pattern "He saw . . ." is considerably changed, and our understanding of it appreciably increased, by the addition of the modifying clause "which had formerly been in section L-2 . . ." If we were to examine the sentence a little more in detail, we would see that its basic pattern is "He saw . . . lathe," and the modifier of the basic pattern is "the." In addition to this single-word modifier, however, the clause "which . . . had been . . ." has been added, and there are also modifying words and phrases within the clause which modifies the basic sentence pattern.

The diagrams on pages 296–297 will show you the organization of the English sentence. The sentence itself could be expanded to greater length if needed. Basic-pattern elements are in bold face type; their functions are stated in small capitals. The words in italics comment on and amplify these identifications.

It is important for you to be able to recognize what the basic pattern of a sentence is. Only in this way will you be able to avoid writing incomplete sentences, a serious grammatical error. The recognition of the basic pattern, however, will insure that your sentence will carry full sense.

Let us analyze a few more sentences into their components of basic-pattern and modifying elements so that you will be able to see a little more clearly the sentence and its components.

Some verbs do not command objects; instead, their sense is filled out by what is called a "complement." In such a sentence as "He became President," the main effort of the verb is merely to reflect the complement *President* back to the subject. In this sentence, the verb is little more than a statement of an equality. Such a change does not, however, affect the the basic-pattern structure. If we were to add to the sentence and make it read, "He became President, which was a great honor," we have added a clause to modify the complement in the same way that we often add clauses to modify objects.

From a grammatical point of view, sentences are divided into four major classes: simple, complex, compound, and compound-complex. If we were to explain this division in terms of the basic-pattern sentence, we might say that the basic pattern itself is always a simple sentence.

If we write two basic-pattern sentences and combine them into one sentence with the use of a semicolon or a conjunction, we have then written a compound sentence. If, instead, we write a basic-pattern sentence which has some parts of that sentence modified by one or more clauses, we have then written a complex sentence. If we write two basic-pattern sentences, connecting them in some way, and add a clause or clauses modifying parts of either or both of the basic pattern sentences, we have then written a compound-complex sentence.

Follow the illustration below, in which the basic patterns are noted and the modifying clauses are also indicated.

Basic pattern: This is a transformer.
Basic pattern plus another basic pattern: This is a transformer and this is a rectifier.
One basic pattern and one modifying clause: Basic pattern, He built a car, *then the modifying clause,* which is like no other.
Two basic-pattern sentences with one modifying clause: He built a car which was like no other; he took it on a nation-wide tour.

In summary, when you sit down to write you should have the basic pattern of the sentence clearly in mind. You can almost always say this basic pattern in five or six words (you will often need to put in word modifiers). Then decide how you wish to change the sense of the basic pattern through the use of appropriate modifiers. You may decide that your sense will require two or three basic patterns to make it clear; if so, you should express each one of these to yourself. The addition of the modifiers whether in the form of phrases, words or clauses can then be made to bring your reader the full sense you intend.

Order in the Sentence

After you have decided on the basic pattern you wish your sentence to have, you will then often wish to introduce modifiers. The placement of these modifiers, however, may give you some trouble. For instance, suppose you were to write such a sentence as this: "The

SUBJECT   clause modi

The new seed **tapes** which had been wound into the reactor being built for

word modifiers   *phrase modifier*   *participial phras*
of SUBJECT   *of clause*   *claus*
                                                    modifier

                                                    SUBJECT *of*
                                                    clause making
                        SUBJECT VERB   *up* OBJECT   *clause modifier of* SUBJECT *of*

Many **people believe** that **scientists,** who ought to be and usually are well in –

word
modifier
of
SUBJECT

                phrase modifier of VERB   SUBJECT

On last Wednesday afternoon, the oldest **member** of our entire staff

fying SUBJECT   VERB   VERB

the Yankee Electric Company **were** originally **produced** at Housatonic

modifier of phrase modifier of   *word*   *phrase*
modifier   *modifier.*   *modifier*
     of VERB   *of* VERB

in the new subsidiary of our plant.

phrase modifier of   *phrase modifier of*
VERB   *phrase modifier of*
     VERB

clause modifier of
VERB *of clause*
word   *making up* OBJECT
clause making up OBJECT   *modifier*

formed about political issues, **are** mere **children** when they act in the area :

VERB   OBJECT *of*   *phrase modifier* :
of   *clause*   *of* VERB :
clause   *making up*   *of clause* :
making   OBJECT   *modifying* :
up   *main* VERB :
OBJECT

of practical politics.

phrase modifier of
phrase modifier of
VERB *of clause*
modifying main VERB

VERB   OBJECT   *clause modifying* OBJECT

was given a farewell **reception** which was attended by our president and :

:   *clause modifying* VERB *of clause modifying* OBJECT

our treasurer, although both of them are extremely busy men.

vice-president countermanded the instructions of the treasurer and wrote a new procedure with the concurrence of the board of directors." To make the intended meaning clear, we must reorder this sentence to read in this way: "With the concurrence of the board of directors, the vice-president countermanded the instructions of the treasurer and wrote a new procedure."

As you were reading the sentence in its original form, you probably thought that only the writing of the new material was done with the agreement of the board of directios; after you had read the second sentence with the placement of the phrase indicating "with the con-currence" at the opening of the sentence, you were clear that the board had agreed with both ideas that the vice-president had indi-cated.

Even the placement of individual words within a sentence may vary its meaning. For example, take such a sentence as "Only he says he likes chemistry." Now, place the word "only" in every other position in the sentence and see what differences in the sense you will get.

To be sure of achieving the exact sense that you want with modify-ing words, phrases, and clauses, place them as close as possible to the word they modify. In this way, you will rarely confuse your reader or express an inexact meaning.

SENTENCE VARIETY

Technical writing usually demands more simple sentences than does writing of any other type.

Since all professional writers shun the use of too many compound sentences because they involve the tiresome repetition of *and, but,* and *for,* the technical writer should also try to avoid their overuse. Too frequent coordination of ideas is the mark of the immature thinker as well as the immature writer. If you want proof of this, listen to the talk of the average child. He seldom subordinates ideas; he coordinates them constantly. A sample of his speech might run some-thing like this:

I went to Aunt Sally's last night. She has a little girl called Susan. I played with Susan's toys, and I had a good time. I liked her new dolly, and I want Mamma to buy me one like it. It had red hair and blue eyes, but it can move its eyes like a real person. I hope I go to Aunt Sally's again, for I did enjoy myself.

The child has failed to express the subtle relationships which exist between the ideas. The repetition of "and," "but," and "for" is also boring. Yet this is the best the child can do. His mental development is not advanced enough for him to comprehend complex thought relationships. The mature man, naturally, cannot take refuge in such an excuse. He must vary his sentence patterns enough to give the reader a proper understanding of his thought process.

Since good writers vary these patterns, the question may be asked, "How is this variation obtained?" Obviously, a writer does not sit down and say, before he begins a manuscript, "I'll make the first sentence simple; the second sentence complex; the third sentence compound-complex; the fourth sentence simple, etc." If he did this, he would lose the continuity of his ideas.

First of all, he has to set down his ideas on paper. After he has outlined his material carefully, his best procedure is to write without paying any special attention to sentence variety, niceties of grammar and punctuation, or precision of word choice. After he has written this rough draft, he goes over it to find whether the ideas are in proper sequence. When this has been established to his satisfaction, he proceeds to revise the whole manuscript. His job is to vary the sentences in type; to make the beginnings of his sentences as different as possible; and to check his grammar and his use of words. He should also make sure that his punctuation is accurate in order to have the relationship among the parts of his sentences clear.

When the writer has had much practice, he finds that his first draft needs less revision than the first drafts of manuscripts he wrote while he was a beginner. The best writers in any field usually have to revise painstakingly to produce a finished piece of work. Their advantage over the amateur is that, by constantly working with sentences, they tend to think in varied sentence patterns.

The following paragraph offers an illustration of good sentence variety. Look at it from the standpoint of variation in sentence types and sentence beginnings.

To understand properly the activities of the molecules making up a given volume of gas, we may think of them from the standpoint of the following illustration. Imagine a toy balloon inside which are a dozen tiny dwarfs, each armed with a shotgun. Each charge of the guns consists of an almost infinite number of tiny buckshot. The dwarfs are so placed that when they shoot, the tiny missiles strike every portion of the balloon's inner surface. The power of the dwarf shotguns is, however, too slight to break the skin of the balloon. Instead, the shot merely stretches the skin. Let us now assume that the weather grows warmer and the dwarfs are stirred to greater activity. They load and fire more rapidly and the balloon, subjected to greater pressure by the tiny missiles striking it, expands more and more. In the same manner the molecules of gas, represented in our analogy by the buckshot, vibrate more rapidly under the influence of heat and strike the enclosing sides of their chamber more often than they did when the temperature was fifty degrees lower. The more often they strike, the greater is the pressure on the enclosing surface.

The sentences fall into the following types:

> Simple sentence
> Complex sentence
> Simple sentence
> Complex sentence
> Simple sentence
> Simple sentence
> Complex sentence
> Compound sentence
> Compound-complex sentence
> Complex sentence.

Their variation is obvious from this listing. All four types are represented. The simple and the complex sentence are the dominant types in the paragraph, with one compound sentence and one compound-complex sentence adding pleasing changes in structure. Consequently, the effect of the whole paragraph is smooth and euphonious, and the idea are put into a related sequence.

The beginnings of the sentences are also varied. A series of sentences each of which starts with subject-predicate-object is monotonous. The skilled writer tries to break up too many recurrences of such openings. In the paragraph reproduced above, the first sentence begins with an infinitive phrase, "To understand properly the activities of the molecules making up a given volume of gas . . . ," which precedes the main thought. Additional variety comes in sentence two by the imperative, "Imagine a toy balloon. . . ." The third sentence opens with subject, predicate, object, and the next two sentences also begin with subject and predicate. To avoid monotony, the following sentence goes back to the imperative, with the next sentence using the subject-predicate opening. As a change, a phrase—"In the same manner"—introduces the next idea, and another phrase—"The more often"—begins the final sentence.

Whenever the sentence can be started with a phrase or a clause instead of by subject and predicate, it is well to find out whether this kind of beginning gives more emphasis to the main idea. If it does not, then the normal order is preferable. Variety in sentence beginnings is a desirable feature in any sort of writing, technical or non-technical. It should always be striven for in the revision of a manuscript.

THE LOOSE AND PERIODIC SENTENCE

The loose sentence, one which completes its main clause before the end of the sentence is reached, is the commonest of English sentences. On the other hand, the periodic sentence has value for the technical writer. In this type of sentence, the reader must wait until the end for the thought to be completed. Details are added within the body of the sentence rather than at the end. Thus the periodic sentence may be used to advantage when the writer wishes to emphasize a point by its position within the sentence.

PERIODIC: If the engineer wishes to succeed, he must be well acquainted with economics.

LOOSE: The engineer must be well acquainted with economics if he wishes to succeed.

SENTENCE FRAGMENTS

Unless constantly on his guard in the construction of sentences, the amateur writer is likely to make costly mistakes. A common error, for instance, is the incomplete (fragmentary) sentence. Sentences of this sort are so easy to write and often sound so plausible that they may go undetected. A well-rounded sentence makes an independent statement; it is complete in itself. To be complete it must usually have a subject and a predicate, either expressed directly or implied unmistakably.

Of course, there are times when an incomplete sentence is justified. If a professor, trying to tell where steam enters a turbine, asks the question, "And where does steam enter this turbine?" and then answers it by saying, "Through a single governing valve," his answer is certainly not a complete statement by itself. When it is considered in relationship to the question, it is clear enough. If he should follow his answer by, "An obvious matter, this," he would be referring to the fact he has just stated. The phrase is not a complete sentence. It needs the previous statement for clarification. Yet it is clear once it is considered in respect to that statement. Incomplete sentences of this kind can be defended; they are often used in speech.

When sentences are fragments not clear to the reader, they are indefensible. The freshman who wrote, "From the governing valve, the steam passes into the nozzle chamber from which it expands through the nozzles. Governing the heat energy.", was not conscious that there is no accurate relationship between the participial phrase and the main idea of the preceding sentence. Participial phrases cannot stand alone.

Participial phrases, prepositional phrases, and subordinate clauses are fragmentary in meaning when used alone. If you read them over, they make no complete sense until you connect them to an independent clause. Look over the following lists:

PARTICIPIAL PHRASES

Being one of the most important substations in Alabama.
Seeing the result of his actions.
Believing one of the statements to be true.

PREPOSITIONAL PHRASES

In the case of the two smallest frames.
By a given volume of gas.
Through every part of the bag's surface.
At the end of each inspection period.

SUBORDINATE CLAUSES

While the engineer is planning his future.
Because the motor needs to be cleaned.
After he had decided what voltage was best.
When he had constructed the model.
Which he had referred to the Division Engineer.

All writers should avoid fragmentary sentences unless they are sure such statements are clear in reference and achieve a specific rhetorical effect.

Types of Technical Exposition

The practicing technical man, the student, and the technical advertising writer are often required to write four particular types of exposition. These are definitions, descriptions of mechanisms and apparatus, descriptions of processes, and analyses. As in all other types of technical writing, the aim is to present the reader with a body of fact expressed with the greatest possible clarity.

To help the student to follow the methods which the writers of the following examples have used, we have attempted to detail in the column at the side of the material the methods and central thoughts occurring in the textual material, prefacing each example with a general statement of the requirements of the particular type of writing.

Definition

Technical writers are frequently concerned with the definition of terms or objects. To write a clear and complete definition of anything is a difficult procedure, for it requires careful and logical thought and the inclusion of all necessary elements so that the readers may grasp easily what is meant by the definition. The American College Dictionary, for instance, defines the word "factory" as a "building or a group of buildings, usually with equipment, where goods are manufactured."

As you examine this definition, you can perceive its essential elements. It must consider the word in relation to the whole group of objects which it symbolizes. It must classify the word in its broadest aspects. It must tell the function of the object being classified.

You will notice that "factory" is allied to a specific class: "buildings." This general classification is then broken down into a subclass, which makes the object more specific. A factory is not any building. It is a building in which manufacturing operations take place. This subclass can, if necessary, be broken down further into a differentiation of various sorts of factories. A building in which aluminum is processed would be an aluminum plant, or factory, or a building in which boxes are manufactured would be a box factory. If the box factory was engaged exclusively in making containers for hand grenades, the definition would have to include this limiting element. In other words, defining anything makes necessary the consideration of all limiting factors.

The following paragraphs, from Dr. Richard D. Hoak's article dealing with stream pollution, illustrate one of the phases of definition. The material does not dogmatically say, "This is *the* definition"; instead, Dr. Hoak examines the background which has given rise to the different definitions of stream pollution, analyzes them, and gives his reasons for adopting the definition with which the paragraphs are concluded.

What Is Stream Pollution? [4]

Pollution is difficult to define precisely. This is partly due to our lack of knowledge, and   *Reasons for difficulties in defining pollution.*

[4] By permission of Dr. Richard D. Hoak.

Statement of difficulty to show the reader the reasons for such a lengthy discussion, followed by the reasons producing the difficulty.

Implication of defects in some other definitions of pollution.

Generalized definition of stream pollution: basic element. Résumé of most definitions of pollution, stated generally.

Here the writer shows the need for differentiating between definitions.

Statement of limitation.

The writer advances the reasons for making general definitions.

The writer shows why rigidity of definition should be avoided.

Statement of the qualities of adequate definitions.

Complexity of definition in California.

Final statement of definition for administrative purposes. General classification: material.

Differentiation: that unreasonably impairs quality of water.

Point of view: public interest (as understood by an administrator).

partly to the fact that definitions usually reflect the aims of those who do the defining. But all definitions (of stream pollution) contain the basic idea that pollution really means the presence of so much of something in streams that it interferes with their use for a particular purpose. It is this concept that causes trouble for the definition-makers. What is called pollution under one set of conditions would not be considered to be pollution under different conditions. Definitions of pollutions thus derive from priorities of stream uses, and these depend upon stream location.

Therefore, no universally applicable definition is possible. All-inclusive definitions are convenient administrative devices, however, and some laws contain them. If improvement in water quality is the objective of anti-pollution legislation, rigid definitions should be avoided. They prevent the flexibility in appraisal of effects that is essential for control of pollution in the broad public interest. Too often they become substitutes for thoughtful analysis of difficult problems.

Definitions must be simple if they are to be both equitable and effective. The problem of practical definitions was recognized by the authors of the California anti-pollution legislation when they defined three categories of pollution. "Contamination" means hazard to public health; "pollution" means adverse effects on other beneficial uses; and "nuisance" means damage from unreasonable disposal practices. If the basic concept behind all definitions is kept in mind, however, further simplification is not only possible, but desirable. *Pollution is the discharge of material that unreasonably impairs the quality of water for maximum beneficial use in the over-all public interest.*

Manufacturing companies concerned with new developments in their field often send out bulletins which are really forms of definition. Particularly when some new product has been developed by the research group of the company is it necessary to tell people about it. The following discussion on polyphenyl ethers (pages 305–307) is

POLYPHENYL ETHERS

General Information

The Polyphenyl Ethers, a new class of fluids, were developed specifically for use in high temperature and/or nuclear radiation environments. They are being extensively evaluated in many aircraft and missile applications, and it is almost certain that they will also be used in numerous industrial applications.

Although their low temperature properties are inferior to those of many other fluids, the Polyphenyl Ethers function in many situations where other lubricants fail. Uses may involve satisfactory short term operation at extreme high temperature conditions, or longer fluid life at moderate conditions.

Three different molecular weight fluids covering a range of viscosity and volatility are available. All are of similar oxidation, thermal and radiation stability. Property and performance data are listed in the following table.

Suggested Uses

Because of their outstanding stability, the Polyphenyl Ethers are suggested for the following uses:

1. High temperature aircraft turbojet engine lubricating oil where bulk oil temperatures of 500°F or higher are expected.

2. Hydraulic fluid at temperatures up to 900 or 1000°F for short periods, or lower temperatures for long periods.

3. Base stock for high temperature greases.

4. All uses requiring lubricating oils, hydraulic fluids or greases for operation in nuclear radiation environments.

5. Electrical insulating or dielectric fluids exposed to high temperatures or nuclear radiation.

Properties

Kinematic Viscosity, cs at 100°F
                                     210°F
                                     400°F
                                     700°F
Pour Point, °F
Specific Gravity, 20/4°C
Flash Point, °F
Fire Point, °F
Spontaneous Ignition Temperature, °F minimum
Boiling Point, °F at   10 mm Hg (extrapolated)
                    at 100 mm Hg (extrapolated)
Refractive Index, n_D^{25}
Specific Heat at 392°F
Dielectric Strength (ASTM D149-59), volts/mill
Dielectric Constant (ASTM D150-54T) at 10^3 cycles
Dissipation Factor (ASTM D150-54T) at 10^3 cycles
Volume Resistivity (ASTM D257-46), ohm-cm

Performance

Evaporation (ASTM D972-56), 6.5 hr at 500°F, weight %
Thermal Stability (isoteniscope decomposition temperature) °F
Corrosion-Oxidation Test, 48 hours, 5 liters air per hour
                                 Viscosity Increase, cs at 210°F
                                 Neutralization Number Change
                                 Fluid Appearance
                                 Evaporation Loss, weight %
                                 Corrosion of Metals
Shell 4-Ball Wear, 600 rpm, 1 hr at 400°F, 52-100 steel **balls,**
                         Scar diameter in mm at 10 kg
                                      30 kg
                                      50 kg
Ryder Gear Scuff Test, lb per inch
Radiation Resistance, % viscosity increase at 210°F after absorption of
                   1×10^9 rads (1×10^{11} ergs/gm)
                   6×10^9 rads (6×10^{11} ergs/gm)

a. 5.7×10^9 rads absorption

ET-378 Bis(Phenoxyphenyl) Ether	ET-492 Bis(Phenoxyphenoxy) Benzene	ET-540 Bis(Phenoxyphenoxy-phenyl) Ether
69.6	390	2770
6.3	13.3	27.2
1.4	2.2	3.1
0.5	0.7	0.9
19	40	59
1.179	1.199	1.216
505	560	610
565	680	735
1100	1100	1100
558	630	725
607	815	870
1.6220	1.6304	1.6361
0.440	0.438	0.441
>300	>300	>300
4.46	4.36	4.30
<0.0002	<0.0002	<0.0002
$>1 \times 10^{14}$	$>1 \times 10^{14}$	$>1 \times 10^{14}$
32.5	3.65	1.14
>800	>800	>800
at 500°F	at 600°F	at 600°F
0.07	4.22	28.4
0.01	0.03	0.05
dark, clear	dark, opaque	dark, opaque
1.0	1.8	1.7
nil	nil	nil
0.770	0.707	0.672
1.197	0.945	0.889
1.281	1.162	1.071
---	2200 to 2600	---
16	27	32
260	320	350[a]

such a paper.[5] You may notice that the method of definition used under the heading of "General Information" is to show what specific applications these new ethers may have.

One of the methods of technical definition is the detailing at considerable length of the various properties of a material. In this example, such a means is used. It is at once clear, of course, that only the person well trained in this field will follow the particular values of the figures; nevertheless, since this is a method of definition very often used, it is reproduced here to show how such kinds of definitions may be used.

Yet technical definitions may be almost as short as those in a dictionary, and often are. Such definitions usually follow the logical requirements discussed in the paragraph preceding "What Is Stream Pollution?" The function of the thing being described is given or is placed within its specific class; then, whenever possible, it is broken down into a subclass and differentiated from that subclass.

Such short definitions are a technical necessity in a field which is just being explored. In older phases of science early workers often failed to define their terms at first, thus leading to confusion among other workers who were attempting to check their results. Phlogiston, for example, was called "fatty earth," a term that helps one not at all to understand its qualities. Priestley, a competent 18th century scientist, misled by such an inaccuracy in definition, called oxygen "dephlogisticated air." The modern technical worker has learned the necessity for precise definition so that when a number of workers in a given field meet, they may understand what is said through their comprehension of an exact definition.

In order that those working in such a new field as nucleonics may be able to communicate with one another exactly, the workers in the atomic energy installation at Bettis Field near Pittsburgh have detailed as exact definitions as possible of the terms used to describe phenomena in this branch of science. By circulating these definitions within the Bettis Field laboratory, they have clarified the vocabulary to a large extent. The following examples [6] will illustrate the method of definition.

Activity

The number of atoms decaying per unit time, measured in curies, 3.7×10^{10} disintegrations per second; a measure of the intensity of emission from a radioactive substance in terms of counts per unit time.

[5] Reproduced through the courtesy of The Dow Chemical Co.
[6] By permission of the Allen B. Du Mont Laboratories, Inc.

Backscattering

The deflection of particles or of radiation by scattering processes through angles greater than 90° with respect to the original direction of motion.

Compensated Ion Chamber

An ion chamber capable of sensing the core flux level between 2.5×10^6 and 2.5×10^{-13} n/cm^2 sec.

Descriptions of Apparatus and Process

When the technical man attempts to describe apparatus, it is rare that he must (or, for that matter, can) limit himself to the actual physical appearance of the mechanism itself. Almost always he needs to add the description of the operation of the apparatus; he must tell what it does and how it does it. This is a logical step, for it supplies the reason for this or that part of the mechanism; and such reasons can be assessed only against the over-all frame of reference, the purpose of the apparatus.

Sometimes, as in the following description, the writer assumes an understanding on the part of the reader of the general reason for being of the mechanism. Every technical person knows, in a general way, why an atomic reactor is or may be a useful device. The particular value of a certain type of reactor is all that needs to be brought to the reader's attention.

In general, description of apparatus includes the following elements, although there is no set order for their occurrence. Often these elements are preceded by a brief history of the apparatus. (The latter element occurs as the second sentence in the example on the next page, rather than formally preceding the body of the description.)

1. Description of the essential parts of the apparatus, although this need not necessarily imply a description of their physical appearance.
2. Details of the apparatus, organized according to spatial, temporal, or logical relationships.
3. Indications of differentiation between the apparatus being described and other apparatus belonging to the same general class. (A phase of definition.)

Although the following description of apparatus confines itself closely to the reactor itself, a knowledge of its operation is quite as important to a reader as is the mere technical description. (See page 310).

Description of Apparatus [7]

Statement of the special qualities of the boiler, designed to arouse interest in the reader.

Short reference to history of water boiler reactor.

An enriched uranium solution makes the water boiler reactor at the University of California, Los Alamos Scientific Laboratory, one of the smallest and most economical chain reactors thus far constructed. In operation since 1944, this homogeneous nuclear reactor has been modified several times, with the present version known as the "SUPO."

Statement of difference between the water boiler reactor and other nuclear reactors.

Description of essential elements making up the reactor.

The model is called the water boiler reactor because water is both the cooler and moderator. In the reactor, the moderator is the neutron reflector, whereas in many others a lattice network of graphite separates the fuel elements. One of the factors that act to control the reaction is the rods which maintain neutron multiplication at approximately one, although it sometimes exceeds unity a little during actual operation. Even if the control rods are withdrawn, the water temperature increases, causing the solution to expand. This in turn decreases concentration of the active materials.

Descriptive details of the water boiler reactor.

Special value of this reactor.

The reactor itself is a 12-inch diameter stainless steel sphere containing an enriched uranyl nitrate solution (88.7% U^{235}). The critical mass is 777 grams of U^{235}, the operating mass 870 grams. Because of the small volume of the reactor, strong fluxes of slow or fast neutrons (in the order of 2×10^{12} neutrons per square centimeter per second) can be produced at an operating power of 30 kw.

Additional descriptive details of the water boiler reactor, with emphasis on spatial relationships. The organizational method (introduced by the word "sphere" in the first sentence of the preceding paragraph) is to show the reactor from the center to the outside. A state-

The sphere is small, but with the shielding needed to protect workers from intense radiation, the external structure measures $15 \times 15 \times 11$ feet. The sphere is surrounded by a reflector which consists of a 55-inch cube of graphite. Between the reflector and two graphite thermal columns are bismuth walls which provide gamma ray protection for the columns. The shielding around the entire assembly comprises $\frac{1}{2}$ inch of boron

---

[7] By permission of *Chemical and Engineering News.*

carbide and paraffin, 2 inches of steel, 4 inches of lead, and 5 feet of concrete.

ment of reasons for the parts ("reflector," "thermal columns," "bismuth walls which provide gamma ray protection," and "shielding") helps to clarify the description.

Description of apparatus often employs the device of analogy to clarify appearance or function. In the following detailing of the Fraunhofer grating, widely used in light and crystal research work, the writer assumes that many people, although technically trained, may not have had any experience with such an apparatus. Consequently, he uses analogy to help his description. The paragraph combines description of apparatus with description of process (the operation of the apparatus).

Description of Laboratory Process and Apparatus [8]

Fraunhofer's earliest grating was simply a comb or ladder of parallel wires with gaps between them—identical wires and exactly equal gaps. . . . There must be hundreds of wires to the inch. If now one projects a beam of sunlight against the comb from the side, it traverses the comb and emerges as a fan-shaped beam, exhibiting the prismatic colors and accompanied on either side by the invisible rays. . . . *The grating treats the light as would a prism,* dispersing a beam and separating its components. The analogy is not perfect—there are differences in detail: for instance, grating and prism disperse the colors in opposite order, so that now the violet is the least deflected and the red the most deflected hue of the visible spectrum. Such details are not important to us now; both devices are capable of sifting out the various components of a light beam, and this is all that matters. My reason for discarding the prism is that its mode of action depends upon the molecules inside the glass and is complicated and obscure, whereas the grating is intelligible. It is in fact the grating which requires the wave theory of light, and which proves the wave theory of light, and which enables us to determine the wave lengths of light. This state-

Description of apparatus by the use of an analogy ("comb or ladder").

Detailed description of apparatus.

Detailed description of process, using nontechnical language.

Description of apparatus by use of a simile. Limitation of analogy.

Results of process.

Interpretation of results of process.

[8] By permission of The Macmillan Co.

Emphatic device of italicizing to ensure that reader will follow the author's interpretation.

ment merits repetition and italics: *the action of the grating is what requires the wave theory of light—what proves the wave theory of light—and what enables us to determine wave lengths of light.* Other instruments possess these features,

Reference to special qualities of apparatus.

but it is the grating which exhibits them most clearly.

Description of Process

The following description of process [9] (in nontechnical form) is organized around a time and space sequence. First appears an introduction which gives the reader the general impression of the entire shop. After this the actual process of hand-blowing glass is taken up in greater detail. Observe the emphasis on the spatial relationship as the glass moves from one craftsman to another.

The Glass Artisan at Work

One's first impression on entering the glass artisan's shop is that of a scene from Dante's "Inferno." Reddish flames lick from the glowing glass furnace, whirling fans draw air across the shop, shadows move along the dark ceiling; forms dash to and fro with red-glowing masses of glass. But the impression of chaos fades as the eyes adapt to the light.

This strange, seemingly disconnected activity turns out to be a well-organized hand-blowing operation where glass tableware is being made. Glass is taken from the pots of glowing liquid on a rod by an apprentice "runner" who delivers it to the first craftsman. With a judicious combination of swinging, blowing, and molding in a wet wooden block at his feet, the craftsman fashions the bowl part of a goblet. Step by step, the glass takes form; at each step the rod with the glass is passed on by a "runner" to the next craftsman. Bit by bit, glass is added and molded and shaped on the rod which is kept in motion by the craftsmen seated on their "thrones." Finally, the glass is cracked loose from its rod, and into a bed of charcoal.

The "bubble top" of the glass is cut off in an unexpected manner. First, tiny jets of flame heat a ring around the lathe-held glass, then at a touch of a sharp tool, the glass breaks cleanly at the lip. With this, the sleek goblet takes its final form but is not yet completed. It will require careful finishing before it is ready for the banquet table.

[9] Reproduced through the courtesy of *The Orange Disc,* the magazine of the Gulf Companies.

Apprentices rush the still-hot glasses to the annealing oven, where they move slowly down the long path to final finishing, where the sharp lip is rounded by careful grinding and flame polishing. The graceful goblets that pass the rigid, last inspection are then carefully packed off to the shippers, ready to appear in the world marketplace.

Sometimes a process which has worked out well in a laboratory is to be transferred to an industrial application. Since one can never be sure that unsuspected defects will not appear, the technical writer often finds it expedient to qualify his description with such phrases as "It may be anticipated that . . . ," or "this apparatus may result in . . . ," etc. The following technical description is limited in this way.

Description of Apparatus, Anticipating Expected Results [10]

Submarines to Obtain Oxygen from Electrolysis of Water

An apparatus for the electrolytic decomposition of purified sea water may enable submarines to remain submerged for long periods of time without resurfacing for fresh supplies of oxygen. A contract for the development and production of such an apparatus has been granted to M. H. Treadwell Co., Inc., of New York, by the U. S. Navy.

Statement of intended purpose of apparatus.

Reference to scientific development.

The purified sea water will be decomposed in the presence of an electrolyte, such as sodium hydroxide or potassium hydroxide, to produce hydrogen and oxygen. The hydrogen will be vented to the ocean, while the oxygen will be sent directly to storage tanks, from which it will be released to the ship's atmosphere. The electrodes used are nickel plated and are separated by a fabric diaphragm that prevents mixing of the two gases. The concentration of the electrolyte is 15 to 20%.

Short and non-detailed description of operation of apparatus.

Description of essential elements making up the apparatus.

One pint of water is said to produce about 10 cubic feet of oxygen. Since one man consumes about 1 cubic foot of oxygen per hour, daily requirements for each person will necessitate the decomposition of about 2.5 pints of water.

Expected demands upon apparatus.

[10] By permission of *Chemical and Engineering News.*

Special qualities of the apparatus.

The cells will be able to operate in positions of extreme inclination and through violent motion. They are designed to produce oxygen directly at pressures of up to 3000 pounds per square inch. In addition, the units will be equipped with automatic control and safety devices never before used in electrochemical equipment.

Short reference to history of apparatus for electrolytic decomposition of purified sea water.

The U. S. Navy contract to Treadwell was awarded on the basis of designs prepared by Robert Spitzer, manager of the electrochemical construction division of M. H. Treadwell Co., in cooperation with L. A. Cook and A. R. Whale of the Bureau of Ships. The new designs are the result of collaborative work conducted over the past 18 months.

Sometimes laboratory work is described on the basis of what actually was done in the laboratory itself, with no reference to any expected results if the process is applied in industry. Under these circumstances little description of standard pieces of apparatus is given, for every technically trained person who is especially interested in the work being done is assumed to be acquainted with them.

Description of a Laboratory Process [11]

Corrosion Resistance of Metals Studied with Interferometer

Statement of results of process, with no emphasis on specific value.

Reference to scientific development.

Short reference to history of use of instrument; indication that a new use is being considered here.

Detailed description of process and essential elements making up laboratory operation.

Reference to conventional phases of apparatus and procedure. (Notice that no description of the interferometer, a

Corrosion to a depth of 0.003 microns can be detected on optically flat specimens by an interferometer procedure devised by R. G. Pike and Donald Hubbard of the National Bureau of Standards' mineral products laboratories. Interferometers, widely used for such problems as checking accuracy of block gages and measuring expansion, have been used very little in corrosion studies, according to NBS.

A sample, ground and polished to optical flatness, is immersed to half its depth in a corrosive solution. It is withdrawn, rinsed and dried, then covered with an optically flat piece of quartz. Interference fringes, seen in a conventional interferometric viewing apparatus of the Pulfrich type illuminated with an unfiltered helium lamp, appear as vertical parallel lines which are continu-

[11] By permission of *Chemical and Engineering News.*

ous. If corrosion has taken place, lateral shifting of the vertical fringes will be noted at the level-of-solution line.

Swelling of the surface, rather than attack, was observed in some cases, crystalline quartz in acid solution, for example. In swelling, the lateral shift of the vertical fringes is in the opposite direction to what it is for corrosion.

widely used and well-known instrument, is given.) Results of process if corrosion has occurred.

Results of process if corrosion has not occurred.
Specific example.
Test for swelling as opposed to corrosion.

Like the organization of the report, descriptions of apparatus are by no means stereotyped. They will not always follow the same pattern. The writer's knowledge of a process, his detailed acquaintance with apparatus used, and his observations of results may dictate a different organization from that used by other scientists or technicians. The marginal notations given for the preceding examples are intended for guidance rather than to suggest any special formula.

Our final example of a description of a process is that of what happens in electrical circuits and why some circuits exhibit different degrees of resistance than others.[12]

Thermoelectricity, Electrical Resistance and Electron Scattering in Metal Alloys

How does the scattering of electrons affect the thermoelectric behavior and the conduction of electricity in metals? Physicists at Honeywell have been able to successfully predict certain features of this behavior on the basis of a simple mathematical model.

Everyone is familiar with the fact that metals are good conductors of electricity and also good conductors of heat. All of the electrical current and most of the heat is carried ordinarily by the electrons in a metal. The flow of electricity is intimately associated with the flow of heat or energy, and we can say that the heat flow "interacts" with the electrical current flow. Whatever gives rise to one of these flows will also give rise to the other. Thus if we connect a wire across a battery we get a flow of energy (heat) as well as a flow of electricity; conversely, if we place one end of a copper wire in a flame, heat will pass down the wire and at the same time an electrical current will flow momentarily so as to "readapt" the electrons to the new situation in the wire—one end of the wire is now hotter than the other. The electrical current flow is only momentary because there is no "return path" by which the electrons can flow around in a closed circuit.

If we connect an iron wire to the copper wire at the hot end, and connect the two free ends to a sensitive voltmeter, there will be a flow of heat

[12] Reproduced by permission of the Minneapolis-Honeywell Regulator Co.

(energy) in both wires, of course, and there will also be a flow of electrons in both wires. But now, since the electrons are free to traverse a closed loop (through the voltmeter), the electrical current flow is sustained as long as we keep the hot junction in the flame.

The experimental facts that heat flow in a pair of wires (called a *thermocouple*) can cause electricity to flow has been known for over a century and is called the Seebeck Effect; the reverse phenomenon, that electrical current flow through a junction of dissimilar metals will cause heat to flow toward or away from the junction, depending upon the *direction* of the current, has been known for nearly a century and is called the Peltier Effect. The Seebeck Effect is used in thermocouples to measure temperature, to detect radiation (which simply heats the junction), to generate electricity from heat, and for many other related applications which involve the conversion of heat into electrical current flow. The Peltier Effect has only recently come into prominence in thermoelectric refrigerators, and in these applications as well as in thermoelectric generators it has been found that semiconductors are often more suitable than metals.

Although the general connection between heat flow and electrical current flow is now well known, the detailed *mechanisms* of electrical and heat conduction in metals is only poorly understood. The extent to which a particular metal conducts electricity or heat is determined in part by the number of electrons which can contribute to the conduction process, and in part by the opposition or "resistance" which these electrons meet as they move along the wire. This resistance results from the presence of various kinds of "obstacles" or "irregularities" in the wire and can be treated as a *scattering* of the electrons from their normal forward motion along the wire. For example, a "perfect" crystal lattice consisting of only copper atoms at *fixed* positions would present no resistance to the flow of electrons; but at any temperature above absolute zero the copper atoms vibrate about their normal positions and behave as "obstacles" to the conduction electrons.

A very effective kind of obstacle or scatterer is an atom of a kind different from that of which the crystal itself is made. Thus if we place a gold atom in a copper lattice, the electrons are confronted with an "oddity" in the otherwise "pure" copper lattice and are thereby scattered: the more gold atoms, the larger the total scattering and the larger the electrical resistivity. Also, some atoms are more effective scatterers than others; thus iron atoms in copper are nearly twenty times more effective than gold atoms. Finally, the scattering ability of a given atom usually depends upon the temperature of the crystal.

Our understanding of the facts just described is at best only qualitative, and the specific *interactions* between heat flow and electrical flow which give rise to the Seebeck and Peltier thermoelectric effects are even more of a mystery! Nevertheless, we have been successful in predicting the thermoelectric behavior of *ternary* alloys on the basis of empirical information on *binary* alloys. We have thus contributed some small amount of order into a technological field (metal thermocouples) which for a century has been within the exclusive domain of alchemy.

Technical Analysis

Technical analysis assumes that the writer is capable of resolving a piece of apparatus, a process, or an idea into its component parts. As an analysis extends deeper and deeper into the ramifications of the subject, its complexity increases. For instance, it is comparatively easy to analyze the entire physical universe into matter and energy; it is also easy to resolve energy into kinetic and potential, and matter into homogeneous and heterogeneous. Yet when one proceeds with the analysis, he finds that he will have all elements and compounds under the heading of homogeneous matter, and millions of other subdivisions under heterogeneous.

In general, one may say that analysis is an extension of the technique of outlining. The writer must divide his topic into its important subdivisions; he must then analyze these subdivisions into their component parts; and he must further subdivide these parts. He makes as many subdivisions as he needs to complete his detailed analysis.

As you examine the following analytical paragraph, dealing with mathematics as looked at through the eyes of the physicist, you will observe that the writer's central thesis is broken down into two subdivisions: how physics calls new mathematical techniques into being, and how physics employs already existing mathematical methods. Each of the subdivisions is analyzed in detail by the citation of examples.

Analysis of Theory and Practice [13]

Mathematics is not a complete and perfected body of doctrine which one goes to seek in the scriptures whenever one has need of it. On the contrary, mathematics is a growing science of which the development—strange as it may seem for so ostensibly pure a science—is affected to a remarkable degree by so crass a law as that of supply and demand. To put the same idea in more respectful words: the existence of a problem in physics which interests many physicists,

Statement of limitations of mathematics.

Statement of general thesis to be analyzed.

Restatement of this same thesis in different phrasing, and with an example

[13] By permission of The Macmillan Co.

(the brilliant physicist and his need) to buttress it.

First phase of analysis of thesis followed by an example to prove the point.

Second phase of analysis of thesis, also followed by an example to illustrate the point the writer makes.

Conclusion to prove that mathematics is actually a growing science ("immense activity"), followed by an analogy.

Restatement of first and second phase of analysis to show the relationship by a cause-effect sequence to the thesis.

or perhaps interests only one physicist but that one a brilliant one, has a strong power of calling into being the mathematical technique which is necessary for coping with the problem. Sometimes a stimulus from physics has evoked an altogether new department of mathematics (the calculus of variations is an instance of this kind). More often it has happened that some variety of algebra or geometry or calculus, which had already been invented and outlined for the sake of the intellectual pleasure which it gave to its designer and to a few other of the mathematical elite, suddenly turned out to be supremely well fitted to the needs of a newly sprouted branch of physics. (Non-Euclidean geometry and matrix algebra are examples of this kind.) Such an event calls forth immense activity in the mathematical field which it involves, and the mathematicians who happen already to be cultivating that field are in the happy situation of a farmer when someone runs up and tells him there is oil beneath his farm. To express this briefly: physics tends to develop, nay, even at times to create, the mathematics which it needs and uses.

Need for Practice

To obtain ease in writing, the beginner should practice. He should not wait for assignments from his professor. If he really wants mastery of English, he should form the habit of writing every day about some interesting event which he has noticed, or of discussing some aspect of his technical experience. People who keep diaries or journals have found that their recording of daily happenings aids them in gaining ease and distinctiveness of style. The professional man who has to write business letters, reports, and articles for the journals also realizes that he improves each time he has to put his ideas on paper. The technical student needs even more practice. He should write and rewrite for at least half an hour each day. If he is willing to do this, he will find it more valuable than classroom lectures or any sort of formal instruction. No one becomes a writer in a few easy lessons. Even the professional, if he is first-class, is never completely satisfied with what he turns out. He is always striving for improvement. And this means work—plenty of it.

Exercises—Words and Sentences

1. By consulting a dictionary, learn the differences between:
    a. lithe, live
    b. homogenous, homogeneous
    c. sympathy, empathy
    d. technological, technical
    e. intrepid, interpret
    f. allow, leave
    g. maternal, maternalistic
    h. agree, accede
    i. guerilla, gorilla
    j. liquefy, liquidate
    k. oculist, optician
    l. persecute, prosecute
    m. sublimate, subliminal
    n. dialect, dialectic
2. Write illustrations of the basic sentence patterns, indicating what parts of the sentence are really basic and what parts are modifiers of basic parts.
3. a. Write a compound sentence consisting of two basic parts with phrase modifiers.
    b. Write a complex sentence consisting of two basic parts with a clause modifier and phrase modifiers.
    c. Write a compound-complex sentence with three basic parts and two clause modifiers as well as phrase and word modifiers.
4. Improve the following paragraph by proper sentence subordination.

    The engineer went to the atomic energy works and was stopped at the gate and was told that he must show his pass and then he could be allowed to go into the works. The engineer thought he had his pass in his car and he went back to get it and it was not there. He went back to the gate and the officer there called his supervisor and the supervisor came down and recognized him and told the officer that it would be all right to let him in.
5. Classify the following sentences as simple, compound, complex, or compound-complex.
    a. After the entire job had been done and the men had been allowed to go home, it was found that through some error a most important phase of the work had not been done.
    b. When it is necessary to run lengthy tests in the laboratory, it is the general practice that at least two men be kept on the night shift so that one may offer the other help in the event of an accident.
    c. Walking down the lengthy aisle of the AD building, we finally were met by one of the oldest employees in the entire shop and office.
    d. New apparatus constantly has to be produced so that industry may move forward in its progress and that scientists and engineers may carry to completion the experiments which they undertake.
    e. We may say, however, that although few people in higher education

have tendencies to mutter and murmur as they speak, nevertheless, there are a few outstandingly poor lecturers.

    f. Feeling that the process which they had worked out was undoubtedly the best one that could be found to carry out such an operation, the three scientists pooled their forces, working day and night, and finally succeeded in producing a working model.

6. Determine which of the following are sentence fragments. If some of them are, rewrite them as complete sentences.

    a. Since the material had already been requisitioned from the storeroom which was in the neighboring building, and since the earliest date that could be hoped for delivery was at least three weeks.

    b. "Nevertheless," said the superintendent of the radiation laboratory, "and this in spite of all we know about the dangers of radiation and its bad effect on human beings."

    c. Knowing that the graduating class at the institution was one of the largest and perhaps the ablest that had ever been matriculated in even so well known and so old a technical school as this one.

    d. The advantages in carrying out careful experimental procedures, although perfectly well known to any technically trained person, are not so well known to the liberal arts graduate.

7. Determine which of the following sentences are loose and which are periodic:

    a. Engineering, although commonly thought of as a relatively new science, is actually very old.

    b. He picked up the peening hammer which had been allowed to drop beside the workbench.

    c. The care with which the drawing is done, the precision used in machining the part, and the accuracy of the inspection are all necessary for adequate quality control.

    d. The engineer carries his work home with him, even if his actual day is finished at five o'clock in the afternoon.

Discussion Questions—Words and Sentences

1. What is the advantage in knowing the etymology of a word?
2. Why should the beginning writer avoid using fragmentary sentences?
3. What is a participial phrase? Why can it not stand alone as a sentence?
4. Why must technical writing be exact and grammatical?
5. What pronunciation should be adopted when two or more pronunciations are listed in the dictionary for the same word?
6. Why is it advisable to vary the types of sentences used in writing?
7. What is the definition of a simple sentence? A complex sentence? A compound sentence? A compound-complex sentence?
8. Why should the technical man learn to subordinate unimportant material?
9. What are the advantages in the use of the periodic sentence?

9

Speaking Techniques

Today's scientists and engineers are being drawn more and more into government decision-making processes. Some of them are helping to solve governmental problems involving science and technology. Some are engaged in projects connected with space research; others are concerned with administrative work in Washington. Increasingly, technical people are also being attracted to areas of foreign policy through their contributions to the development of backward nations. As a result, the scientist and the engineer have discovered common interests with the social scientists in their efforts to deal with some of the problems of twentieth-century man.

Because of the broadening of their activities, technical people are called on frequently to interpret their work to groups of laymen and other scientists and engineers. They are expected to have enough facility in speech to talk to various groups in a logical and interesting way. To do this, they need to know basic speaking techniques. Let us examine a few of these.

Preparing To Speak

Sound preparation for speaking is a necessity if an individual is to be successful either before a large audience or as a participant in a relatively small conference. Such preparation is especially needed if the speaker is to interest his audience. This preparation involves the following steps:

ANALYZING THE AUDIENCE AND THE OCCASION

Because speaking involves capturing the interest and attention of human beings, you will first have to know what kind of people you will be addressing. Suppose you are asked to speak before the local branch of the Institute of Electrical and Electronic Engineers. You know in advance that the meeting will be open to all engineers who belong to the I.E.E.E. You find out, however, that these members have been invited to bring their wives and their friends. There will also be a few other guests, perhaps some visiting engineers from other organizations and some members of local clubs. Because the group will be mixed and will include many individuals who have no technical training, you will have to put your remarks into nontechnical language. You will also have to use more illustrations than if your audience were composed only of technically trained people; and perhaps you will need such pictorial material as charts and graphs, slides, or films. Your preparation to speak will pose more problems than it would if you had an audience composed exclusively of your fellow workers.

Likewise, the occasion will affect what you say. If a group is celebrating its centennial, you will have to adjust your remarks to recognize this event. Should you be speaking on rocketry to laymen at a dinner meeting, you will have to choose as many vivid illustrations as you can to hold their attention, for they will expect to understand the various phases of the subject that you discuss. If you use the language you would employ for space scientists or physicists, you would be likely to lose your audience quickly. Thorough analysis of your audience and the special demands of the occasion will help you to appeal to the existing interests of your hearers.

CHOOSING A SUBJECT

Your analysis of the audience not only suggests your method of treatment, but it also limits the kind of subject you will choose. Obviously, you cannot select a topic which will be so specialized as to appeal to only a few people in your audience. Instead, if your audience consists of laymen or a mixture of specialists and laymen, you will have to select a subject that will appeal to both groups.

Finding a suitable subject is one of the most difficult steps in speech preparation. If you have been working on some phase of voltage regulation as it affects transmission lines, or arrester location as it affects transformer protection, you will have to decide against these subjects if your audience is composed of nonspecialists. The nontechnical person will find it hard to become excited about such topics unless you can simplify them and relate them to his established interests. On the other hand, you may have been working in Kansas City on a single-unit steam power plant which will give that community low-cost power. You may want to propose the building of such a plant in your own community. Here is a subject ready-made for you and your audience. Your hearers will be interested in how your project will result in lower electric bills for them. The subject represents your work and your detailed knowledge of your job. Moreover, it is not too extensive for discussion in a thirty- or forty-five-minute talk.

Selecting a proper subject involves the following process: (1) thorough analysis of what you know, since a speaker can be confident in presentation only when he is sure of what he is talking about; (2) examination of what you know in the light of whether it will be suitable for the particular audience you will address; (3) decision on whether the subject is limited enough in scope so that it can be developed with some degree of completeness within the time allotted.

NARROWING THE SUBJECT

Knowing how to limit a subject so that it can be covered with some degree of completeness within the speaker's time allowance is highly important. If the speaker chooses too broad a subject, he will be able to give his audience only a hurried outline of it or a series of generalizations. Unless the audience has each point illustrated as well as explained, it will not understand what is being talked about.

If you were preparing to talk to a mixed audience—one composed of technical and nontechnical people, of both men and women—and chose the subject "Recent Developments in the Research Laboratories of My Company," you would find that there has been so much work done that you could not possibly do more than touch the subject in a general way. No one development could be made clear and emphatic. Three recent developments would limit your remarks to reasonable bounds. Perhaps you could pick out the most important one and center all your attention and energy on it. It is far better to inform an audience thoroughly about one idea than it is to talk sketchily about several.

Assume that for your mixed audience you have chosen the topic "Womanpower: A Neglected Resource in the United States." This topic fulfills all the requirements. It is centered around one concept. You know the subject because you have just returned from a visit to the Soviet Union, where Russian women are used in both the professions and industry. You know that your audience will be interested in it because the men are chiefly engineers and interested in manpower problems, and the women are concerned about the status of their sex in the economy. The men and women present will have a common eagerness to know about the subject. The topic is narrow enough, for it concerns womanpower as a resource in the United States rather than in the world.

Presenting the Subject: Possible Methods

Now that you have analyzed your audience and determined their interests, chosen the topic and narrowed it, your next step is to decide how you can best present your material. You examine it from every possible angle. You could trace historically the economic position of women in the United States; you could deal with woman's struggle to enter the professions and the degree of success she has attained; you could explain the growing importance of women in industry and the professions since World War II; or you could spend your time on womanpower as a present economic resource and outline what the future holds.

You decide on the last method. From the data you have, you will have charts prepared to show the audience. If you decide to make a comparison between womanpower in the Soviet Union and its industrial utilization and that in the United States, you will be able to illustrate your points by slides.

Although you know your subject well, you want to obtain the latest facts and figures. To obtain them and to find out what has been written on your subject, you will have to do some research in the library.

USING THE LIBRARY [1]

To obtain the necessary information, you go to the library. You realize that you must search for what has been, and what is being, done on your subject. You know, too, that your self-confidence will increase in proportion to your detailed mastery of your topic.

Outlining the Speech

After you have checked your facts and figures and have taken sufficient notes, you are ready for the next step: outlining your subject.

Most speakers are impatient about outlining. They have a provocative topic, they know the subject thoroughly, both in historical background and in modern developments, and they feel qualified to speak about it. The very fact that they do know so much is a danger. The

[1] For the technique of using the library, see pages 200–204.

more knowledge one has the more likely he is to be diffuse and rambling in presentation unless he has made an outline.

Speaking involves a selective process. The effective speaker is the one who chooses only that material which will communicate to others most efficiently what he wants to say. And this selection of material involves a knowledge of the psychology of an audience. What basic interests does the audience have already? What type of material will appeal to these basic interests? What illustrations will keep and hold attention the best? What material should be omitted as irrelevant to the subject; what material must be included? These are questions which the speaker must put to himself before he begins to outline. They emphasize the need of outlining, too, for it is only by going through the whole process that the speaker, by thought and by trial and error, can reach conclusions about what he is actually going to tell his hearers.

TYPES OF OUTLINES

Although there are a variety of outlines which can be used by the speaker, three types are most common: the topical outline, the key-phrase outline, and the sentence outline. The last type, being the most complete, is the one which is recommended for the beginner. The first two types are for those people who have done a great deal of speaking and who, because of this experience, have gained self-confidence.

THE TOPICAL OUTLINE

The topical outline, as its name suggests, consists of a series of main topics arranged in an order which is logical and emphatic. A topical outline on "Womanpower: A Neglected Resource in the United States" might read:

 I. Approach to the audience
  A. Trip to Soviet Union
  B. Russian women
  C. Failure to use American women
 II. Purpose: Use of American women in economy
 III. Development of purpose
  A. Present use
   1. Industry
   2. Facts and figures

        B. Future use
           1. New jobs
           2. Space projects
        C. Professions
           1. Use of women
           2. Facts and figures
        D. Future use
           1. Eliminate shortages
           2. Increase supply of engineers
           3. Supplement teachers
    IV. Conclusion
        A. Marriage and childbearing
        B. Future prosperity
        C. Necessity for increasing use

This outline is for the expert. He knows his subject so thoroughly that, like the actor, all he needs is a series of cues to recall to his mind the plan of his talk. He can develop this plan by specific details because he has worked with his subject long enough to master it. If you have made this kind of preparation, you can speak from a topical outline.

THE KEY–PHRASE OUTLINE

The beginning speaker finds the key-phrase outline of greater help than the topical outline because the phrases, complete and specific, bring to mind in some detail the material about which he is to speak. Sometimes the phrase outline, moreover, gives him a start on sentences which will lead into his ideas because they are part of the sentences which he plans to use. A key-phrase outline of the same topic, "Womanpower: A Neglected Resource in the United States," might be planned as follows:

    I. Approach to the audience
        A. Brief mention of recent trip to Soviet Union
        B. Importance of Russian women to Soviet economy
        C. Failure to utilize women in the United States
    II. Purpose: To stress the need to use American women to the greatest extent possible in industry and the professions
    III. Development of the purpose
        A. Present use of women in industry
           1. Women in laboring and managerial roles
           2. Facts and figures to illustrate these roles (use charts)

     B. Future use of women in industry
       1. Women to do a variety of new jobs as well as those already being done
       2. Women on space projects and as possible astronauts
     C. Present use of women in the professions
       1. Women in medicine, dentistry, law, engineering, etc.
       2. Facts and figures (use charts)
     D. Future use of women in the professions
       1. To help eliminate shortage of doctors, dentists, and medical technicians
       2. To increase the supply of engineers
       3. To supplement the decreasing number of qualified teachers
IV. Conclusion
     A. Marriage and childbearing in relation to increasing use of women in our economy
     B. Future prosperity of the country in relation to increasing use of women in our economy
     C. Necessity for increasing use of women in our economy

From this outline, the speaker gets more help in recalling his speech and its phrasing than he does from the topical outline. By glancing at each point slightly before he puts it into finished sentences, he has enough material set down so that the actual phrasing is suggested to him. Many speakers find this type of plan sufficient for their needs.

THE SENTENCE OUTLINE

For the beginning speaker, the sentence outline has advantages beyond those of the key-phrase outline. Each point is expressed in a complete sentence; therefore the speaker gets more than a mere lead into each part of his talk. Every sentence is really a topic sentence for a new idea. Because of this completeness of statement, phrasing the talk is simplified further. Notice how this works out in the following outline:

Womanpower: A Neglected Resource in the United States

    I. Approach to the audience
     A. During my recent trip to the Soviet Union, I was surprised to notice in what a variety of ways the Russians are utilizing women in their economy.
     B. Russian women have helped to make the Five-Year Plans of the Soviets successful.
     C. The United States, on the other hand, has failed to utilize its womanpower as effectively as it could.

   II. Purpose: My purpose in this talk is to stress the acute need for the United States to use its womanpower to the greatest extent possible in industry and the professions.

  III. Development of the purpose

     A. Since World War II, we have been using women to a greater extent than ever before in industry, but we have by no means reached maximum use.

       1. Women are used in a variety of laboring jobs as well as in managerial positions.

       2. Let us look at a few charts that illustrate to what extent we are lagging behind the Soviets in our use of womanpower.

     B. From now on, women in the United States are destined to play a more important part than ever before in industry.

       1. New inventions, scientific discoveries, and technological development will create new jobs for women in addition to the jobs they are already performing.

       2. Women will also be utilized to help on space projects and perhaps to become astronauts.

     C. Relatively few women are now in the professions.

       1. Medicine, dentistry, law, and engineering could use intelligent women.

       2. The charts I have brought will demonstrate the present proportion of women to men in the professions.

     D. The future for women in the professions holds unlimited possibilities.

       1. They will be needed to help eliminate the present shortage of doctors, dentists, and medical technicians.

       2. They will be needed to meet the increasing demand for more skilled engineers.

       3. They will be needed to supplement the decreasing number of qualified teachers.

  IV. Conclusion

     A. The increasing use of women in our economy will by no means jeopardize marriage and childbearing.

     B. The future prosperity of our country is tied in with our more intelligent use of our womanpower.

     C. If we are to meet our chief competitor, the Soviet Union, on some common ground, we must use women in industry and the professions as the Soviets do—on an equal basis with men.

The sentence outline means more hard work in preparation than the speaker would do ordinarily. It takes more time to get ready than the other types. But for the man who has a poor memory or who wants the maximum aid in phrasing his ideas, it is the best. All beginning speakers should start by preparing their talks in this way. After they have gained confidence and skill, they can use the key-phrase outline or even the topical outline.

The Approach to the Audience

After the speech has been thoroughly outlined, the speaker must decide how he will develop each part of his outline. He will begin with the introduction. This part of a speech offers special problems, for it represents the speaker's first meeting with his audience. If he fails to make a good impression from the opening minute, he may lose the group for the rest of his speech.

The introduction may be divided into three parts: (1) the approach to the audience; (2) statements to relate the approach to the purpose of the speech; and (3) statement of the purpose.

The approach to the audience relies on the speaker's appeal to the established interests of the group. These interests are those that human beings have in common, such as their liking for stories and jokes, their interest in quotations from authorities, their enjoyment of descriptions or history, or their curiosity about comparisons or contrasts. The aim of the approach to the audience is to get the group into a receptive and friendly state of mind, and to prepare them to hear and pay attention to the statement of the speaker's purpose.

Any one of the following devices can be adapted to the introductory remarks of a speaker. These devices should be so carefully chosen that they will lead easily into the speaker's main purpose.

THE NARRATIVE

Any narrative arouses interest, for people like to hear stories. A story gives a specific situation in which particular people are involved. By its graphic quality it gets involuntary attention; that is, the members of the audience do not have to make themselves listen. They are caught and held by the story. A narrative, therefore, is always a good device for beginning, provided that it leads into the purpose of the talk and is short.

THE QUOTATION

Another device practiced by many effective speakers is opening a speech by the use of a quotation. An audience is impressed by the words of an authority such as Einstein or Von Braun. The trick is to choose a quotation that is relevant to the speech and that will point toward the statement of purpose. The quotation must be apt and timely so that it will capture the attention of the audience.

THE RHETORICAL QUESTION

The rheorical question serves to center attention on the purpose and compel the audience to think about it. Consider the following question in its relation to the speaker's aim: "Since the scientist has invented the hydrogen bomb, what is the likelihood that it will be used by unscrupulous statesmen to wipe out whole sections of the world's population? Because this likelihood may become a reality, I should like you to consider the moral responsibility of the scientist in this matter." Here the question leads into the purpose of the speech. The chief danger in using the rhetorical question is that speakers often tend to shoot a barrage of questions at the audience. The result is that hearers cannot concentrate on any one of them. One well-phrased question is better than several.

DESCRIPTIVE OPENINGS

The speaker sometimes has occasion for a descriptive opening. If he is dealing with a new invention, he may arouse interest by describing that invention before he introduces the purpose of his talk. But the description of an invention, or of a piece of equipment, must lead naturally into the main purpose. Description for its own sake is mere ornamentation.

THE HISTORICAL APPROACH

Before the speaker can begin talking about his subject, he may wish to summarize what took place in the past. If his subject is the development of atomic power, for instance, he may have to give a summary of the experiments carried out in the past on atomic power in order to make his hearers aware of the possibilities of present-day research. Such a beginning should be used with discretion. The speaker should find out whether his audience needs historical orientation. If it is made up of scientists, they will doubtless know the history of nuclear physics. If they are laymen, they would find the historical survey helpful.

THE STARTLING STATEMENT

A startling statement is meant to shock people into attention. "The hydrogen bomb means the end of civilization!" would be surprising enough and abrupt enough as an opening assertion to put everyone on edge to hear how the speaker intends to defend his remark and merge it with his purpose. This kind of opening should be used only occasionally. Since audience interest tends to fall off after such an opening because it is so dramatic, the speaker should examine other means of beginning before deciding to use the startling statement.

COMPARISON OR CONTRAST

Comparisons or contrasts make neat openings. A comparison of the effect of the invention of gunpowder with that of the atomic bomb, or a contrast between the optimism of the late 1920's and the caution of the present era, could be used as opening devices. An engineer might want to compare a piece of equipment made in 1910 with another piece manufactured in the latter part of the twentieth century, or he might want to contrast the two.

NEGATIVE STATEMENTS

Negative statement has the effect of heightening the suspense of hearers. A speaker might begin as follows: "This evening I do not want to underestimate the scientist as a human being. Nor do I want to say that he is without a sense of moral responsibility. I would certainly not affirm that the scientist is indifferent to the effects of his discoveries on other human beings. Yet I do want to impress you scientists with the fact that the public expects you to accept the moral responsibility devolving upon you to work for world peace and the use of scientific discoveries for peaceful ends." This opening would make the audience wonder right up to the last sentence what the statement of the purpose was going to be. The positive sentence, coming after a series of negative statements, gains additional emphasis. Since the device exploits the effect of novelty, it should be used sparingly.

THE ANALOGY

Analogy is one of the most useful methods for leading into a talk. It consists of paralleling the unknown with the known, of explaining the unfamiliar in terms of the familiar and showing how the two are alike. Suppose a talk opened in this way: "The scientist says that although he has developed the atomic bomb and the hydrogen bomb with their infinite capacity for destruction, he is not responsible for the uses to which they may be put. He is like the big game hunter who has built a trap to catch a lion. The hunter has forgotten to tell his wife, and the poor woman falls into it and breaks her neck. Is the hunter responsible for her death? Will the scientist be responsible for the wrecked cities of Europe and the United States if atomic or hydrogen warfare comes? Yes, society will hold him morally responsible. That is why he must do everything in his power to promote world peace." Since everyone can settle in his own mind the degree of the hunter's responsibility for the death of his wife, each member of the audience will be able to grasp in some measure, by the aid of this illustration, the degree of the scientist's moral responsibility for the immensity of destruction which will come from the type of warfare mentioned. The analogy will have done its work.

THE SERIES OF PARTICULARS

A series of facts about the structure of the uranium atom, a demonstration of how the neutron, as a result of collision with an atom of uranium-235, has liberated two neutrons and has started a chain reaction, would demonstrate the destructive possibilities of the atomic bomb. These facts would lead the speaker to relate them to the scientist's responsibility for promoting world peace. A series of concrete particulars or a set of vivid details furnishes the speaker with a convenient device, if the particulars relate to the purpose.

THE JOKE

A joke well told is a device that people always like. No speaker should tell one, however, unless he is capable of doing it well. To find this out, he should try telling a joke to his friends at the luncheon table or to his family at dinner. It is far better to fail before a small group of sympathetic hearers than to have the joke go flat before a strange audience. If the joke succeeds with the small number, the speaker may be fairly sure that it will be equally successful with a large group. He must make certain that the joke is new and that its point will lead into what he wants to say next. The joke that has little or no relation to the succeeding remarks is quickly labeled as wind. Jokes which really "ring the bell" are rare.

GRADUAL NARROWING

A more dignified approach to a serious subject can be gained by starting with a broad statement and then narrowing it gradually until the main purpose of the speech is stated. This type of opening goes from the general to the specific, from the broad statement to the narrowed point of view. When a speaker is certain that the members of his audience have a common background and that they have come to hear him discuss his topic seriously, he may use this beginning to advantage.

OPENING BY STATEMENT OF THE SPEAKER'S PURPOSE

The most obvious device, and perhaps one of the most useful, is the statement of the speaker's purpose at the beginning of the talk. When the listeners are known to have a direct interest in what the speaker will say, this type of opening is recommended. Any speaker should be sure that this condition is met before he discards a more arresting device in favor of a direct statement of purpose as an opening sentence.

SUMMARY OF THE APPROACH

Making a favorable impression on the audience during the first few minutes is basic to the success of any speech. Any one of the devices mentioned, if used skillfully, will help to make this impression. Sometimes the speaker will want to combine two or more devices for introducing his purpose. He should feel free to do so or to use his ingenuity in devising other methods. The fundamental aim is to catch and hold attention.

Because there are so many ways of beginning, the speaker should rid himself of the notion that he must be a professional humorist and amuse his audience by telling them jokes before he states what he wants to talk about. There is no need to rival stage or television comedians. Determine what you can do best in the light of what your particular audience will want and will listen to. If you do this, you should be able to attract the interest of any group.

The Development of the Purpose

No matter what device the speaker chooses for introducing his speech, the introduction should put the audience in a receptive mood, should arouse their interest and curiosity, and should emphasize the speaker's purpose. The audience should be ready to listen to the analysis of the purpose.

LOGICAL THINKING

A large part of the success of any speech, at least with those people in the audience who really think, depends on the speaker's ability to analyze his purpose logically. This is done in a preliminary way when the speaker makes his outline. In the body of the speech, when he actually delivers it, he has to take up each major division of the purpose and make it so vivid and emphatic that it will remain in the minds of his hearers. He cannot allow himself to stray from the idea under discussion, for how well he focuses attention on that idea will determine its effect on his listeners.

He may need to break down any one of the main points into its subdivisions. In this, he will be guided by his judgment. Throughout the body of the speech, however, the audience will need to perceive the unity of thought and the speaker's deft interrelating of ideas.

The inexperienced speaker should guard against merely stating a main point without bringing forward enough proof to make the point convincing to the audience. Unless facts and statistics, or several specific instances, are brought to bear on the point, it will fail to be accepted by thoughtful hearers.

MAINTAINING ATTENTION THROUGHOUT THE BODY OF THE SPEECH

One hazard in speaking is that the introductory device may have been so vivid and successful that the interest it stimulated will be dulled by insufficient illustrations in the body of the speech. To maintain the attention of the audience, the speaker will have to use a number of varied illustrations. He may wish to use (1) definition, (2) the rhetorical question, (3) facts pertinent to his subject, (4) quotations, (5) comparisons and contrasts, (6) anecdotes, or any other devices he considers appropriate to keep attention at a high pitch. If he can use some visual aids he will add to the attention-getting values of his other devices, providing he does not depend too heavily on any one visual aid. Pieces of equipment for demonstration, pictures, charts, maps, graphs, or the use of an overhead projector, can heighten the interest of the audience if they are used at appropriate places in the speech.

The Conclusion

Speakers will generally work hard to construct an interesting opening for their speeches and will take unusual pains to find the right kind of illustrations for their main points. If they neglect any part of a speech, that part is usually the ending. Actually, a poor ending can destroy everything that has been accomplished by an excellent introduction and a well-developed series of ideas. The conclusion should really be the climax of the speech, the most forceful part of the entire discussion.

DEVICES FOR CONCLUDING THE SPEECH

The same kind of devices used in the introduction may also be used in the conclusion: the narrative, analogy, historical material, negative statements, reference to the interests of the audience, the startling statement, vivid facts and statistics, or the anecdote. Most of these devices have been explained in the discussion of the introduction. They are just as valuable for ending the talk as they are for introducing it or developing it. If you decide to use statistics, however, be sure that the statistics are expressed in round numbers. Figures given in detail may be interesting to an audience versed in the subject; they become boring to a lay audience.

RESTRESSING MAIN POINTS

One rather obvious method for concluding is to restress the main points of the speech. This is a popular type of ending, but one which is often unnecessary if the clarity and simplicity of the subject matter are self-evident. In any complicated analysis of the purpose such restressing of the main points is recommended. It helps the audience to keep the whole speech in mind and to go away able to recount to others what has been said.

RESTATEMENT OF THE PURPOSE

Sometimes a restatement of the purpose of the speech makes an effective ending. As far as possible, this should be made in words different from those in the original statement. On the other hand, it is sometimes wise to repeat the purpose in the same words that were used in the opening statement. Listeners like to have the main purpose repeated. The repetition helps everyone fix in mind what the speaker has been talking about.

CONCLUDING BY AN ANECDOTE

An apt anecdote often drives home the speaker's point. If this anecdote relates directly to the speaker's purpose, and to its development, the hearers are likely to go away from the hall feeling that they will never forget what they have heard. An anecdote of this sort generally does more good than detailed summary. Yet such an anecdote is difficult to find. If you have one which will focus attention on what you have said, it will help to point up your message.

CONCLUDING BY A QUESTION

A well-phrased question that re-enforces the purpose is also effective. If the question is short, it may remain in the mind of each hearer long after some details of the talk have been forgotten. Phrasing a pertinent question, however, is more difficult than it may appear. The question should embody in itself the basic idea of the speech.

CONCLUDING BY STATING A FUTURE PROGRAM

Often the speaker wants to put forward a future program which should result from what he has been discussing. If this is the sort of conclusion that will galvanize your hearers into thought or action, it is probably the best technique. The findings of scientists often lead them to enunciate programs for the future. Generally speaking, audiences are appreciative of knowing the implications of an idea that follow from what a speaker has told them.

Types of Presentation

The speaker's real problem is how he shall present his material to his audience. In general, there are four methods:

1. The impromptu speech
2. The memorized speech
3. The read speech
4. The extemporaneous speech

THE IMPROMPTU SPEECH

An impromptu speech is one delivered without previous preparation and without advance notice given the speaker. The engineer often has to express himself impromptu in conferences with his colleagues.[2]

THE MEMORIZED SPEECH

The speaker who has prepared an outline for his talk often prefers to write out in full what he intends to say. He then revises his manu-

[2] See Interviews, pp. 93–97, 346–349; Conference Discussion, pp. 4–9, 349–350.

script and polishes the phrasing. If his speech is an important one which may be taken down by reporters, or if he doubts his ability to phrase ideas while he is speaking, he will probably memorize it.

The dangers of this method are obvious. At high school commencements, for instance, the student speakers frequently get help in the writing of their speeches from well-meaning teachers. After the speech has been written and approved, they take it home and memorize it—often with great pain to themselves. They attempt to learn it sentence by sentence, going from sentence one to sentence two, repeating the first two sentences, then adding sentence three and repeating the whole thing to that point, and so on. The results can be disastrous. If the student has an unusual memory, he will be able to deliver the talk in a facile way; but he may give it without expression, since the ideas are not entirely his own; or he may give the audience the impression that he has a "canned" speech, one that has been gone over so many times that it is parroted. If, on the other hand, the student's memory is average, he is likely to forget a key phrase in one of his sentences. He stops; there is a pause which gradually lengthens; the audience grows uneasy; the prompter whispers the key phrase from the wings; and when the student does catch that phrase, he is so confused and uneasy that he rattles ahead without expression or good enunciation.

Do not memorize your speech unless you are certain that you can give it with expression and without faltering. One lapse of memory might cause you to be a failure and so undermine your confidence for a long time to come.

If you do have to memorize your speech, here are a few suggestions which ought to prove helpful:

1. Read over the whole manuscript several times so that you become familiar with its contents and establish in your mind a logical association of the ideas and sentences.
2. Try to memorize a whole paragraph at a time.
3. Aim to find a memory device which will help you to associate the last idea in one paragraph with the succeeding idea in the following paragraph.
4. Practice giving the speech aloud several times.
5. Know the whole speech as a unit so well that, if you should forget, you will be able to improvise.
6. Deliver the speech with as much animation as you can. Feel the importance of what you are saying. Only an earnest speaker makes an impression on an audience.

If, after following these directions, you are still afraid that you may forget, take your manuscript with you to the auditorium and put it on the lectern. While you speak, slide each completed page to one side; if you should forget, you can then glance at your manuscript and renew your train of thought.

THE READ SPEECH

On occasions, a speaker has to read from a prepared manuscript. His speech may be developed by such complex data that it can neither be memorized nor given extemporaneously. Or he may know that it will be reported by the press and that he will have to submit a copy of the complete speech. Occasions like these call for reading from the manuscript.

To read well, go over the manuscript aloud a number of times. If necessary, place light pencil marks at points where you intend to pause. Underline words which need special stress. Take note of those words which are difficult for you to pronounce; then see whether you cannot substitute simpler words. If not, practice the difficult words until you can pronounce them easily. Above all, when you rehearse the reading of your manuscript, know it so well that you can look away from it and at your audience. Unless you can look at your audience, you will lose all sense of communication with them. People don't fidget if you talk to them directly and fluently. The able reader will:

1. Read over his manuscript so that he will know it almost by heart.
2. Try to convey the full meaning of every sentence to his audience.
3. Decide when and where he will pause.
4. Enunciate crisply.
5. Speak in a tone that can be heard by the people in the last row.
6. Be earnest.

THE EXTEMPORANEOUS SPEECH

The best type of speaking is extemporaneous. This requires:

1. Memorizing the outline thoroughly.
2. Phrasing precisely the ideas and their illustrations as the speaker develops each point.

At first, this method may appear to have the disadvantages of the memorized speech. "Suppose I forget a part of my outline," you ask. "What am I to do then?" If you should forget, no one in the audience will be conscious of it because you will be able to proceed with some allied point you do remember. You are not limited to any specific wording as you are in the memorized talk; therefore you can change the order of your ideas to suit the demands of the moment. Since outlines are relatively short, memorizing them is comparatively easy. The person with only an average memory can do this without much danger of forgetting.

The chief advantage of extemporaneous speaking is its flexibility. You can adapt your speech to the needs of the audience. You may find that the group before you is well acquainted with certain issues you had expected to discuss. If they are, you can cut those issues from your talk as you speak and spend more time on ideas which are new to your hearers. If your audience needs enlightening on certain phases of your subject, you can add points or illustrations at will.

But the method will not be successful unless you memorize the outline completely and keep your attention centered upon it during your delivery. If you follow carefully the procedure below, you ought to be able to use the extemporaneous method successfully:

1. Make an outline of your subject and include in it the main illustrations you want to use.
2. Memorize the outline.
3. Practice the whole speech aloud, putting each part of the outline into words as you speak.
4. Pay attention to the meaning of your phrases and give them proper inflection and emphasis.
5. Place your outline on 3- by 5-inch cards and take these with you to the auditorium. Having the outline with you will help to keep you from becoming nervous.

In practice, of course, you will think out your phrasing. Although you may change this phrasing when you are before the audience, the fact that you have previously put your ideas into words will help you. Knowledge of your subject and much practice are essential.

Delivering the Speech

Up to now, this chapter has concentrated on the preparation of the speech: the choice of the subject, outlining the subject, the devices used for getting the initial attention of the audience and introducing the main purpose, ways of keeping the attention of the audience throughout the body of the speech, and methods for ending.

A speaker might have followed all these stages in speech preparation and yet have a poor speech. Certainly what the speaker has to say is most important of all. Too many people get to their feet and then have nothing worth communicating. But how something is said—the delivery of a speech—can make all the difference between a talk that is boring and one that is alive and appeals to the mind and the emotions of every hearer.

POSTURE

Although posture is a minor part of delivery, it has a vital effect on what the audience may think of a speaker. There are occasions when a man may slouch over a desk or stand with his hands in his pockets and yet make a successful speech.

Yet for the best effect, be alert. After you have been introduced by the chairman, walk to the rostrum and face the audience. Instead of beginning to speak immediately, take time to look over the gathering and get a general impression of the persons who will be listening to you. This momentary pause before you utter the first words will give you a chance to compose yourself and adjust to the situation.

When you face the audience, stand in a comfortable position. If you will observe various speakers, you will notice that each one has his own particular stance. There is no standardized posture, but there are ways to avoid awkward positions.

Standing with the heels together and the toes pointed out at an angle of forty-five degrees will tend to make you rock up and down. Standing with the feet apart, as though you are trying to keep your balance on the deck of a rolling ship, will also lead to an annoying, rocking motion.

Most speakers find that if they keep the feet approximately eight to ten inches apart and place either the left or the right foot forward (in this position, the heel of the foot which is forward is about in line with the instep of the other foot), thus allowing their weight to rest on the foot which is back, they have a satisfactory posture. This also facilitates easy movement when the speaker wants to walk toward his hearers or when he wishes to move to left or right.

Once you have found a restful position, one in which you can relax without any obvious sagging, stand still. The speaker who is constantly in motion directs the attention of the audience to his aimless movements rather than to his ideas. The speaker, like the actor, should move about on the platform only when there is purpose in his movement. If he has to walk back to a chart or a blackboard, if his emphasis of a point makes him want to get nearer his audience by walking to the front of the stage, or if he wants to move right or left in order to address one part of the audience for a few moments, he has movement directed by proper motivation. If you want to change your position on the platform because you need bodily relaxation, do this between the main divisions of your talk.

GESTURES

The untrained speaker is likely to be self-conscious about the gestures he should use. Sometimes he is led into the ridiculous situation of making a gesture after the need for it has passed. Any gesture should be a natural result of strong feeling about a subject. If your entire attention is on what you are saying, if you are feeling deeply about your subject, the gestures will come at the proper time and place in your speech; they will be realistic and effective.

Notice the average man in a conference. He may be smoking a pipe, but he will at times take it out of his mouth and point it at you, or wave it away from him when he is disgusted about something, or keep it in his mouth and pound with his fist on the desk when he is angry or when he wants to re-enforce an idea. Such gestures are spontaneous; they come as the result of his concentration on what he is saying.

For the beginner, no better advice can be given than the need for complete attention to ideas, emotions, and feelings. In practice at home, you would do well to stand before a full-length mirror and watch yourself in action. Bear in mind the five basic gestures which speech authorities recognize, although they decry an artificial use of them:

1. The open hand, palm up and fingers together, with the thumb away from the fingers a little, to express persuasion or assent
2. The pointed index finger to address a particular part of an audience
3. The hand turned with the palm down, fingers and thumb together, to brush away an idea as useless
4. The clenched fist, used to express strong emotion about some aspect of your topic
5. The raised hand, palm toward the audience and fingers together, to obtain silence or emphasize negation.

These gestures are used more often than any others. You are free, nevertheless, to use the hands in any way which will increase the effectiveness of your speech.

When you do practice before a mirror, find out whether you have a tendency to move your hands aimlessly. Are you constantly sawing the air to no purpose? If you have this habit, practice delivering your speech with no gestures at all for a while. Once you overcome needless movements, you will find that your earnestness about your subject will lead to expressive gestures. Every movement you make with your hands should help the audience to interpret your ideas.

GETTING OFF THE PLATFORM

When some speakers near the end of their talk and realize they are about to sit down, they are likely to speed up the rate of delivery as though they cannot wait to finish and run off home.

Since the end of any talk should be its strongest point, round out your conclusion. Speak the final sentence in a firm voice. Then, instead of turning on your heel as you say the last word, wait a few seconds. After that, walk off the platform in a natural way or turn and go back to your seat behind the rostrum. You make a bad impression on your hearers if you scuttle to your seat before they have had time to think with you to the end of your last sentence.

Above all, avoid mumbling "I thank you," as you turn to leave. This is an antiquated ending. Instead of letting the audience think about your final idea, you make them wonder about the "I thank you."

PHRASING

Proper phrasing of the speech allows your hearers to follow each sentence. Most of us have been to meetings where speakers have chopped up their phrases into such small and insignificant segments that it has been hard to follow the meaning. "I—want to—talk to—you this evening—about—the recent—developments in—nuclear physics, but —particularly—I want—to—stress—two—directions which—research—is taking." In this kind of delivery the speaker is putting weight on words which are unimportant in meaning. *To, about, and, but,* and *which* are useful as connectives and as reference words, but they should be subordinate to nouns, verbs, adjectives, and adverbs which convey ideas, emotions, or feelings.

Try not to stress prepositions, conjunctions, or pronouns unless there is good reason for emphasizing them occasionally. Put your thought into units which communicate something directly. "I want to talk to you this evening about the recent developments in nuclear physics" should be spoken as one complete idea, with no breaks within it. "But I want to stress two directions which research is taking" is another complete idea which should be given without a break.

Practice in phrasing ideas will help to establish proper speaking habits. To do this, take any paragraph from a book of prose. Mark off places where an idea, or part of an idea, stops. Then read the paragraph aloud, pausing where you have put your notations. Go from the single paragraph to a whole article. Mark off the logical pauses and then read it aloud. Although you will find that the punctuation of the piece helps you in phrasing, you will also notice that there are times when such marks should be disregarded. If a comma comes after a *but* or an *and,* it is frequently better to run the conjunction into the next phrase and to emphasize the important words in that phrase rather than to stress the individual *and* or *but.* Break up your sentences into parts which can be grasped easily by your audience.

VOICE

The quality of a speaker's voice is another important aspect of delivery. Justly or unjustly, an audience tends to evaluate a speaker in part by the way he sounds. If his voice is resonant, if it has flexibility enough to convey shades of feeling and emotion, if his tones are strong, they listen with pleasure. If his voice is high or nasal or harsh, he may lose the attention of part of his audience.

Although the mechanism of the voice differs with each individual —there are differences in lung construction and power, teeth, nasal passages, and vocal cords—every speaker can try to make the most of his physical equipment unless he has some pronounced speech defect. If you do have a marked defect, you will have to consult a physician to find out whether anything can be done to eliminate it. For any speaker, however, relaxation on the platform is necessary. If you are tense, if your muscles are constricted, your voice will reflect this tension.

To make the most of your voice, you should slow down your delivery to a rate which will let you enunciate each word clearly. If you speed up beyond about 135 words a minute, you run the chance of having to slur your enunciation. Since all good speaking implies that your audience should be able to think with you as you talk, a proper rate is essential. Slowing down too noticeably, however, is almost as annoying as talking too rapidly. Dragging out phrases and sentences gives the listener the feeling that he wants to supply words to the speaker.

The force a speaker uses in delivery is as important as the rate of speaking. The best rule to keep in mind is: Talk to the people in the last row. In a room of average size, you need only ordinary conversational tones. But if your audience is large and the hall spacious, you will have to raise your voice correspondingly. Such an increase in force does not imply the necessity of bellowing. If you shout continuously, you will tire any group. Vary the force so that you can place emphasis on main ideas and important parts of your talk.

This variation in force must be accompanied by a variation in pitch. Your tones should be low or high according to the meaning you want to give each sentence. If you are enthusiastic about your subject and are thinking through each part of your speech, you will vary your pitch unconsciously. It is the speaker who talks in a monotone and thus conveys an apparent disinterest in his subject who is dull at any time. Since most people cannot estimate how they sound to others, try to get a recording of your voice made, either in a speech laboratory, or on a record cut at a music store. If the recording indicates that you speak in a monotone, practice reading aloud to someone who can give you intelligent criticism. Your voice should go up and down the scale according to the degree of earnestness and emotional quality you want each sentence to carry. The quality of your speaking is determined largely by this variation.

NERVOUS TENSION

It is natural for any speaker to feel a little anxiety about the speech he is to make. The tension which results from this anxiety is, however, often more of a benefit than a hindrance. The speaker has a mental spur which results in his putting forth his best effort. Even the most practiced orators have testified that they feel some tension just before they take the platform. If they have prepared well and if they are enthusiastic about what they have to say, this tension goes almost with the opening few words, just as the actor forgets himself and his uneasiness as soon as he hears his cue and pronounces his first line.

Absolute mastery of one's feelings comes only with much practice in speaking. The beginner is naturally more likely to feel nervous than the accomplished speaker. Since nervousness is one of the chief causes of poor speaking, the following suggestions will help you to eliminate it:

1. Realize that your audience will usually be sympathetic with you and will want you to do your best.

2. Know your subject completely. This is the best armor against nervousness. The man who knows his subject and who really wants to tell other people about it has no time to feel nervous.

3. Concentrate on your outline. If your mind is on what you are saying, it cannot be diverted to yourself. The self-conscious fellow, whose attention is on the impression he is making and not on his plan for the speech, is most likely to become nervous.

4. Avoid rushing to the platform and beginning to speak immediately. When you reach the rostrum, face the audience and take time to get a general impression of the people to whom you will speak. While you pause for several seconds, breathe deeply. The man whose breathing is normal and who has plenty of air in his lungs can express himself to the best advantage.

5. Pause slightly between paragraphs. Pause for several seconds between the main divisions of the speech.

6. Speak deliberately. A speaking rate between 125 and 150 words per minute allows the best enunciation and also lets your audience think along with you.

7. Let yourself relax before you begin to speak. This relaxation is especially helpful to the throat muscles. A tense speaker usually has a squeaky voice and an unnatural delivery.

Microphone Technique

The increasing use of the microphone to amplify the voice gives speakers less reason than they have had in the past for speaking in tones which cannot be heard at the back of a hall. But the microphone in itself will not assure a speech which can be understood by everyone. It increases the need for careful enunciation and pronunciation, for a speaker's faults as well as his pleasing qualities are emphasized by electrical amplification.

Using a microphone, whether the lapel or the stationary type, is simple enough if the speaker will pay attention to a few rules. Almost everyone has learned that if he shouts into a telephone the person on the other end of the line will get blurred and unpleasant sounds. The same thing happens when you shout into a microphone. The first rule is to speak in your natural tone of voice. When you reach the emotional climaxes of your talk—if there are any—stand away from the microphone a little, so that the increased force will not be magnified unduly; but be sure always to speak into the microphone.

This is the second rule. On impromptu programs over the air, when people who have never spoken to a radio or television audience are brought on, the announcer frequently has to tell them to speak into the instrument. The position which will bring the best results will have to be determined by practice. If you know that you will be using a microphone for the delivery of your talk, try to arrange for a practice session in the hall where you will be speaking. Get someone—a sound engineer if possible—to listen to you. Ask him to tell you at what position your voice sounds best. You should not stand closer to a microphone than six inches, although the distance will vary according to the strength and quality of your voice.

Don't be afraid of the instrument itself. It won't bite. Insofar as you can, forget it. Give your talk as you would ordinarily, with enthusiasm and energy. The inexperienced speaker is likely to have his consciouness of the microphone lure him into speaking monotonously, or he may exaggerate his enunciation by biting off his words artificially. As in all speaking, be natural.

If you are using a stationary "mike," do not move away from it for any distance. As soon as you get a few feet to one side, your voice will not carry to all sections of the audience. For this reason, the lapel microphone is becoming popular for public addresses. It gives freedom of action and eliminates the speaker's consciousness of the amplifying system.

The stationary "mike," moreover, tends to make the speaker look at it instead of at his audience. Once you lose eye contact with the people before you, you may lose their attention. Talk directly to your hearers, even though you do have a public address system.

And if you want to make the best impression, never cough or clear your throat into a microphone unless you want to sound like an elephant trumpeting. Turn your head away from the microphone and hold a handkerchief close to your mouth. Inarticulate sounds emerge from loud speakers as peculiar, sometimes grotesque, noises.

Interviews

Although the technical man has to make special types of speeches for various occasions, he will use speech methods more often in interviews than in formal speaking. He has to talk with people, take part in conference discussions, or have interviews. In the discussion of the letter of application in Chapter 3, it has been pointed out that this letter is designed to secure an interview for the applicant rather than to get him a job. The real hiring is done when the executive or the personnel manager can meet and talk with the man. But there are other kinds of interviews than those for jobs: talks with persons who are interested in design problems, informal interviews with executives who want to get constructive ideas on policy, meetings with personnel from other firms, etc. Since the technical man has to interview people almost every day, he should know how to do his best under such circumstances.

To some extent, an interview will develop naturally from the questions which the interviewer will ask. Yet there are methods of preparation which will help any man to make the most of his opportunities.

Before you go for an interview for a job, keep in mind certain obvious steps. Any businessman will expect you to be neat in dress. The more conservative your suit and your tie, the better impression you will make. No one will expect a fashion plate; but the ordinary businessman will look for evidences of care in dress and taste in choosing your clothes.

Certainly you will be expected to report promptly. Although the interviewer may not be able to see you in his office at the exact minute designated, he would be justified in feeling that you were inefficient if you came late. Promptness is one quality which any employer looks for.

You can also anticipate some of the things which you will be asked. Set down on paper questions which may come up during the conference. Talk over with your friends the main topic of the forthcoming discussion. Get their ideas and suggestions. Then make an outline of the probable topics and endeavor to have ideas on each of them. The interviewer will want to know something about your education, your experience, and your chief interests. He will also want to ask you what salary you will expect. Prepare to give specific answers to each of these points. Try not to be caught off guard.

Or suppose you are asked by your employer to attend a conference concerning your company's opening a branch in Peru. If you know that this subject will be the basis of the conference, you should read up on Peru. This will entail work in the library. By such work, you should be able to anticipate a few of the directions which the discussion will take. You should also be so well informed that you will be able to contribute constructive ideas.

During an interview, you should try to be a good listener. Too many people aim to impress the employer with what they know. The man who is doing the hiring or who is your superior may want to do most of the talking. You should cultivate the art of listening intelligently. Keep in mind every important point which the interviewer makes; when you are asked for an opinion, give it concisely and clearly. If you are the one who is in a subordinate position, be ready to defer to your superior.

It is always a mistake for the person being interviewed to introduce new points when he has not had time to think about them. Be sure of your facts. Only when you have them clear in your mind can you arrive at conclusions. If you have not thought about a point or if you have no knowledge of a subject, don't hesitate to admit your lack of knowledge. Any interviewer would prefer to have an honest confession of ignorance than to have a person try to bluff.

It is always assumed that you can use good English. As a professional man, you will be expected to speak correctly. Mistakes in grammar make a bad impression on the interviewer. Cultivate the habit of expressing yourself in simple, clear, and correct language.

Perhaps the most awkward part of the interview is the leave-taking. If the interviewer looks at his watch, allows the conversation to lag, or begins to gather up papers on his desk, take these actions as signs that he wants you to go. Thank him for the time he has given you, express interest in what he has said, and get out of the office as graciously as you can. The man who overstays his time defeats his own purpose. You must be sensitive of other people's attitudes if you want to make the best impression.

If, in other words, you want your interview to be successful, take the point of view of the man across the desk. Just as the "you" attitude is important in business letters, it is essential in every interview. Unless you are willing to listen to the other man, to consider his interests, to watch for signs which will tell you when you are pleasing or boring him, you are not likely to get the results you want. Preparing for an interview, then, means:

1. Being neat in appearance and prompt in keeping appointments.
2. Understanding the purpose of the interview.
3. Outlining beforehand the probable points of discussion.
4. Doing any necessary library work to inform yourself about the subject for discussion.

5. Listening intelligently to what the interviewer says.
6. Avoiding too much talk or a display of egotism.
7. Being able to give considered opinions when they are asked for or expected.
8. Making the most of what you know.
9. Using good English.
10. Leaving when you feel the interview is at an end.

Conference Discussion

Like the interview, the conference discussion is likely to require preparation. Since the purpose of any conference is to get a group of people together for the interchange of ideas and opinions, the individual who has to take part should first formulate in his mind the main purpose of the conference. Unless he can sum up concisely what he is going to confer about, he will find it hard to follow what his conferees are saying.

The end of any conference should be the bringing together of opposing points of view. Something constructive should result. To accomplish this, each member of the conference must listen carefully to what the other members say. Beginning to speak before the other man has finished his remarks, allowing the mind to wander, or introducing irrelevant matters are all symptoms of the poor listener.

The conferee must remember that there should be order in the discussion. Only one person should speak at a time. The rest should be courteous enough to consider his remarks and weigh them against their own opinions. No one should go into the conference with settled views. Give and take is the first rule for successful conferences. The aim is to discuss as many points of view about a problem as are necessary. Only by the cooperation of the group can the conference accomplish anything.

And this accomplishment will be worth while only if each man knows the facts about the subject, follows the discussion, and contributes what he can to it. This means reviewing the facts, interpreting them, and coming to tentative opinions or conclusions. These, of necessity, must be tentative, for often a conference will lead to a change in opinion. The chief benefit from any group discussion is that by bringing several different points of view to bear upon a problem, the conferees will be led toward a solution or toward some constructive methods of approach which will help in solving it. Each man must contribute his views as tactfully as he can.

If you have a specific plan which will resolve the problem, study each member of the group to find out how you can win him to your solution. One man may be known as a person who jumps to conclusions without adequate knowledge of facts. Base your arguments so conclusively on facts that he will be led to accept them. Another man may be obviously prejudiced. Try to show him tactfully the real truth. Your judgment of each conferee and his strong points and weaknesses will help you to win over other men to your ideas. You should be willing to accept the other person's point of view if you are convinced it is superior to your own. Compromise is the basis of any fruitful discussion.

To be a useful member of a conference, you must

1. Know the subject of the discussion.
2. Analyze each member of the group.
3. Evaluate the opinions of others.
4. Be ready to offer any reasoned opinions of your own.
5. Be willing to compromise.
6. Be courteous in voicing your opinions.

If you should be chosen as chairman of the conference, prepare an agenda. This is a list of the order of business. Be sure that this agenda can be covered in the time allotted for the conference. If there is no limitation of time, reduce your agenda to the smallest number of items possible consistent with completeness of discussion. Try to anticipate what the group should do or what questions will be asked. As chairman, too, you will have to know the group with whom you will deal, for diplomacy and tact are prime qualifications. It would be well to read over *Robert's Rules of Order*, so that if any questions arise concerning motions to be passed, recognition of speakers, or the precedence of one item of business over another, you will have authoritative answers. An efficient chairman will go into a conference with a well-prepared plan of action. If he doesn't, he is likely to let the talk become aimless.

More than anything else, he should be able to summarize the points brought up by members of the group. A good chairman will never let the discussion wander. He will keep each man to the main purpose. By his analysis of the issues, his evaluation of these issues, and his application of them to the chief purpose, he will direct talk toward an intelligent solution of the problem. And every man wants the time he spends in conference justified by practical results.

Summary

This chapter does not pretend to be a substitute for a complete textbook in public speaking. It has aimed to examine speech techniques from the standpoint of what the technical man, rather than any speaker, should know. It has been designed to give you a concise set of principles for use. By applying them intelligently, you should be able to transmit your information to others in a straightforward, planned, and efficient way.

Discussion Questions

1. What speaking situations does the technical man most often have to meet?
2. Why should a speaker occasionally read his speech?
3. What is the proper procedure to follow when it is necessary to read a speech?
4. What disadvantages may result from memorizing a speech?
5. What dangers appear in the impromptu speech? What is the fatal mistake in this sort of talk?
6. Why is the extemporaneous method so effective?
7. Why should a speaker attempt to analyze his audience before he begins to plan his speech?
8. What three types of outlines are common among public speakers? What are the advantages of each?
9. Are demonstration devices, such as miniature models, slides, etc., of advantage to the speaker? What dangers lie in their use?
10. What must the opening of the speech accomplish?
11. Should the funny story or the anecdote be used?
12. What danger lies in the use of the quotation device to open the speech?
13. Why is the descriptive opening particularly applicable when speaking to a technical group?
14. What is the possible danger in the use of an historical approach?
15. How does the speaker maintain attention throughout the body of the speech?
16. What is the best position for a speaker to take on a rostrum?
17. What is wrong with the speaker striding to and fro across the platform? When should a speaker change his position on the platform?
18. What are the basic gestures in public speaking?
19. Is the analogy more likely to be used when one is speaking to a group made up entirely of engineers or to one in which the members are drawn from different professions?
20. How should a speaker conclude his speech?
21. Why is the "I thank you" ending inappropriate?

22. Where should the accents in the sentences fall? Why should one not accent prepositions, conjunctions, and the like?
23. At about what rate should a speaker deliver his address?

Oral Assignments

1. Prepare an introduction (approach and statement of purpose) for a speech on "The Possibility of a Third World War" or "A Few Technical Developments Which May Be Utilized in a Third World War."
2. Prepare an introduction for a speech on any subject which will illustrate gradual narrowing to the main purpose of the talk.
3. Prepare an introduction for a speech on any subject which will illustrate the descriptive opening.
4. Choose from the introductory devices listed, but not included in the questions given above, one device which will best open a topic of your own choosing. Name the device you have used.
5. Develop a sentence outline for a five-minute speech based on your main interest in your technical field.
6. Deliver the speech which you have outlined in assignment five. Be prepared to tell what devices you have used to maintain attention and what device, or devices, you have used to conclude your speech.
7. Prepare a complete manuscript of a five-minute speech on a subject which might be presented before any convention. Read your manuscript to the class, following the suggestions given for reading manuscripts to an audience.
8. Using the same subject as you took for assignment seven, prepare an outline and deliver your speech by the extemporaneous method. Pay attention to posture and natural gestures.
9. Choose a five-man committee from your class. Assume that your function as a committee is to interview a man for a job. Choose another man as the person to be interviewed. Conduct the interview and get suggestions and criticism from the class after you have concluded.
10. Prepare for a conference discussion on "utilizing womanpower." Choose a conference group from your class and have the rest of the students criticize the procedures used.

INDEX TO
ENGLISH USAGE

Index to English Usage

The following index to English usage has been designed to meet the problems in usage which the technical writer most often experiences.

The index has been arranged alphabetically and has been planned to give the reader information on points of grammar, on words and phrases commonly misused, on technical abbreviations, on punctuation, on capitalization, on spelling, and on other matters directly pertaining to technical writing.

Cross-references have been given throughout. If, for instance, the reader wants information about nouns and their uses, he may find it under "Nouns." Beside this entry the authors have referred him to other parts of the index which have to do with nouns, such as "Parts of Speech" and "Predicate Nouns." Such a cross-reference gives not only the most common uses but also the less common ones. As far as possible, the authors have tried to follow contemporary usage accepted by the best writers and speakers. In almost all instances, the examples have been adapted to the kind of writing which the technical man has to do constantly. "Literary" illustrations have been left out.

Whenever a topic or a word has been treated in detail in "Language Essentials," the reader is referred to the page number of that chapter which treats the subject. For the pronunciation of words, the authors advise the reader to consult a recent edition of a good dictionary, such as *Webster's New World Dictionary of the American Language*, *The American College Dictionary*, or any other well-edited dictionary. An unabridged dictionary is always to be preferred to the desk size; but unabridged editions are usually not so easily available as the abridged editions.

A.—An. See also ARTICLE.

Any word prefaced by the article *a* should begin with a consonant, as "*a* king," "*a* cat," "*a* dog." Exceptions:

1. If the word following the article begins with a silent *h, an* is used, as "*an* honorable man," "*an* honorarium."

2. If the word following the article begins with a vowel that combines the sound of a vowel and a consonant, *a* is used instead of *an*, as "*a* European," "*a* unified country."

3. Variations occur as the result of a change in the accent from one syllable to another. Thus one may say, "*an* historical novel," "*a* history book."

Abbreviations

Abbreviations are useful to the technical man. He can save time by adopting those abbreviations for technical terms given by the American Standards Association. Occasionally, particularly when material is being tabulated, abbreviations of commonly used words are needed, and there can be no objection to using them whenever they are warranted. Keep in mind that an abbreviation is of no use unless it is clear to the reader.

Abbreviation rules:

1. Abbreviate only after a definite quantitative value.

   The motor is rated at 275 *hp*. The power consumed by this circuit is 320 *kw*.

2. Use all abbreviations in their singular forms.

   This machine rotates at 1800 *rpm;* 560 *kva* is the capacity of the transformer. (Exceptions: *pp, ff, Bros., Messrs., mss.* for *pages, following pages, Brothers, Misters, manuscripts.*)

3. Use no punctuation to follow standard engineering abbreviations, unless there is a possibility of confusion, as in *in.* for *inch* or *am.* for *amplitude.*

4. Do not abbreviate "Company" in firm names unless such abbreviation is part of the official name of the firm.

5. Do not abbreviate "multiply" as "x." Use "by" instead.

6. Do not abbreviate the name of any city.

7. Do not abbreviate any word or set of words which has not become well known in engineering. Do not, for instance, abbreviate "*ionization constant*" as *ic.*

8. Do not abbreviate titles unless the first name or the initials of the holder are present, as *Prof. Edmonds* instead of *Prof. Walter D. Edmonds.*

9. Do not abbreviate the names of months or days.

As a technical man, you should adapt yourself to the system of abbreviations commonly used in your own shop or office.

Following is a list of common abbreviations recognized by the American Standards Association.

absolute	abs	amplitude, an elliptic	
acre	spell out	function	am.
acre-foot	acre-ft	Angstrom unit	A
air horsepower	air hp	antilogarithm	antilog
alternating-current		atmosphere	atm
(as adjective)	a-c	atomic weight	at. wt
ampere	amp	average	avg
ampere-hour	amp-hr	avoirdupois	avdp
		azimuth	az or α

barometer .... bar.
barrel .... bbl
Baumé .... Bé
board feet (feet
    board measure) ... fbm
boiler pressure ...... spell out
boiling point .... bp
brake horsepower .... bhp
brake horsepower-
    hour .... bhp-hr
Brinell hardness
    number .... Bhn
British thermal unit ... Btu or B
bushel .... bu

calorie .... cal
candle c
candle-hour .... c-hr
candlepower .... cp
cent .... c or ¢
center to center ...... c to c
centigram .... cg
centiliter cl
centimeter .... cm
centimeter-gram-
    second (system) ... cgs
chemical .... chem
chemically pure ..... cp
circular .... cir
circular mils .... cir mils
coefficient .... coef
cologarithm .... colog
concentrate .... conc
conductivity .... cond
constant .... const
continental horse-
    power .... cont hp
cord .... cd
cosecant .... csc
cosine .... cos
cosine of the ampli-
    tude, an elliptic
    function .... cn
cost, insurance, and
    freight .... cif
cotangent .... cot
coulomb .... spell out
counter electromotive
    force .... cemf
cubic .... cu

cubic centimeter ..... cu cm, cm³
                         (liquid,
                         meaning
                         milliliter,
                         ml)
cubic feet per minute . cfm
cubic feet per second . cfs
cubic foot .... cu ft
cubic inch .... cu in.
cubic meter .... cu m or m³
cubic micron .... cu μ or cu
                         mu or μ³
cubic millimeter ..... cu mm or
                         mm³
cubic yard .... cu yd
current density ...... spell out
cycles per second .... spell out or
                         c
cylinder .... cyl

day .... spell out
decibel .... db
degree .... deg or °
degree centigrade C
degree Fahrenheit ... F
degree Kelvin .... K
degree Réaumur ..... R
delta amplitude, an
    elliptic function ... dn
diameter .... diam
direct-current (as
    adjective) .... d-c
dollar .... $
dozen .... doz
dram .... dr

efficiency .... eff
electric .... elec
electromotive force ... emf
elevation .... el
equation .... eq
external .... ext

farad .... spell out
                         or f
feet board measure
    (board feet) ...... fbm
feet per minute ..... fpm
feet per second ..... fps
fluid .... fl

foot	ft
foot-candle	ft-c
foot-Lambert	ft-L
foot-pound	ft-lb
foot-pound-second (system)	fps
foot-second (see cubic feet per second)	
franc	fr
free aboard ship	spell out
free alongside ship	spell out
free on board	fob
freezing point	fp
frequency	spell out
fusion point	fnp
gallon	gal
gallons per minute	gpm
gallons per second	gps
grain	spell out
gram	g
gram-calorie	g-cal
greatest common divisor	gcd
haversine	hav
hectare	ha
henry	h
high-pressure (adjective)	h-p
hogshead	hhd
horsepower	hp
horsepower-hour	hp-hr
hour	hr
hundred	C
hundredweight (British 112 lbs; U. S. 100 lbs)	cwt
hyperbolic cosine	cosh
hyperbolic sine	sinh
hyperbolic tangent	tanh
inch	in.
inch-pound	in-lb
inches per second	ips
indicated horsepower	ihp
indicated horsepower-hour	ihp-hr
inside diameter	ID

intermediate-pressure (adjective)	i-p
internal	int
joule	j
kilocalorie	kcal
kilocycles	kc
kilocycles per second	kcps
kilogram	kg
kilogram-calorie	kg-cal
kilogram-meter	kg-m
kilograms per cubic meter	kg per cut m or kg/m^3
kilograms per second	kgps
kiloliter	kl
kilometer	km
kilometers per second	kmps
kilovolt	kv
kilovolt-ampere	kva
kilowatt	kw
kilowatt-hour	kw-hr
Lambert	L
latitude	lat or ϕ
least common multiple	lcm
linear foot	lin ft
liquid	liq
lira	spell out
liter	l
logarithm (common)	log
logarithm (natural)	$\log_e$ or ln
longitude	long
low-pressure (adjective)	l-p
lumen	l
lumen-hour	l-hr
lumens per watt	lpw
mass	spell out
mathematics	math
maximum	max
mean effective pressure	mep
mean horizontal candle-power	mhcp
megacycle	spell out

megohm .... spell out
melting point .... mp
meter .... m
meter-kilogram ...... m-kg
microampere .... μa or mu a
microfarad .... μf
microinch .... μin.
micromicrofarad ..... $\mu\mu$f
micromicron .... $\mu\mu$ or mu
               mu
micron .... μ or mu
microvolt .... μv
microwatt .... μw or w
mile .... spell out
miles per hour ...... mph
miles per hour per
  second .... mphps
milliampere .... ma
milligram .... mg
millihenry .... mh
millilambert .... mL
milliliter .... ml
millimeter .... mm
millimicron .... mμ or m mu
million .... spell out
million gallons per
  day .... mgd
millivolt .... mv
minimum .... min
minute (angular
  measure) .... ′
minute (time) .... m
mole .... spell out
molecular weight .... mol.wt
month .... spell out

National Electrical
  Code .... NEC

ohm .... Ω or spell
               out
ohm-centimeter ..... ohm-cm
ounce .... oz
ounce-foot .... oz-ft
ounce-inch .... oz-in.
outside diameter ..... OD

parts per million ..... ppm
peck .... pk
penny (pence) ...... d

pennyweight .... dwt
pint .... pt
potential .... spell out
potential difference ... spell out
pound .... lb
pound-foot .... lb-ft
pound-inch .... lb-in.
pound sterling .... £
pounds per brake-
  horsepower hour ... lb per
               bhp-hr
pounds per cubic foot . lb per cu
               ft
pounds per square
  foot .... psf
pounds per square
  inch .... psi
pounds per square
  inch absolute ..... psia
power factor .... spell out or
               pf

quart .... qt

radian .... spell out
reactive kilovolt-
  ampere .... kvar
reactive volt-ampere .. var
revolutions per
  minute .... rpm
revolutions per second . rps
rod .... spell out
root mean square .... rms

secant .... sec
second .... sec
second (angular
  measure) .... ″
second-foot (see
  cubic feet per
  second)
second (time) (in
  astronomical
  tables) .... s
shaft horsepower ..... shp
shilling .... s
sine .... sin
sine of the amplitude,
  an elliptic function . sn
specific gravity ...... sp gr

specific heat	sp ht	temperature	temp
spherical candle		tensile strength	ts
power	scp	thousand	M
square	sq	thousand foot-pounds	kip-ft
square centimeter	sq cm or cm²	thousand pound	kip
		ton	spell out
square foot	sq ft	ton-mile	spell out
square inch	sq in.		
square kilometer	sq km or km²	versed sine	vers
		volt	v
square meter	sq m or m²	volt-ampere	va
square micron	sq μ or sq mu or μ²	volt-coulomb	spell out
square millimeter	sq mm or mm²	watt	w
		watt-hour	whr
square root of mean		watts per candle	wpc
square	rms	week	spell out
standard	std	weight	wt
stere	s		
		yard	yd
tangent	tan	year	yr

Absolute Phrases. See Participles; Infinitive.

Abstract Noun. See Nouns.

Active Voice. See Voice.

Ad. See also Clipped Words.

This is the clipped form for "advertisement." Although quite acceptable in ordinary speech, it should not be used in writing or in formal English speech.

Adjective. See also Comparison; Predicate Adjectives.

An adjective defines some quality of a noun or pronoun: it makes the noun or pronoun more explicit. Although adjectives aid in precise identification, the writer is cautioned against their overuse. Too many adjectives clutter a sentence rather than clarify it.

The *blue* finish was very *effective* on the motors.

Blue differentiates "finish"; it sets it apart from all other finishes used by the company. *Effective* gives another quality of the finish.

Varieties of adjectives:

1. *Descriptive* adjectives give a quality or tell something of the condition of the word modified.

An *inaccurate* potentiometer.

2. *Limiting* adjectives usually show amount, number, and quantity, as well as pointing out the noun modified.

This steam line; *seventeen* kva.

3. *Proper* adjectives are derived from the name of some individual, nation, or sect.

The *Ziemann* effect; a *Bunsen* burner.

Sometimes proper adjectives have come into such common use that they are no longer capitalized, as

pasteurized milk

Occasionally, adjectives have become so closely related to nouns that they are really parts of a compound noun, as *court-martial*.

Sometimes adjectives precede and sometimes they follow the nouns or pronouns they modify. This is usually dependent on the effect desired by the writer.

They are always separated from the noun or pronoun modified when they fulfill the function of a predicate adjective.

The turbine is *old*.

Adjectives are usually compared (that is, raised in intensity of meaning) by the addition of *-er, -est.*

sick, sicker, sickest.

Sometimes, *more* and *most* or *less* and *least* precede the word itself, but without hyphenation, as

intelligent, *more* intelligent, *most* intelligent.
intelligent, *less* intelligent, *least* intelligent.

Nouns often substitute as adjectives, as

a *brass* bell; a *copper* wire.

Adjective Clauses. See also PUNCTUATION, COMMA.

An adjective clause is a group of words which includes a subject and a predicate and is used to modify either a noun or a pronoun.

The generator *which was recently installed* burned out its bearings.

Here the italicized clause modifies "generator"; it limits the meaning of the modified word.

People *who work with high voltage electricity* soon learn to handle it with the greatest care.

The italicized adjective clause modifies "people"; it differentiates them from other people who perhaps have not learned to use such care.

Often adjective clauses are introduced by such words as *which, who, that*, although occasionally they are introduced directly into the sentence without any preceding word, as

The rectifier *John was attending* carried a heavy overload.

Adverb

An adverb is a word used to modify a verb, an adjective, or another adverb by answering the questions of *how, when, where, why, to what degree*, or *how much*.

Adverbs can be classified according to the types of meanings they convey.

How?—manner.
    He threw the breaker out *quickly*.
When?—time and order.
    The transformer *then* caught fire and interrupted the power supply.
Where?—place.
    The operator went *below* to look at the Diesel.
How much?—quantity.
    The switchboard was *totally* destroyed.
Why?—cause.
    He was *consequently* replaced as foreman.
Responsive and Introductory.
    Yes, it is. *However*, that's true.

Adverbs are compared in the same manner as adjectives, with the addition of *-er, -est, more* and *most, less* and *least*, as:

    soon, sooner, soonest; rapidly, more rapidly, most rapidly; fearfully, less fearfully, least fearfully.

Most adverbs end in *-ly*, although in speech it is not uncommon to omit this ending in some cases.

The generator is running *slowly*. The power factor varies *quickly*.

"Drive *slowly*" has become "drive *slow*" in colloquial usage.

Conjunctive adverbs connect main clauses in compound sentences. The most important conjunctive adverbs are: *also, besides, consequently, however, hence, accordingly, therefore, nevertheless, then, to, so, further, moreover, indeed, still, only, thus, otherwise.*

Adverbial Clauses

Adverbial clauses are groups of words which contain a subject and a verb and act as adverbs; that is, they express *time, place, cause, quantity, manner*, and *degree*. Such clauses modify verbs, adjectives, adverbs, or, occasionally, whole sentences, and are often introduced by such words as *where, how*, or *when*.

When he went to the section, they were building dynamometers.
Although I have worked for General Electric for the past fifteen years, I am only beginning to learn the business.
While I started the motor, he ran for the foreman.

Affect—Effect

For words likely to be confused in meaning, see "Words Often Confused" in "Language Essentials," pages 289–290.

Agreement. See also CORRELATIVE CONJUNCTIONS; PRONOUNS, AGREEMENT OF.

1. Lack of agreement of the subject with the verb (subject plural, verb singular, or the opposite) is a common fault when the subject has been followed by a prepositional phrase which has a noun or pronoun of different number for the object of the preposition.

The *engineer,* in opposition to the stand taken by all his colleagues, *is* determined to go ahead.

Always determine the number, whether singular or plural, of the subject of the sentence. The verb must agree.

2. Pronouns must agree with their antecedents in both number and gender.

The *policeman* at the gate feared *he* had lost *his* badge.
The *policemen* at the gate feared *they* had lost *their* badges.

3. An adjective used to point out agrees in number with the word it modifies.

Those dogs are defective and may cause an accident.
This dog is defective and may cause an accident.

4. When a compound subject connected by *and* is used, the verb must be plural in form.

John and his brother who is in the Navy *are* now at home.

When *either—or, neither—nor, or,* or *not* is used as a connective of the compound subject, a singular verb is used.

Either the motor-generator or the rectifier *has* to be replaced.

5. When a compound subject is connected by *either—or, neither—nor, nor,* or *or,* and one member of the subject is singular and one plural, the verb agrees with that part of the subject closest to it.

Either the supervisor or the men *are* at fault.
Either the men or the supervisor *is* at fault.

6. Sums of money and titles of books and articles are singular.

English and Engineering is a good text; four dollars is its cost.

All

All ready is an adjective phrase, and should not be confused with *already*, an adverb.

> The vat was *already full*. (The meaning is a time value.)
> The machine was *all ready* to be started. (Here we have a description of the state of the machine by an adjectival modifier.)

All together is an adjective phrase; *altogether* is an adverb.

> The parts for the automobile are *all together*. (*All together* modifies the noun *parts*.)
> Rectification is *altogether* different from alternation. (The difference described is complete.)

All Right

This phrase should be written as two words, not as *alright*.

Almost—Most

Avoid using *almost* and *most* interchangeably. *Most* is the clipped form for *almost*, as in "*Most* everyone in the shop bought a raffle ticket." *Almost* is an adverb.

> I have *almost* finished the drawing.
> *Most* people in industry nowadays carry group life insurance.

In the last example *most* is an adjective.

Ambiguity

Ambiguity, the capability of being understood in two or more ways, is a common fault in writing. Communication must be sufficiently exact so that two meanings, perhaps of equivalent value grammatically, cannot be taken from one's writing. Ambiguity arises from a number of causes:

1. Misplaced modifiers.

> The foreman said *when the turbine stopped* that the workmen could go home.

Here two meanings may be taken. Either the turbine has already stopped, and the foreman is sending the men home, or he is telling them that they may go when the turbine stops.

2. Indefinite pronoun references.

> He entered the gate of the mill *which* was two miles from his home.

Again, two meanings are quite possible. Either the mill itself is two miles from his home, or if the shop is a large one, it is possible that the mill extends past his house, and the particular gate he entered is two miles away.

He cut a hole in the oxygen line and *it* escaped rapidly.

Here the pronoun *it* has no antecedent. The writer will avoid ambiguity by stating,

After he had cut a hole in the oxygen line, the *gas* escaped rapidly.

Among—Between

In formal writing, use *among* to imply more than two and *between* to imply only two.

The incentive system set up intense competition *among* the men.
The choice of a man to be shop foreman lay *between* Thomas Held and Frank Turets.

Amount—Number

Amount is used only when things are considered in their totality as a mass.

There was a large *amount* of sand in the grout.

Number refers to things of which the totality can be estimated precisely.

A *number* of people (perhaps seventeen) came to the powerhouse.

Antecedent. See also Pronouns, Antecedents of.

An antecedent is the word or phrase to which a pronoun or a pronominal adjective refers. In informal English, the pronoun sometimes refers to a clause. In formal English, this kind of reference should be avoided.

When the *superintendent* was found, *he* was unconscious.
Although the women stayed on the job, *all the men* went on strike. *They* stayed out fifteen months, supported by their wives and daughters who were still in the plant.
Give me the *files.* I want to examine *their* arrangement.

Any and Its Compounds

Any is used either as a limiting adjective,

Any good man can string that line,

or as a pronoun which implies the existence of a noun.

Any of these will suffice.

The compounds of *any* are confusing because of doubt whether they should be separated or spelled as single words, and whether their pronoun references need be singular or plural.

1. Write *anybody, anyhow, anything,* and *anywhere* as single words; use no hyphen or any other separation.

2. Write *anyone* and *anyway* as one word when the accent falls on *any*. If special emphasis is placed on one person out of many, the words are written separately: *Any one* of the engineers can answer the question.

3. *Anybody* and *anyone* are singular in grammatical form and require a singular pronoun reference and a singular verb.

> *Anybody* who *is* an engineer *realizes* the need for training.

Apostrophe. See Punctuation.

Apposition

Apposition is the placing of a word, phrase, or clause beside another word which means the same thing. The appositive should be in the same case and number and should have the same grammatical value as the word with which it is in apposition.

> John, *the turbine operator,* is not on duty. (In this sentence, *turbine operator* means the same as John and has the same grammatical value.)

Appositives are always set off by commas if they are not essential (non-restrictive) to an understanding of a sentence.

> My work, *doing research on halogens,* is interesting.

If the appositive word is essential to an understanding of the meaning, it is not separated by commas (restrictive).

> *Westinghouse the inventor* was one of our foremost Americans.
> *Westinghouse the citizen* was a benevolent philanthropist.

Article. See also A—An.

The articles in English are classified as follows: *the,* the definite article; *a* and *an,* the indefinite articles. *The* points out a specific person or thing; *a* and *an* have no specific reference.

As. See also Conjunctions.

This word may act as:

1. A conjunction. In this use, it helps in transition; it ties clauses together with a meaning of degree, time, circumstance, or cause.

> Degree: He increased the load *as* far *as* he could.
> Time: He came in *as* I was finishing the article.
> Circumstance: The Chief Engineer was busy *as* the experiment continued.
> Cause: *As* the power load was dropping, he did not think it necessary to stay.

2. An adverb.

All the manufactured apparatus was shipped *as* soon as we could crate it.

3. A preposition,

He worked in the plant *as* a coil-winder.

4. A pronoun.

It was such a problem *as* pleased him.

As . . . as. This form is used in comparisons.

The oil-type breaker is *as* efficient *as* the air breaker.

When a negative comparison is used, *so . . . as* is preferable.

Testing switches is not *so* interesting *as* working in a laboratory.

As though (as if). After these introductory words, use the subjunctive mood when the following statement is contrary to fact.

The boiler acted *as if* it *were* going to explode.

As to. Try to avoid the use of this phrase within the sentence, as it is almost always an awkward and undesirable substitute for *concerning, of,* or *about.*

He spoke *as to* (of) the value of rotary convertors.

Auxiliary Verbs. See also LINKING VERBS.

These are verbs which combine with others to produce a variation in tense, mood, or voice. The commonest of these verbs are *to be, to have* and their several forms.

I *am* coming to work tomorrow.
He *had* decided on a procedure for testing the pump.

Other common auxiliary (helping) verbs are *may, can, must, might, could, would, should, shall, will.*

Because. For incorrect use see WHEN.

Because is used correctly when it denotes the reason for something occurring. It signifies *for the reason that.*

Because I have been ill for five weeks, I must leave work early. I shall play golf *because* I have nothing else to do.

Behind—In Back of

In formal English, *behind* is preferred to the more informal *in back of.*

"He darted *behind* the Buick" instead of "He darted *in back of* the Buick."

Being as—Being that

Being as and *being that* are colloquialisms. Use *since* or *because.*

Beside—Besides

These two words are often confused. *Beside* means *by the side of.* *Besides* means *in addition to.*

> I sat *beside* my secretary, Wilma Green.
> *Besides* seeing the shop foreman and the superintendent, I interviewed the president.

Between—Among. See AMONG—BETWEEN.

Brackets. See PUNCTUATION.

But

But is a coordinate conjunction; that is, it should connect only words, phrases, and clauses of equal grammatical value.

> John went, *but* Henry did not go with him. (*But* here connects two independent clauses.)

But also carries the sense of the two connected parts being in opposition.

> He liked the foreman, *but* the foreman did not like him.

But is a part of the clause which it introduces. If it is necessary to use a comma, it should precede *but.*

> I cannot understand your meaning, *but* I will do my best.

But—Only—Hardly—Scarcely

These words have a negative connotation. Do not use them with another negative.

> WRONG: I *hadn't* but one slide rule.
> RIGHT: I had only one slide rule.

> WRONG: He *wasn't* out of the shop *only* five minutes.
> RIGHT: He was out of the shop only five minutes.

> WRONG: I *don't hardly* (*scarcely*) know what to do about the survey.
> RIGHT: I hardly (scarcely) know what to do about the survey.

Can—May

"*Can* you integrate for this value?" The question here is one of possibility: whether the person addressed is able to perform the operation.

May when used as a verb implies a permission to do some requested action. *Can* indicates an ability to perform some action.

"*May* I ask whether you approve of these union activities?" In such a sentence, the person speaking is asking permission.

Can Not—Cannot

Cannot is the more common form, although sometimes emphasis is gained by the use of *can not*.

Cannot Help But

Because of the double negative, *cannot help but* should be avoided.

> FAULTY: I *cannot* help but smile at the way he handles a chisel.
> RIGHT: I cannot help smiling at the way he handles a chisel.

Capital Letters

Uses:

1. The first letter of a sentence is always capitalized.
   The breaker failed.

2. Proper nouns are always capitalized.
   One of the most famous of nineteenth-century mathematicians was Clark Maxwell.

3. Proper adjectives are always capitalized unless usage has made them so familiar that they are considered as common adjectives.
   He investigated the subject of Roentgen rays.

4. The beginning letter of a direct quotation is always capitalized. If the quotation is broken by other words, the second portion is *not* capitalized.
   John said, "The chlorine gas line is broken," then, after coughing, went on, "and the valve is stuck."

5. The first letter of a line of poetry is usually capitalized.
   "Like a cloud of fire
   The deep blue thou wingest."

This rule is often not true in modern poetry. E. E. Cummings commonly uses small letters throughout his work.

6. Important words in titles of books and articles are capitalized.
   The Dynamo and the Generator
   The Most Famous Story

7. Names of deities are always capitalized. The pronoun references to them are also capitalized if they are worshipped at the present time.
   "My God, why hast Thou forsaken me?"
   Jupiter
   Saviour

8. "Oh" and "I" are always capitalized if "Oh" is considered as an exclamation; "I" as a personal pronoun.

"*Oh, I* am sick to my very soul!"

9. Subjects of study which contain national names (*English* history, *Spanish, German, French*) should always be capitalized. Those subjects that do not refer to national names are not capitalized unless they refer to particular courses in the college catalogue.

I am studing *b*iology, *p*hysics, and *c*hemistry.
I am studying *P*ortuguese, *E*nglish, and *G*erman.
I have on my schedule *P*sychology I, *H*istory III, *A*stronomy I, and *English* I.

Case. See also GENITIVE CASE; NOMINATIVE CASE; OBJECTIVE CASE.

Case represents the various forms taken by nouns and pronouns to indicate their grammatical values within the sentence structure. In English, case is by no means so important as it is in either Latin or Greek, where the form of the noun changes decidedly according to its sentence use.

The English cases are:

1. Nominative: the form taken by a noun or pronoun when it is used as
   a. Subject of a sentence (The *mechanic* fell.)
   b. In apposition with the subject (John, the *mechanic*, fell.)
   c. Complement of a verb or predicate nominative (That man is *John*.)

2. Possessive: the form used to
   a. Indicate ownership (the *mechanic's* hat)
   b. Accompany nouns or pronouns with a gerund (*His* fixing the machine helped to maintain production.)

3. Objective: the case used when the noun or pronoun is
   a. The direct object of the verb (He struck the *mechanic*.)
   b. The object of a preposition (He talked to *him*.)
   c. The object of a verbal (He went to get the *mechanic*.)

Case forms do not vary so extensively for nouns as for pronouns. The cases of the personal pronoun "I" in the singular and plural follow:

	Singular	*Plural*
NOMINATIVE:	*I*	*we*
POSSESSIVE:	*my, mine*	*our, ours*
OBJECTIVE:	*me*	*us*

If the pronoun is to act as subject or as complement (predicate nominative), it requires the nominative case, or *I*. Grammatically, "It is I" is the correct form, although common usage has reduced this to "It's me" in ordinary speech.

Clauses. See also ADJECTIVE CLAUSES; ADVERBIAL CLAUSES; CONDITIONAL CLAUSES; NOUN CLAUSES.

Clauses are usually classified as independent (main) clauses and dependent (subordinate) clauses.

Independent clauses can stand alone and make a complete statement.

Dependent clauses cannot stand alone but depend upon an independent clause for their meaning and fulfill the same functions in the sentence as nouns, adjectives, or adverbs.

> Independent (main) clause: *The freight is always delayed* whenever there is a strike.
> Dependent (subordinate) clause: The freight is always delayed *whenever there is a strike.*

Clipped Words

These are words which usage has shortened from their longer forms. *Taxi* and *taxicab* are clipped forms of *taximeter-cabriolet.* *Ad, phone,* and *bus* are further examples. Sometimes these clipped words, which as a rule are quite correct for informal English, descend to the slang level. Examples are *prof, gents, doc.*

Collective Nouns. See also NOUNS.

These are nouns which, although singular in form, have a plural sense. "An audience," for example, requires a singular verb, although it implies the presence of more than one person, when the writer means the group as a whole. If the writer wishes to refer to the individuals who make up the audience, he should use a plural verb.

College Subject Names. See CAPITAL LETTERS (9).

Colon. See PUNCTUATION.

Comma. See PUNCTUATION.

Comma Fault. See PUNCTUATION.

Common Nouns. See NOUNS.

Compare To—Compare With

One person or thing is *compared to* another person or thing when the first is represented as being similar to, or like, the other. When two persons or things are examined for the purpose of bringing out points of resemblance or difference, they are *compared with* one another.

> He compared the machine to a balky mule.
> He compared the machine shop at Tarentum with that at Sharon.

Comparison (Adjectives and Adverbs)

Adjectives and adverbs are increased or decreased in intensity by the process known as comparison. Comparisons are made in one of three ways: *-er, -est* is added; *more, most* or *less, least* are used; or the word is completely changed in form.

Positive	*Comparative*	*Superlative*
quick	quicker	quickest
fast	faster	fastest
enormous	*more* enormous	*most* enormous
erroneously	*less* erroneously	*least* erroneously
many	more	most
good	better	best

Often adjectives and adverbs may be compared either by the addition of the *-er, -est,* or by the addition of *more, most* or *less, least.* When there is an option, the writer must judge which method will sound better.

Some adjectives represent absolutes. If one is dead, he cannot be "deader," but objects do vary actually in shades represented by such adjectives as "white" and "black." There is no reason why these words should not be compared.

Complement. See PREDICATE ADJECTIVES and NOUNS.

Complex Sentence, Compound Sentence. See "Language Essentials," pages 298–301.

Compound Words. See also DIVISION OF WORDS; PUNCTUATION, HYPHEN.

Compound words are made up of two or more words and often are connected by a hyphen. The only difficulty the student is likely to experience is the question of when to use the hyphen and when to omit it. In general, the rule is:

1. Write as one word, *without* the hyphen, when the word through long usage has come to have little or no meaning if the parts are separated.

airplane	railroad	setscrew
switchboard	drydock	bedplate
substation	however	fireproof

2. If each part of the compound word represents some engineering term commonly used alone, hyphenate the word.

rotary-converter	ton-mile	horsepower-hour
volt-ampere	pound-foot	foot-second
ampere-hour	kilovolt-ampere	acre-foot

3. Cardinal numbers from *twenty-one* through *ninety-nine* should be hyphenated.

4. Ordinal numbers should always be hyphenated.

   forty-ninth; twenty-first

5. Use the hyphen to connect fractional parts, as modifiers.

   three-fourths interest; quarter-inch

6. Use the hyphen when a term originally hyphenated has been abbreviated.

   ft-lb; a-c circuits

7. Use the hyphen to show that the part of a word at the end of a line belongs to the other part which begins the next line.

The best rule to follow is to use the hyphen as little as possible. Unless there is clear sanction for a hyphen, omit it. Look up doubtful hyphenations in the dictionary.

Concrete Nouns. See NOUNS.

Conditional Clauses

Conditional clauses are those which express a state of being or an action necessary to make valid the action of the main clause which follows.

   If the induction regulator operates, the voltage will return to normal.

In this illustration, the second clause is true only if the action occurs which is proposed in the conditional clause which begins the sentence.

Usually conditional clauses are preceded by such words as *if, in the event that, considering that, whether,* and phrases or words of the same general type.

Condition *contrary to fact* is one of the more important uses of the conditional clause.

   If I were the superintendent, I'd fire Hank.

Here the conditional clause indicates a state that is not true, but upon which the following clause is predicated.

Notice that formal usage requires the use of the subjunctive mood in the conditional clause. In informal English, the indicative ("If I *was* . . .") is more often found. Sometimes, rather than expressing a condition contrary to fact, the conditional clause will state a reasonable supposition under which the following clause will hold true.

   If the shop air pressure is up to sixty pounds, the shot blast can be used.

Statements of this sort do not require the subjunctive mood even in formal English.

Conjugation. See VERBS.

Conjunctions. See PARTS OF SPEECH.

Conjunctions vary in meaning. If *but* is used, the clauses usually are opposite in effect. *While* is restricted to a time sense in good writing; *as* is a weak form of *because*. It is a good rule to look up the precise definition of conjunctions.

Conjunctive Adverbs. See ADVERB.

Contact Clauses. See PUNCTUATION, COMMA FAULT.

Contractions

Contractions are devices which save more time in speaking than in writing. A student may as well write out "cannot" as use the shortened form, "can't." The use of contractions tends, however, to make writing far less formal and such use is quite correct under certain circumstances. If the engineer is writing formally, he should not use contractions.

It is necessary to know where to place the apostrophe which signifies the omission of a letter or series of letters in a contraction.

can't	doesn't	won't	weren't	shouldn't
don't	aren't	I'll	they'll	couldn't

Copulative Verbs. See LINKING VERBS.

Correlative Conjunctions. See also AGREEMENT.

The correlative conjunctions *either . . . or, neither . . . nor* connect words, phrases, and clauses of equal rank.

Dangling Modifier. See also PARTICIPLES.

These are modifiers which have been misplaced and are too far removed from the words they modify to be clear.

He walked toward John, *looking at the machines.*

In this example, the modifier (looking at the machines) should be placed at the beginning of the sentence.

It is a point of clarity to allow neither participles, infinitives, clauses, nor phrases to dangle. Placing them as close as possible to the words they qualify will usually overcome this fault.

WRONG: Coming around the corner, the machine was seen.
RIGHT: Coming around the corner, I saw the machine.

Dash. See PUNCTUATION.

Data—Strata—Phenomena

These words are much used by technical men; sometimes they are over-used. Each of these words is a plural form in itself (the singular forms are *datum, stratum, phenomenon*). *Data* has grown to have a collective meaning and so may properly be used with a singular verb.

He collected the *data* which *is* before you.

Many writers still prefer to use *data* with the plural verb. Plural verbs are always used with *strata* and *phenomena*.

Demonstratives

These are either pronouns or adjectives which are used to point out specific nouns or substantives in the sentence. The demonstrative words are *this, that, these, those*.

Those are the things that are not good shop practice.
This is the sort of thing that is not good shop practice.

Dependent Clauses. See also Adverbial Clauses; Adjective Clauses; Conditional Clauses; Noun Clauses; also "Language Essentials," pages 294–297.

These are clauses which in themselves do not contain sufficient meaning to make a complete statement. They should always be supplemented by an independent clause to express a complete meaning.

He decided to go *when the relay tripped out*.

In this sentence, the italicized clause does not of itself state a complete meaning. It must be read in conjunction with the preceding clause for a complete sentence.

Dependent clauses are grouped according to their functions as *noun, adjective*, and *adverb* clauses.

Descriptive Adjectives. See Adjectives.

Different Than—Different From

Standard usage is to write *different from* in almost all cases. *Different than* is sometimes used if it is followed by a clause instead of a single word.

He took a new job on coil-winding that was entirely *different from* his old position.
The coil-winding machine was a good deal *different than* he had expected.

Direct Address

This occurs when a writer or speaker addresses another person or persons by name or by an equivalent designation.

John, go to the tool room and fetch me a new micrometer.
Men, why strike now?

Direct Objects. See OBJECTS.

Ditto

Ditto marks are often used in tabulated lists. In any other type of writing they are out of place.

Division of Words. See also COMPOUND WORDS; PUNCTUATION.

In typing it is often a problem to know precisely where a word should be hyphenated when it is necessary to continue the remainder of it on another line. When it is necessary to hyphenate, break the word between syllables. If there are consecutive vowels, include both before the division is made if they represent separate syllables in themselves. For proper syllabification, consult your dictionary.

Done

The principal parts of the verb *to do* are *do, did, done. Done* must always be used with an auxiliary verb such as *to have* or *to be.* Avoid using *done* for *did.*

> CORRECT: I have *done* the job.
> CORRECT: When he is *done* he may go home.
> INCORRECT: I *done* it yesterday.

Don't

This is the contraction for *do not.* Never use it when you mean *does not.*

> CORRECT: I *don't* know when the district engineer can see you.
> INCORRECT: He *don't* know when he can get to the Chicago plant.
> CORRECT: He *doesn't* know when he can get to the Chicago plant.

Double Negatives

Double negative clauses are those in which two negative particles are employed. They are not used by the educated person in either formal or informal writing or speaking. Contrary to the saying, two negatives do not make a positive.

> INCORRECT: I *didn't* do *nothing.*
> CORRECT: I did nothing.

Due to

This phrase has come to have a prepositional use in informal English. It should not be used in this way in a formal report or paper.

> INCORRECT: *Due to* the continuing backlog of orders, we have decided to increase the personnel of your department.

CORRECT: Because of the continuing backlog of orders, we have decided to increase the personnel of your department.

"Owing to" is a legitimate usage.

Each

When *each* is used as a pronoun, it is considered to be singular, and must employ the singular form of the verb for agreement.

Each of the men *has* his place on the assembly line.

Effect—Affect. For words likely to be confused in meaning, see "Words Often Confused" in "Language Essentials," pages 289–290.

Ellipsis. See PUNCTUATION.

Equally as Good

The *as* is not needed in this expression. *Equally good* is the correct phrase.

Etc.

This abbreviation, meaning "and so forth," is useful to the engineer if it is used in a strictly limited way. It must include meanings of the same class as those previously stated.

He called attention to the types of rotating machines manufactured by the company, such as motors, generators, turbines, rotary converters, *etc.*

Avoid the repetitive and incorrect *and etc.*

Every

In formal writing, *everybody* and *everyone* are grammatically singular and should take singular verbs. In informal speaking, these words are likely to take plural verbs. Even in informal writing (as distinct from conversation) they should be followed by a singular verb.

Everybody starts his machine at the same time.

Exclamation Mark. See PUNCTUATION.

Farther—Further

These words are often used interchangeably, but *further* means an advance in degree, sort, kind, or manner, whereas *farther* means advance in distance.

Figures. See NUMBERS.

Figures of Speech

These are phrases in which an occurrence is described in language which really belongs to another type of description. The engineer should make slight use of figures of speech unless he is writing for a nontechnical group.

> The broken high tension lines snaked across the field, spitting long arcs of blue flame.

Phrasing of this sort is of little value to the engineer when he is writing a factual report. He also incurs the danger of mixing his figures of speech, as:

> It is a sad thing to be killed by the hand which has sworn to protect you and ought to serve you on bended knees.

Fractions

In all tables, fractions are written in Arabic form (½, ¼, etc.). When used in a sentence, or where there are not a large number of figures in the paragraph, they are spelled out (*seven sixty-fourths, thirty-three fifty-sevenths,* etc.). If the engineer needs precision, he should use decimals rather than fractional forms. His slide rule will determine the values quickly. Always precede a decimal with a zero and a point: *0.6529, 0.00115.*

Genitive (or Possessive) Case. See also CASE; PLURALS.

NOMINATIVE	GENITIVE		
	Singular	*Plural*	
dog	dog's	dogs'	Regular
Ralph	Ralph's	Ralphs'	formations
Jones	Jones'	Joneses'	Wording already
Charles	Charles'	Charleses'	ending in *s*

The genitive case of most words which represent inanimate objects is formed by the addition of *of.*

> The lines *of the motor;* the weight *of the box.*

Often the genitives of such words are formed by the addition of the apostrophe and *s* as well, just as the genitives of the first group are sometimes formed by the addition of *of.* In informal English it is quite correct to say, "The *motor's* lines"; "the *box's* weight." One may also refer to "that child of *John's,*" thus using both methods of showing genitive.

Gerund

The gerund is a verbal which has the qualities of both a noun and a verb. It indicates action as a verb; it may also have any of the functions of a noun. Comparatively easy to recognize by its form (all gerunds end in *ing*), it may be confused with the participle. The gerund usually requires the noun or pronoun used with it to be in the possessive case.

The motor's *humming* sounded over the test floor.

In this sentence, *humming*, a gerund, indicates the action of making the noise; it also indicates the name of that action.

Hunting for breaks in the high tension line was his job.

In this example, the gerund acts as the subject of the sentence. Because of its function as a verb, it may also take an object or a predicate complement.

Gerund Phrase. See PHRASES.

Get

Get means to secure, but it is widely used as an auxiliary verb without a great deal of meaning being attached to it. "Have you got armatures in stock?" for instance, asks a question, but the *got* is superfluous. *Gotten* is often looked down on by purists, but it is frequently used informally as the past participle of this verb. In formal writing, however, it is better to use the simple *got* rather than the more unwieldy *gotten*.

Hardly. See BUT; ONLY; SCARCELY.

Have

Like *got, have* has the value of a full verb in its meaning of "to own, to possess." It is also used widely as an auxiliary verb to form the present perfect tense of all verbs: "I *have* come; I *have* succeeded." In this form its meaning is restricted to a time-value word.

He—She

These pronouns in their masculine and feminine forms stand for some noun which has preceded them. The English language has the disadvantage of not having a third personal pronoun which can include both genders; hence when it is necessary to refer with one pronoun to persons of different sex, "he" or "one" is the accepted form.

No teacher can achieve perfection, even if *he* is the best in *his* school.

Here the pronoun "he" may refer to both masculine and femine teachers. In a coeducational school, the same practice is followed in speaking of students.

Every student, be *he* rich or poor, receives the same instruction.

Himself—Herself

These pronouns are properly used in two ways, one of which is to refer to a preceding pronoun.

He told *himself* that the transformer was perfectly safe.

The second use is that of intensifying the preceding noun or pronoun.

I was asleep, and who should come in but the *boss himself.*

However

The main use of *however* is as a connective word. It is valuable as a transition device, but it has little or no meaning in itself.

> The engineer has a duty to mankind; a duty to produce the best that is in him for the benefit of others. It does not follow, *however,* that he is merely a drudge.

However is also used as a simple adverb.

> The lineman is expected to repair the break, *however* bad the weather might be.

Usually, *however* should not be used to begin a sentence; instead, it should take a position within the sentence.

> This problem, *however,* is not too difficult.

Hyphen. See PUNCTUATION; COMPOUND WORDS.

Idiom. See PREPOSITIONS for illustrations of the idiom.

The engineer has a duty to mankind; a duty to produce the best that frequently defies logical explanation. A writer or a speaker sometimes says that he is "possessed by" an idea, or that clerks "wait on" customers. Such idioms use prepositions in a seemingly arbitrary way. A writer has to train himself to remember idioms.

Imperative Mood. See MOOD; VERBS.

In—Into—In to

In usually indicates a place or condition; *into* usually shows the way and indicates a direction.

> He was *in* the shop. (Location; place)
> He went *into* the shop. (Progress toward; direction)

In to, as separate words, represent the adverb *in* plus *to,* which is either a part of an infinitive or a preposition.

> He went *in to* cut the power off the crane.
> He went *in to* eat.

These are both examples of the adverb plus the *to* which begins the infinitive.

> He came *in to* lunch.

If "lunch" is here assumed to be a noun, *to* is the preposition which precedes it.

In Back of. See BEHIND.

Indefinite Pronouns. See PRONOUNS.

Indicative Mood. See MOOD; VERBS.

Indirect Object. See OBJECTS.

Infinitive

The infinitive, like the gerund and the participle, is a verbal. It may act as a combination of verb and noun (*To work* well is a craftsman's aim.) and, as in the example, may be used as a subject. It may possess all the qualities of a noun while still carrying the implication of action, as do almost all verbs. It may also be a combined verb and adverb (He turned *to leave* the switchboard.) and answer the tests of the adverbial questions. (See ADVERBS.) It may also modify a noun or pronoun, as does an adjective. (He has a lot of wiring *to finish*.)

The infinitive is invariably prefaced by *to*, which may be considered as part of it.

The infinitive also takes part in what is called the "absolute" construction. This construction has no grammatical relation to the rest of the sentence.

> *To be sure*, I don't know.
> *To proceed* to a consideration of these matters, I might tell you that we are opening a new plant in Xenia, Ohio, on September 10.

Infinitive Phrase. See PHRASES.

In Regard to—In Regards to

In regards to is an incorrect usage and should not appear in writing.

Intensive Pronouns. See PRONOUNS.

Interjections. See PARTS OF SPEECH.

Interrogative Pronouns. See PRONOUNS.

Intransitive Verbs. See TRANSITIVE VERBS.

Italics

When typing, indicate italics by underscoring. This method is a printer's mark and is commonly used for:

1. Indicating titles of books or periodicals.

Harper's; Rotating Machines.

2. Indicating foreign words and phrases if they are not well known.

Ça va sans dire; comme il faut; ave frater.

3. Showing emphasis. When a single word or perhaps a phrase or a complete sentence appears in italics in a paragraph which is otherwise printed in plain type, it draws the attention of the reader to the italicized portion.

4. Considering words, phrases, or figures under discussion.

In the bulletin on transformers, the phrase *single or three-phase* should be deleted.

Its—It's

It's conveys the meaning of *it is.* It should never be confused with the pronoun whose possessive form *its* does not require an apostrophe.

Kind of—Sort of

Adverbial. The technical writer has little use for these phrases in their adverbial usage. They are about equal to "rather" or "somewhat." They belong to informal English, and should not be used in written communication.

Substantive. These phrases when used as substantives are quite correct, but they apply to classes of objects rather than to individuals.

He was the *sort of* man who would make a good superintendent.
That *kind of* apparatus can be sold at a good profit.

Kind of a, sort of a are common variations of these phrases, but they should be avoided in formal writing. *Those kind* is incorrect.

Lay—Lie

These words are often confused, particularly when they are in past tenses. *Lay* implies no conscious action or volition on the part of the object; it means to "put or place." *Lie*, on the other hand, implies that the action be done by the subject of the sentence; it means to "recline." The principal parts of these two verbs follow:

lie, lay, lain
lay, laid, laid

The two verbs are likely to be confused only in the past tense of *lie* and the present tense of *lay.*

He *lay* down under the test bench to examine the wiring.
I *lay* the anode head on the cloth.

Lie never takes an object. It is an intransitive verb. *Lay*, a transitive verb, always requires that the action be carried over to some object.

Lead—Led

The principal parts of *to lead* are:

lead, led, led.
I *lead* the meeting of the American Society of Mechanical Engineers.
Yesterday I *led* the meeting of the American Society of Mechanical Engineers.

Do not confuse the spelling of the first person present indicative of *to lead* with the past tense, *led*.

Learn—Teach

These are often confused in meaning. As far as a student is concerned, *to learn* is an active process; *to be taught* is passive. A student *learns* a formula; his instructor *teaches* it to him.

He *learned* to wire a transformer in either star or delta.
The test floor instructor *taught* him to wire a transformer in either star or delta.

Less—Fewer

Like *number* and *amount*, the difference between *less* and *fewer* is one that has to do with quantity in the gross, and with number. *Fewer* deals with numbers and things that may be counted.

There are *fewer* people at the meeting than there are in the department.

Here one may count the people; hence *fewer* is the correct term.

He used *less* cement to make the grout than he usually did.

Here the cement is measured, rather than counted; it is an *amount* rather than a *number*.

Let—Leave

Leave means to allow to remain behind, to fail to take. *Let* means to permit, to enable to do.

WRONG: *Leave* the vacuum pump operate to dry the induction regulator.

This sentence shows a common error in the use of *leave*. If *let* were used, the wording would be correct.

RIGHT: *Let* the vacuum pump operate to dry the induction regulator.

But:

> *Leave* your pay in the office to accumulate for the vacation period.
> *Let* the foreman take care of the construction.

Leave is generally used with inanimate objects; *let* is more likely to be used of persons.

Let's

This contraction means "let us," and always requires an apostrophe to indicate that it is a shortened form.

Like—As

Like means similar to or resembling, when used as a conjunction or a preposition; *as* means equally, in the same manner. *Like* is often erroneously used for *as* or *as though:*

> It looks *like* we'll have to work overtime on this job.

Here a clause of probability or comparison is intended, and *as if* or *as though* should take the place of *like*.

Correct usages are:

> He works *as if* his life depended on getting the motor repaired.
> After all, one transformer looks a good deal *like* another.

Likely—Apt—Liable

The student should make a careful differentiation in the meanings of these words.

> Likely: probably, expected
> Liable: responsible legally, exposed to damage
> Apt: suitable, pertinent, quick of understanding and comprehension.

Limiting Adjectives. See ADJECTIVES.

Line

Line may be either a verb or a noun. When used as a noun, it must be used precisely.

"What line of business are you in?" is really equivalent to "What business are you in?" *Line* can be omitted to advantage. *Line* is almost business or industrial slang.

Linking Verbs

The linking, or copulative, verb resembles certain conjunctions and auxiliary verbs in regard to its value in the sentence. It has little or no meaning of its own, but merely serves to connect the parts of the sentence which do carry the information. *Be, become, seem, feel,* and *appear* are among the more common of the linking verbs. Almost any sentence that uses these has its meaning in the subject and the predicate noun or adjective.

"The motor *appeared* burnt out." In this example, "motor" and "burnt out" are the important, meaningful words; "appeared" merely connects them. "The thyratron *is* one of the most useful tubes in modern industry." *Is*, like *appeared* in the previous sentence, does little else than connect the important parts of the sentence.

Lot—A Lot—Lots of

These words are often used in speech, but writing would use their equivalents, "many," "a certain amount."

Main Clause. See CLAUSES.

Man—Woman

Modern usage prefers *man* or *woman* to *gentleman* or *lady* in references to persons unless one wishes to emphasize qualities of gentility or to address an audience. In the latter case, "Ladies and Gentlemen" is customary. Instead of saying, "This is the *gentleman* who designed the relay," it is better to say, "This is the *man* who designed the relay." But in the sentence "He is a *gentleman* in every particular," the writer is focusing on the qualities of gentility.

May—Can. See CAN—MAY.

May Be—Maybe

May be is a verb form only. It cannot act as an adverb.

It *may be* that the condenser will improve the power factor.

The assumption is that possibly the condenser can improve the power factor. *Maybe* is an adverb meaning "perhaps" and implying considerable uncertainty. As in,

Maybe I will attend the convention.

Messrs.

Messrs. is the plural form of *Mr.*

Miss

This title is used to differentiate the unmarried from the married woman. When in doubt as to the marital status of a correspondent, *Miss* should be used. The plural form is *Misses.*

Modifiers

In English the exact meaning of a word may be made clearer by modifiers which are dependent on the word which carries the essential meaning. If one speaks of a piece of dicarta, he may differentiate it from other pieces by a modifier—"It is a piece of *red* dicarta." Modifiers of nouns and pronouns are adjectives and their various forms; verbs are usually modified by adverbs.

Mood. See also VERBS; CONDITIONAL CLAUSES.

Mood is a grammatical term which indicates the manner in which the action or state expressed by the verb is understood by the writer or speaker.

There are three basic moods in English: the *indicative*, the *subjunctive*, and the *imperative*. Of these, the indicative is the commonest. It states a fact or makes a declaration. The subjunctive expresses a condition contrary to fact, a doubt, a wish, or a condition that may be possible. The imperative mood is used to give a command.

> Indicative: He *ground* down the rough surface of the weld.
> Subjunctive: If he *were* to come, the house could be sold.
> Imperative: *Get* the tools from the box.

Moreover

Moreover as a conjunction applies to the engineer's strictly formal writing more than to any other kind. It should not be used unnecessarily, as its effect is ponderous.

Most—Almost. See ALMOST—MOST.

Mr.—Mister; Mrs.—Missis

Mr. is the common form of address usually used before the name of any man to whom you are writing. It should *never* be written in the form *Mister*, although this is the pronunciation. When addressing a feminine correspondent, the same is true of *Mrs.* as opposed to *Missis* or *Missus*.

Neither—Either. See CORRELATIVE CONJUNCTIONS.

No.

When this abbreviation for *number* is used, as before the number of a patent or a motor number, it is capitalized.

> Take motor No. 586731 to the shop.

In engineering writing this is often typed as #586731.

Nobody—Nothing—Nowhere

These are single words and should not be written as "no body," "no thing," or "no where"; nor is a hyphen used between their parts. *Nobody* and *nothing*, being singular, take the singular form of the verb, as in the following illustrations:

> *Nobody* wants that kind of man in his organization.
> *Nothing* comes from *nothing*.
> The letter is to be found *nowhere*.

Nominative Absolute. See PARTICIPLES.

Nominative Case. See also CASE.

Nouns and pronouns which are the subjects of verbs are put in the nominative case. The personal pronouns *I, you, he, she, it, we, you, they* are nominative forms; the relative pronouns *who, which,* and *that* are also nominative.

When parenthetical expressions such as *I think* or *he says* are part of a sentence and follow *who*, be sure to keep the *who* in the nominative case.

> WRONG: He is a trustworthy businessman *whom*, I think, will make an excellent member of the Board of Governors.
>
> RIGHT: He is a trustworthy businessman *who*, I think, will make an excellent member of the Board of Governors.
>
> WRONG: The engineer *whom*, he says, will solve our problem is W. T. Grant, Division Engineer for Koppers.
>
> RIGHT: The engineer *who*, he says, will solve our problem is W. T. Grant, Division Engineer for Koppers.

When a pronoun is the subject of a clause used as the object of a verb or of a preposition, the pronoun is in the nominative case.

> WRONG: Hire *whomever* can run the machine.
>
> RIGHT: Hire *whoever* can run the machine.
>
> WRONG: He had a liking for *whomsoever* could help him attain his goal.
>
> RIGHT: He had a liking for *whosoever* could help him attain his goal.

After conjunctions such as *than* or *as*, use the nominative case.

> He is a better engineer than *I*.
> He is as efficient as *they*.

After forms of the verb *to be* (a linking verb), nouns or pronouns which follow are in the nominative case.

> The president of the company is *he*.
> These are *they*.

None—No One

No one is considered more emphatic than *none*. It is always singular. Modern usage sanctions either the singular or the plural with *none*. The number depends mainly on the meaning of the writer.

> *No one* is to leave this room until the culprit is found.
> *None* of them have found the right solution to the problem.
> I have attempted several methods, but *none* is the right one.

Nonrestrictive Modifiers. See PUNCTUATION, COMMA.

Nouns. See also PARTS OF SPEECH and PREDICATE NOUNS.

Nouns are names of persons, places, things, qualities, actions, or ideas: *George Westinghouse, engineer, Pittsburgh, turbine, virtue, acceleration, calculation.*

The classification of nouns follows:

1. Names of particular people, places, or things are proper nouns. They are always capitalized.

> *George, Helen Keller, Paris, United States, Bay of Fundy, Manual of Style, Declaration of Rights.*

2. Names of members of a group of persons, places, things, or ideas are common nouns and are not capitalized: *man, person, town, machinery, efficiency.*

3. Names of groups or classes considered as units are collective nouns: *crowd, team, group, mob, congregation.*

4. Names of things that can be perceived by any of the senses are concrete nouns: *dynamo, voltmeter, yell, grinding, oiliness, sludge.*

5. Names of things that can be perceived by the intellect alone, especially names of qualities and ideas, are abstract nouns: *acumen, efficiency, steadfastness, faithfulness, honesty.*

Nouns may be used as:

> Subject of a verb: The *machine* stalled.
> Object of a verb: The operator stalled the *machine.*
> Object of a preposition: I called for the *operator.*
> Predicate nominative: The engineer is *Mr. Johnson.*
> Appositive: The engineer, *E. B. Nelson,* diagnosed the trouble.
> Possessive: The *engineer's* hat blew off.
> Adjective: The *design* problems connected with the work are annoying.
> Adverb: *Afternoons* he slept.

Noun Clauses

A clause used as the subject, the direct object, an appositive, a predicate nominative, or the object of a preposition is a noun clause. *That, what, who, whoever, whatever* are words which usually introduce noun clauses.

> Used as subject: *Whatever is,* is right.
> Used as direct object: I trust *that you are satisfied.*
> Used as appositive: The statement, *"These motors are to be shipped tomorrow,"* appears in the letter.
> Used as predicate nominative: You are *what you profess.*
> Used as object of a preposition: I shall ask for *whatever I like.*

Number. See also No.

The grammatical term used to denote whether the writer or speaker is referring to one, or more than one, person or thing. The distinction is usually made by inflection, such as *group, groups; ox, oxen; child, children.*

Number—Amount. See AMOUNT—NUMBER.

Numbers

1. When writing dates, use figures except for social notes, in which dates are written out.

July 10, 1954   September 25, 1954

1st, 3rd, 5th may be used when no year is given with the date. They are not used when the year is given.

2. Use figures when a.m. or p.m. follows.

6 a.m   7 p.m

When the time is written out, write out the numerical designation.

RIGHT: six o'clock   WRONG: 6 o'clock

3. Use figures for street numbers. Do not put a comma between thousands.

6184 Michigan Boulevard   Suite 6, Washington Arms, 6810 Beechwood Boulevard

4. Use numbers for pages and other references to parts of a work.

page 842   pp. 651–723   Chapter 18 (or Chapter XVIII, if the chapter in the work is given in Roman numerals)   Vol. II, p. 649, (for line) 28.

5. Use figures for sums of money.

$182.11 $0.84

Note: Sums in round numbers or sums that can be expressed in two or three words are usually written out, except in a series of sums.

two million dollars   sixty-two

6. Use figures always for statistics or for a series of more than one or two numbers.

There are 283 graduates in electrical engineering, 158 in mechanical engineering, 175 in chemical engineering, and 310 in general engineering.

7. It is general practice to use figures with per cent. (Also, "per cent" normally is spelled out.)

Labor turnover in the plant only varied occasionally from a steady 17–19 per cent.

8. Use figures always for order numbers, numbers on machinery, or numbers used for any specific trade designation.

Order No. 185362 Motor No. S186325
Trade Bulletin No. 162
or
Order #185362 Motor #S186325

9. Avoid beginning a sentence with a figure. Spell out the initial figure.

Five to 10 per cent of all the machines were found to be defective; another 10 to 15 per cent did not operate efficiently.

Usually a writer can arrange his sentence so that he need not begin it with a figure written out. This practice is recommended.

10. Plurals of figures are formed by adding *s* or *'s* to the figures.

Eight 6s, eight 6's

11. In any series of figures involving fractions, write the fractions as figures. In expository writing when only one or two fractions occur, write out the fraction (or fractions).

He had to order the following items:
500 filing cards 6½ in. by 4¾ in.
1000 notation cards 8¾ in. by 3½ in.
50 reams of 8½ in. by 11 in. second sheets

12. Figures are used throughout in graphs, charts, and tables.

Objective Case

Nouns or pronouns used as objects of verbs or of prepositions are in the objective case.

The mechanic fixed the *machine.*
The president called *him* into the office.
The engineer asked for *help.*
He walked into *it.*

The subject of an infinitive is in the objective case.

The foreman asked *him* to be chief helper. (*Him* is the subject of the infinitive *to be.*)
The manager *whom* I thought to be the president was arrogant. (*Whom* is the subject of the infinitive *to be.*)

The predicate substantive completing an infinitive is also in the objective case.

He thought the Division Engineers wanted to find *him.* (*Him* is the predicate substantive which completes *to find.*)

Objects

1. *Direct object:* Any noun or pronoun that receives the action of a transitive verb is its direct object.

Sanders adjusted the *voltmeter.*
He asked *what was needed.* (The whole clause is the direct object.)

2. *Indirect object:* A noun or pronoun which is indirectly affected by the action of the verb is the indirect object. It usually precedes the direct object unless it is used with a preposition, such as in the sentence "I gave the book to *John.*" *Book* takes the direct action of the verb; *John* is indi-

rectly affected by the action of the verb. The common form would be: "I gave John the book."

> He offered the *engineer* a slide rule. (*Slide rule* is the direct object; *engineer*, the indirect object.)

3. *Object of a preposition:* The word, phrase, or clause whose relationship to the rest of the sentence is shown by a preposition is the object of the preposition.

> He walked over to the *engineer*. (*Engineer* is the object of *to*.)
> He was related to *a few officials*. (The phrase *a few officials* is the object of *to*.)
> He relied on *what I told him*. (The clause *what I told him* is the object of *on*.)

Of—Off

Avoid using *of* in place of *have* in verb phrases.

> WRONG: I could of done it.
> RIGHT: I could have done it.

Off of is an unnecessary doubling of prepositions. Use *off* by itself.

> WRONG: He took the specifications *off of* the shelf.
> RIGHT: He took the specifications *off* the shelf.

One. See also VIEWPOINT.

1. Usually the impersonal pronoun *one* can be avoided in writing. The use of a specific name or of *I* or *you* is preferable. The repetition of *one* is too formal for present-day style.

> *One* must be careful if *one* wants to be accurate in all things.

Use *he* to refer to *one* in a sentence of this sort.

> *One* must be careful if *he* wants to be accurate in all things.

2. When *one* is used in a phrase it often can be omitted.

> The blueprint was an unusual one.
> The blueprint was unusual.

3. When *one* is used in combination with *any-, every-, some-* to make an indefinite pronoun, it is written as one word: *anyone, everyone, someone.* If the writer wishes to emphasize *one*, he writes these combinations as two words, as *some one of the motors*.

> *Anyone* can solve the problem.
> *Any one* of the four engineers will be satisfactory.
> *Everyone* knows he is president.
> *Every one* in the group was surprised.

One of Those Who

After the expression "one of those who," the clause which follows takes the plural verb.

> He is one of those engineers who *read* a number of technical journals. (The reference for *who* is *engineers*.)
> It is one of the journals which *explain* technical processes in simple language. (*Which* refers to *journals*.)

Only

Although *only* should be placed before the word or phrase it modifies, there are many instances in which this order should be changed for proper emphasis. The following sentence has the *only* in its most logical position.

> The engineer lacks *only* three more sales to reach his monthly quota.

On the other hand, the order of this sentence could be changed to read:

> The engineer *only* lacks three more sales to reach his monthly quota.

In informal speech and writing, the meaning of the two sentences is practically unchanged.

Sometimes *only* is so restrictive in meaning that it can be placed in only one position.

> During his interview with the vice president, the engineer asked for *only* $7,000 per year.

Placing *only* before the verb is a careless usage in speech and in writing.

> Actually we *only* want to stay five minutes.
> The techniques needed can *only* be acquired after much study and practice.

Adverbs like *even, ever, nearly, just, exactly* have to be used as prescisely as *only*. If they are misplaced they, too, can spoil the emphasis which the writer needs. Like *only*, they may stand before the verb.

Onto—On To

When *onto* is a preposition it is written as one word.

> The engineers dashed *onto* the desert.

If *on* is used as an adverb and *to* as a preposition, they should be written separately.

> The golf champion drove *on to* an ultimate victory.

Paid—Payed

The principal parts of the verb *to pay* are *pay, paid, paid*. As a past tense, *payed* is used only in *he payed out a line, rope*, etc. Even in this usage *paid* is common.

Pair

The plural of *pair* in greatest use is *pairs*. After a number the form *pair* is correct according to business usage.

Eight *pair* of telephone lines.

Parallel Constructions

When a writer wants to establish the similarities which exist between statements that have a direct relationship to the main part of the sentence, he puts those statements in the same grammatical structure. This is known as parallelism. It is an excellent device for making parts of an idea emphatic.

> The engineer wanted *to establish his main thesis, to analyze it into its logical parts,* and *to make each part effective by citing relevant illustrations.* (Note: The parallelism is kept by having a series of infinitive phrases: *to establish, to analyze, to make.*)
> I want to know *what you are going to do to solve the problem, what means you will use to gather your data,* and *what method you will employ in analyzing the data.* (Note that the series of *what* clauses keeps the structure parallel.)
> The engineer *should know his special field thoroughly, have a general knowledge of allied engineering fields,* and *read widely outside his specialty.* (Note: Here the repetition of verb forms, *should know,* (*should*) *have,* (*should*) *read,* keep the parallelism.)

Failure to keep parallelism is a violation of good English usage. Examine the following sentence for lack of parallelism.

> The engineer *wanted to establish* his main thesis, *analyzing* it into its logical parts, and *hoped* to make each part effective by citing relevant illustrations.

The illustration "First the *engineer* set up his tripod and then *you* know he is ready to mount his transit" is a violation in parallelism because the point of view is shifted from "engineer" to "you."

In the sentence "*I* believe the engineer's position in modern society is more important than it was even twenty years ago, and *one* can observe this by looking at the accomplishments of engineers," there is a different violation of parallelism. The writer has gone from the personal "I" to the impersonal "one." Keep the same pronoun point of view.

In the following illustration the writer has passed from the active to the passive voice: "The students *ran* onto the field and a little later *were to be seen* tearing down the goal posts." It should read: "The students *ran* onto the field and a little later *tore* down the goal posts."

In a sentence like "First *check* the electrical system and then you *should find* out whether the carburetor is in good working order," the writer has changed from the imperative mood to the conditional. The imperative, once it starts the sentence, should be kept consistently. "First *check* the electrical system and then *find out* whether the carburetor is in good working order."

Outlines particularly require parallel structure. See "Language Essentials," pages 267–270.

Parenthesis. See PUNCTUATION.

Participial Phrases. See PHRASES.

Participles

Participles are verbal adjectives. They modify nouns or pronouns. Avoid confusing the present participle ending in *-ing* with the verbal noun (gerund), which also ends in *-ing*. (See GERUND.) The endings of the past participle are *ed, d, t, en, n.* In verbs like *go, went, gone,* the form of the past participle is irregular.

> Present Participles: *machining, welding, working, fixing, lining*
> Past Participles: *machined, lost, risen, set*

These participles are used as parts of verb phrases.

> I am *machining*. He is *welding*. I have been *fixing* the machine.
> I have *machined* the piece. I had *lost* the nut.
> He is *risen*. The rings have been *set*.

Since participles are verbal adjectives, they must modify clearly some noun or pronoun.

> *Sitting* on the crane, I looked over the machine shop. (In this instance, *sitting* clearly modifies the subject *I*.)
> *Considered* from the standpoint of efficiency, the electric locomotive is more satisfactory than the diesel locomotive. (*Considered* properly modifies *electric locomotive*.)

When participles modify the wrong noun or pronoun, they are called dangling participles.

> *Sitting* on the crane, the machine shop looked like a disorganized place to me. (Obviously, the machine shop cannot be sitting in this instance.)
> *Considered* from the standpoint of efficiency, I find that the electric locomotive is more satisfactory than the diesel locomotive. (Here *considered* modifies *I* and is not accurate in reference.)

Uses of the participle as a verbal adjective are found in the following sentences:

> The men *walking* in the street often talked about the coming strike.
> The *coming* Utopia in the United States will give every man security.
> The tool *used* in this operation is the best for the job.

In the sentences above, the participle always modifies a noun or a pronoun.

Try not to overuse participles. Unfortunately, many writers use participles in places where main verbs would be preferable.

POOR: The engineer was one of our best, *making* us hope not to lose him.

BETTER: Since the engineer was one of our best, we hoped not to lose him.

POOR: He *being* our most experienced workman, we let him try to do the job.

BETTER: Since he was our best workman, we let him try to do the job.

In absolute phrases—phrases which relate to the whole sentence rather than to a particular word or phrase in the sentence—participles are often used. These should not be confused with the participle as verbal adjective.

Generally *speaking*, we consider him a reliable man.
Judging from his actions, he is the most radical fellow in the shop.

A noun or pronoun followed by a participle is known as a *nominative absolute*.

The foreman having ended his talk, the men filed back to work.
The welders having been dismissed, there was talk of a strike.

Parts of Speech. See also NOUNS; PRONOUNS, etc.

A part of speech is the name of that classification under which a word is placed according to its use in the sentence. The technical man cannot hope to find out what is wrong with his writing unless he knows how to recognize the parts of speech.

In the English language, there are eight parts of speech. Often a word cannot be classified unless the writer knows the grammatical function of the word (whether it is subject, object, modifier, etc.), its meaning (whether it names something or describes something), or its form (the *'s* to signify the genitive—possessive—or the *er* to denote the comparative of an adjective).

Nouns—These are name words, names of people, places, things, qualities, ideas: *James Watt, New York, generator, noise, calculation.*

Pronouns—These are words which stand in place of nouns and refer to them: *I, she, he, it, we, they, someone, which.*

Adjectives—These are words which describe, limit, or qualify a noun or a pronoun: *greasy, dirty, both, hot, earnest, Georgian.*

Verbs—These are words which state actions, states of being, emotions, conditions, etc.: *charged, electrocuted, hated, am, were, become.*

Adverbs—These are words which limit the meaning of verbs, adjectives, or other adverbs. They tell how, when, where, why, to what degree an action was performed: *quickly, well, swiftly, then, more.*

Prepositions—These are words which relate nouns and pronouns to other words in the sentence: *by, at, in, behind, after, within.*

Conjunctions—These are connecting words which link words, phrases, or clauses. There are two kinds: coordinating conjunctions which join words, phrases, and clauses equal in rank; subordinating conjunctions which join subordinate clauses to main clauses.

The principal coordinating conjunctions are: *and, but, for, or, nor, either . . . or, neither . . . nor.*

The principal subordinating conjunctions are: *after, as, although, because, before, in order that, since, unless, until, when, whenever, while, wherever.*

Interjections—These are words which express strong emotion or feeling: *Help! Heavens! Bravo! Hurrah!*

Passed—Past

The principal parts of the verb *to pass* are:

Infinitive	*Past Tense*	*Past Participle*
pass	passed	passed

Past is used as an adjective, an adverb, or a preposition.

As adjective: *past* communications
As adverb: He walked *past.*
As preposition: He went *past* the door.

Passive Voice. See also VERBS.

Untrained writers use the passive voice too often. Active voice is usually more effective. "The nut was tightened by the engineer" is not so economical or emphatic as "The engineer tightened the nut."

In active voice, the subject performs the action.

In passive voice, the subject is acted upon. Notice the following examples of passive voice:

The turbine *was put* into the warehouse.
Many activities of the workmen *could be seen* from the window.
The Bunsen burner *was placed* on the laboratory table.

Use the passive voice when the thing acted upon is more important than the actor.

Per

Since *per* is borrowed directly from Latin (*per* has the meaning of *through, by, among*), it should be used in phrases which are closely related to their Latin sources: *per cent, per annum.* It is also used in business phrases: Twenty dollars *per* day; forty hours *per* week. In technical writing, it is quite proper to talk about "revolutions *per* minute." Avoid using *per* in noncommercial or nontechnical writing.

Per Cent

This may be written as either one or two words. Do not use a period after *cent.*

Period. See PUNCTUATION.

Person. See also VERBS.

Verbs and pronouns change their form to designate first person (the person speaking); second person (the person spoken to); third person (the person or thing spoken about).

First person: *I* called the mechanic.
                We called the mechanic.
Second person: *You* called the mechanic.
Third person: *He* (or she) called the mechanic.
                It fell on me.
                They asked for water.

English verbs have only one form to distinguish person. This is the third person singular:

I grease.	We grease.
You grease.	You grease.
He greases.	They grease.

Personal Pronouns. See PRONOUNS.

Phenomena. See DATA.

Phrases

Groups of words which have no subject or predicate but which form a functional unit in the sentence are phrases. They are most important to the sentence because they express fine shades of thought. The subject, the verb, or the object may be a phrase, as in the sentence *"Engineers in college have heard the challenge of their older brothers in the profession."* "Engineers in college" is a phrase which forms the complete subject; "have heard" is a verb phrase which makes the complete predicate; "the challenge of their older brothers in the profession" is the complete object.

Phrases are classified as follows:

1. *Prepositional phrases*—These begin with a preposition: *in the shop, by the machine, on the locomotive, into the office.*
2. *Infinitive phrases*—These begin with an infinitive: *to go in comfort, to live with others.*
3. *Participial phrases*—These begin with a participle: *going home, buying a car, locked in the machine.*
4. *Gerund phrases*—These result from a gerund and a modifying phrase: *Driving into town* is a luxury.
5. *Verb phrases*—These are formed by an auxiliary verb and a participle: *have greased, am running.*

Phrases have different functions in the sentence and are used just as single parts of speech would be used.

Noun phrases	—*The first ball was fast.* (Used as subject.)
	He pitched *a fast ball.* (Used as object.)
	He gave the book *to the engineer.* (Used as indirect object.)
	He saw the girders *of the bridge.* (Used as genitive.)
Verb phrases	—I *have solved* many problems. I *will go* with you.
Adjective phrases	—The problem *of the day* is to make six drawings. *Catching the wire,* he drew it taut.
Adverbial phrases	—He worked *beyond his capacity.* He performed the job *in approved fashion.* He is going *in the morning.*

Prepositional phrases—*in place of, in spite of, in view of, in order to, in regard to.*

Plenty

Plenty should not be used as an adverb, as in the sentences "He was plenty mad" or "The machine is plenty efficient." In very informal speech this use is accepted.

Plurals

1. Plurals of most nouns are formed by adding *s* or *es* to the singular form of the noun. Add *es* if the plural forms an extra syllable.

engineer	engineers
pinch	pinches
machine	machines
winch	winches
locomotive	locomotives
dash	dashes

Some words ending in *s* have the same form for the plural as for the singular.

mathematics   morals   ethics   (and all words ending in *-ics*)

2. Nouns ending in *y* preceded by a consonant change the *y* to *i* and add *es*.

supply	supplies
caddy	caddies
cry	cries

For irregular plurals, the student should consult a reliable dictionary.

Possessive Case. See also GENITIVE CASE.

This is the case in English (Latin, genitive) that is used to show possession. The commonest way of forming this case consists of the addition of an apostrophe, either before or following an "s."

Predicate. See also VERBS.

The predicate of a sentence is the word or words which express what is said about the subject.

> The welder *insulted* his helper.
> The helper *has been insulted.*

A compound predicate consists of two verbs which are dependent upon the same subject.

> The engineer *kicked* the casting and *swore.*

Predicate Adjectives and Nouns

Nouns or adjectives which complete the meaning of a linking verb are called predicate nouns or predicate adjectives. Either a predicate noun or a predicate adjective is called a subjective complement.

> *Predicate adjective*—He is *peculiar.* He feels *bad.* He becomes *ill.*
> *Predicate noun*—He is *president.* Nelson became a licensed *engineer.*

Prepositional Phrase. See PHRASES.

Prepositions. See also PARTS OF SPEECH.

Prepositions show the relation of a noun or a pronoun to some other word or words in the sentence. The noun or pronoun following the preposition is the object of the preposition.

A selected list of prepositions follows: *about, above, across, after, against, along, among, around, at, as far as, back of, before, below, beside, between, by, concerning, down, for, from, in, in place of, in spite of, into, like, near, of, off, on account of, onto, over, since, through, to, toward, under, until, unto, up, upon, via, with,* and *within.*

Note: Some prepositions are also used as conjunctions, such as *after, before, since,* etc. If conjunctions, they are followed by a subject and a predicate.

Prepositions are often used in idiomatic expressions. Be sure that you use the right preposition with an idiom.

Incorrect Idioms	*Correct Idioms*
abhorrence for	abhorrence of
acquitted from	acquitted of
adverse against	adverse to
aim at proving	aim to prove
all the farther	as far as
all-around	all-round
among one another	among themselves
angry at (a person)	angry with
anyplace	anywhere

Incorrect Idioms	Correct Idioms
as regards to	as regards
blame it on him	blame him for it
cannot help but say	cannot help saying
comply to	comply with
conform in (a principle)	conform to, with
correspond with (a thing)	correspond to
desirous to	desirous of
die with	die of
different than	different from
equally as bad	equally bad
feel of	feel
have got to	must
identical to	identical with
in accordance to	in accordance with
independent from	independent of
inside of a year	within a year
kind of a	kind of
listen at (music)	listen to
no doubt but that	no doubt that
oblivious to	oblivious of
over with	over
plan on going	plan to go
remember of	remember
stay to home	stay at home
superior than	superior to
there is no doubt but that	there is no doubt that
unequal for	unequal to
very interested	very much interested
vie against	vie with
want in (off, out)	want to get in (off, out)
where are you at?	where are you?

Although it was considered inappropriate until recently to end a sentence with a preposition, modern usage sanctions this unless the preposition at the end results in awkwardness. Sometimes the attempt to put the preposition within the sentence causes unnecessary formality, as in "What is it to which you object?" rather than "What is it you object to?" The writer must base his final judgment on whether the sentence reads more naturally, easily, and clearly with the preposition at the end or in the body of the sentence.

Present Tense. See TENSES.

Principal Parts. See VERBS.

Consult a good dictionary for the principal parts of any verb about which you may be in doubt.

Professor

Avoid clipping this word to *prof.*, except in very informal conversation. On an envelope and in a letter, the word should be written out unless the professor's name is long. Always give the professor's initials as well as his last name.

> Professor E. T. Weatherby
> Head, Department of Chemistry

Pronouns. See also PARTS OF SPEECH.

DEFINITION: A pronoun is a word used in place of a noun.

ANTECEDENT: The noun to which the pronoun refers is called its antecedent. Since the pronoun itself names no specific person or thing, it gets its meaning from the antecedent, as in "The Industrial *film* 'Coal' is too long. *It* bores our customers."

REFERENCE OF PRONOUNS: Be sure that the antecedent of each pronoun is clear to your reader.

> *Men* who work in machine shops are in constant danger. *They* may be maimed unless *they* are careful. (*Men* is the antecedent of *they*.)
> The *shop* closed for the duration of the war. *It* reopened after the proclamation of an armistice. (*Shop* is the antecedent of *it*.)

The beginning writer often places a pronoun in such a position that the reader is unable to tell what it refers to.

1. The pronoun may have no antecedent.

> Engineering is the most interesting subject in school. That is why I want to be *one*.

In the example above, *one* has no preceding word for reference. The sentence can be corrected by changing the pronoun so that it has a proper reference or by using the word "engineer."

> *Engineering* is the most inteersting subject in school. That is why I chose *it*.
> Engineering is the most interesting subject in school. That is why I want to be *an engineer*.

2. The pronoun may have an ambiguous reference.

> He passed the gate of the stadium *which* was just above the Chemistry Building.

Here *which* may refer to either *gate* or *stadium*. The sentence may be corrected by clarifying the reference.

> He passed the stadium gate *which* was just above the Chemistry Building.

3. In formal writing, the pronouns *you* and *they* should not be used in the indefinite sense.

INCORRECT: I noticed the unrest in the shop. *You* could feel it.
CORRECT: I noticed the unrest in the shop. *It* could be felt.

INCORRECT: *They* say that the shop will go on strike tomorrow.
CORRECT: *It* is said that the shop will go on strike tomorrow.

KINDS OF PRONOUNS:

1. **Personal Pronouns.** The personal pronouns are *I, thou, you, he, she, it,* and their inflexional forms.
2. **Demonstrative Pronouns.** The demonstrative pronouns are *this, that, these, those.* They point out specific persons or things.
3. **Interrogative Pronouns.** The interrogative pronouns are *who, which, what.* They are used to introduce direct questions. *Whoever* and *whatever* are sometimes used as interrogative pronouns.
4. **Relative Pronouns.** The relative pronouns are *who, which, that,* and the compounds *whoever, whichever,* etc.
5. **Reflexive Pronouns.** The reflexive pronouns are *myself, yourself, herself, himself,* etc. The action of the verb is directed back to the subject by these pronouns, as in "*I* went *myself.*"
6. **Indefinite Pronouns.** The indefinite pronouns are *any, anyone, some, someone, no one, nobody,* etc.
7. **Intensive Pronouns.** The intensive pronouns are *myself, yourself, himself, herself,* etc. They put additional stress on the subject, as in "I *myself* did it."
8. **Reciprocal Pronouns.** The reciprocal pronouns are *each other* and *one another.*

AGREEMENT OF PRONOUNS:

1. Agreement in number. If the antecedent of a pronoun is singular, the pronoun must be singular; if the antecedent is plural, the pronoun must be plural.

The *manager* lost his wallet. *He* offered a reward for its return.
The *strikers* battled valiantly; *they* lost.

Use singular pronouns to refer to *each, every, either, neither, someone, somebody, anyone, anybody, everyone, everybody, no one, nobody.* Notice the reference for *everybody* in the following sentence: "*Everybody* has been assigned *his* seat for the game." Avoid using a plural pronoun to refer to *everybody* in formal English. The reference to *everyone* in the sentence following is typical of the references to the pronouns named above: "*Everyone* in the plant has *his* button."

2. Agreement in person. Pronouns agree with their antecedents in person as well as number.

I asked the personnel manager to give *me* a reference.
You wanted a reference for *your* new employer.
She asked for *her* reference.

DECLENSION OF PERSONAL AND RELATIVE PRONOUNS.

PERSONAL

	Singular	*Plural*
Nom.	I	we
Poss. (Gen.)	my, mine	our, ours
Obj.	me	us
Nom.	you	you
Poss. (Gen.)	your	your, yours
Obj.	you	you
Nom.	he, she, it	they
Poss. (Gen.)	his, her, hers, its	their, theirs
Obj.	him, her, it	them

RELATIVE

Nom.	who	who
Poss. (Gen.)	whose	whose
Obj.	whom	whom

Proper Names

In business letters and personal correspondence, the technical man should take pains to spell out proper names according to the spelling used by the person (or persons) concerned. Check names of people carefully, since the average man is proud of his name. The same care should be taken with names of companies and corporations, names of institutions, and names of places. Only a careless writer guesses at these things.

Proper Nouns. See NOUNS.

Proposition

Try not to use this word too often. Aim for a substitute which will be more accurate: *proposal, plan, offer, business transaction.*

Proved—Proven

The past participle *proved* is preferred to *proven.*

Punctuation

Before the invention of printing, there were comparatively few marks of punctuation used in manuscripts. Material was written in block form; consequently, the reading of a manuscript was difficult. Today, we have a well-defined system of punctuation. We not only mark off our writing into large units called paragraphs, but we have a system of marks which help to show the relationship between parts of the sentence, or which set off parts of an idea for special emphasis. These marks make communication more efficient.

In the first part of this century, punctuation marks were scattered liberally throughout writing. Today, the trend is toward economy in their use. The careful writer will set down a mark of punctuation only when it is necessary for clarifying thought. When he revises his manuscript, he will check to find out whether his punctuation is accurate in this sense.

Many publishing houses have style books which set the standard for punctuation of all printed material. Essentially, these books are in agreement concerning the use of punctuation marks. Their differences are usually minor.

A check of the practices advocated by editors and publishers reveals that there are two systems of punctuation: open and close punctuation. The general trend is toward open punctuation, in which as few marks as possible are used. Close punctuation uses many marks which are not vital to the clarity of the communication. The result is often a slowing down of the movement of the sentence. For instance, it is optional whether one puts "After he had greased the motor, he sat down to rest" or "After he had greased the motor he sat down to rest." The omission of the comma does not result in ambiguity; it gives the sentence faster tempo and makes the reader feel the unity of the thought being transmitted. One could write "Men, machines, and power are vital forces in modern society" or "Men, machines and power are vital forces in society." This last rendering is just as clear as the first and does away with a comma which is actually unnecessary. These practices are optional. The main thing to remember is that whether the writer chooses the open or the close system, he should be consistent. In formal writing, of course, close punctuation is often adhered to. This type of writing frequently is complex in style. For a simple style, open punctuation is best. The authors of this book have chosen to use a moderately close punctuation. The student can make his own choice according to his preference and the best practice in the technical journals.

Apostrophe. See also GENITIVE (or POSSESSIVE) CASE. The apostrophe has two main uses. The first is to indicate possession; the second is to indicate an omission. It is also used with the plural of figures and quoted words.

> *John's* work—the work belonging to John.
> The *corporation's* building.

1. In most cases, the plural possessive is indicated by placing the apostrophe in the space after the *s*. When the singular of the word ends in *s* the apostrophe is placed after it to indicate singular possession; the plural is often formed by the addition of the apostrophe after *es*.

> *Burns'* work on turbines, or *Burns's* work on turbines.

2. In indicating an omission.

> He *can't* start the diesel. They *won't* have the drawing done.

3. The apostrophe is used to show plurals of letters, words, and dates which are being spoken or written about.

They met in the middle *1930's*. The second of two *that's*.

The apostrophe is *never* used to indicate the possessive case of pronouns. Incorrect: *It's*—belonging to it. Instead, write *its*.

Brackets. In business and professional writing, brackets are used to enclose comments and explanations inserted by the editor or to point out errors in material written by another. They are to be used judiciously.

1. Editorial explanation: The reason [for the power failure] was that someone had fired several bullets from a high-powered rifle through the transformer.

2. Author's insertion: The union leader [George Morgan] was considered one of the most stubborn men in labor's ranks.

3. Insertion of *sic* to show that an odd spelling or an actual mistake in the text appeared thus in the original document from which a quotation is made: "George Westinhouse [*sic*] contributed his scientific research; his friends gave their money to finance his experiments."

Colon. The colon, consisting of two periods, one above the other (:), is a mark that indicates almost as complete a stop as a single period. It is often used by the engineer (1) to preface tabulated data: "The various elements are placed in three tables, as follows:"; (2) to introduce an extended quotation; (3) to separate clauses when the second is merely a restatement of the first: "Let me restate my point: if the sine curve indicates a voltage of less than 660, the machine will not operate."; (4) to separate the hours and minutes when these are written in figures: "11:23 a.m."; (5) to salute the reader or readers of a letter: "Dear Mr. Jones:", "Gentlemen:".

Usually the colon is followed by a small letter, although some writers prefer to begin with a capital after using a colon.

Comma. The most commonly used mark of punctuation is the comma. Since it occurs so frequently in writing and is often optional, it is the mark which gives untrained writers most trouble. Its misuse leads to costly errors. Business firms have been involved in expensive legal proceedings through carelessness of employees in including or omitting commas in documents. Every day newspapers print sentences which amuse their readers because of the mishandling which the comma has received.

In spite of the minor variations in customary uses of the comma, there are a few rules which can be learned from the practice of the best writers and editors.

1. The comma is used to separate long coordinate clauses connected by *and, but, for, or,* or *nor.*

    a. I went for the set of blueprints in the morning, *and* in the afternoon I had to go back for another set.

b. I like the average engineering student's willingness to work hard on his studies, *but* I admire still more his determination to extend his usefulness as a human being.

c. The outstanding engineer likes to see his ideas published, *for* they represent the best part of his life crystallized in words.

Warning. Do not confuse coordinate clauses with the parts of a compound predicate. These are not ordinarily separated by a comma.

> *Example:* The engineer *directed* his workmen to fill in the ditches and *told* the foreman to have the job completed by August 1.

2. The comma is used to separate a long subordinate clause or a long phrase from the main clause which follows.

a. After the engineer had given his orders to the workmen and had talked to a few of them, he drove home.

b. Before you choose engineering as a profession and commit yourself to it, analyze your capabilities to make sure that you are a fit candidate.

c. In talking to any practicing engineer, try to find out the qualities which have made him successful.

d. By paying strict attention to the rules of punctuation and by checking your sentences in revision, you will save yourself trouble.

Exceptions: If the clause or the phrase which precedes the main clause is short and if the main clause itself is short, the comma may be omitted *if its omission does not result in ambiguity.* This is one instance of open punctuation.

a. If you go to Pittsburgh take me with you.

b. After the job is done I will go to Detroit.

c. By going to New York you will be able to see the President.

d. While racing to Bill's rescue the electrician slipped and fell.

In the following examples the comma cannot be omitted without causing the reader to misread the sentence:

a. As he ate and ate, the boss felt that he could never satisfy his hunger.

b. Because of his eagerness to start, the president almost went without his brief case.

c. At the moment of leaving, the students cheered the coach.

3. The comma is used to separate words, phrases, and clauses in a series. When *and* joins the last two members, conservative practice puts a comma before the *and*.

a. There was a jumble of flywheels, nuts, bolts, and screws on the floor.

b. He bothers me in the field, in the office, and even in my car on the way home.

c. Because I know the procedures to be followed, because I am well acquainted with all the technical details, and because I have a comprehensive view of the problems which business faces today, I am always called upon to do the more difficult jobs.

Note: Writers who favor open punctuation omit the comma before the *and* which joins the last two members of the series, providing that no misreading of the sentence will result.

a. There was a jumble of flywheels, nuts, bolts and screws on the floor.

b. He bothers me in the field, in the office and even in my car on the way home.

Under the following conditions semicolons are used to separate members of the series: (1) if each is long; (2) if one or more have commas within them; (3) if the members are not closely connected in thought.

The engineer, he was told, reads history because he wants to increase his general knowledge; likes biography because, since he wants to be successful, he is eager to know what made the subject of the biography outstanding; enjoys music because it gives him complete relaxation.

4. Nonrestrictive modifiers are set off from the rest of the sentence by a comma or, if the modifier comes within the sentence, by commas. Such modifiers usually add information or descriptive detail to the sentence. If this material were to be omitted, it would not change the basic meaning of the sentence. The italicized material in the following sentences is nonrestrictive:

a. Mr. A. E. Edwards, *who was visiting the Chicago office last week,* will be in the New York office next Tuesday.

b. Arthur Braun, *deceased employee of the company,* was careless in his bookkeeping.

c. The Division Engineer was moved to Philadelphia, *which happens to be his native city.*

d. The engineer, *especially as the general public pictures him,* is supposed to be a man without much aesthetic appreciation; but this judgment does not do him justice.

e. One engineer, *who said he had been with the company for twenty-five years,* refused to sign the petition.

5. Restrictive modifiers limit the meanings of words in such a way that their omission from the sentence would change its basic meaning; consequently, they are never set off by a comma or commas.

a. The engineer *who is particularly harsh with his men* is George Hicks.

b. Economic changes *which result in bettering the lot of the average man* are good.

c. He knew how to handle customers *with the least possible amount of ceremony.*

6. Commas should set off parenthetical words and phrases like *naturally, of course,* etc.

 a. I need not tell you, *of course,* that he is our best salesman.
 b. You are to go, *naturally,* as soon as possible.
 c. He is a man who, *strangely enough,* prefers to work alone.

Phrases and clauses which cause the reader to pause and thus interrupt the movement of a sentence are set off by commas.

 a. The President said, *if I heard him aright,* that I was fired.
 b. My work with Westinghouse, *if it has revealed nothing more,* has shown me my errors.
 c. My plan, *therefore,* is to attend the convention of the American Chemical Society.

Note: Sentences which begin with *and, but,* or *yet* should have no comma following such opening words. They are an integral part of the whole sentence.

7. Commas should always be used to clarify a sentence which might be misread without the use of some mark (or marks) of punctuation.

 a. When the motors stopped, the workmen telephoned the Chief Engineer. (Without the comma, *workmen* might be taken as the object of the verb *stopped.*)
 b. After the men had eaten, the President of the United States began his speech. (The comma avoids a misreading of the sentence, which would give the false impression that the men had eaten the President.)
 c. Whoever you are, are you not trespassing? (In this instance, the same word occurs twice consecutively. It is customary to put a comma between the two words.)

8. Common uses of the comma are:

 a. To separate the day of the month from the year: May 19, 1963.
 b. To separate the month from the year, although the comma here is optional: December, 1848 or December 1848.
 c. To separate the town from the state or country when they are written on the same line in addresses: Washington, Pennsylvania; Dubuque, Idaho; London, England.
 d. To separate millions from thousands, etc., in figures: 8,642,343.
 e. To separate degrees and titles from names:
  R. F. Stone, M. D.
  Rufus H. Brown, Ph. D.
  John Mackintosh, Esq.

Comma Fault. Sometimes the writer falls into the error known as the comma fault, or comma splice. This results from separating two complete statements by a comma instead of a period. The sentences below all contain this error. They may be corrected by using a period in place of the comma, by using a conjunction to join the two clauses, or by having a semicolon to indicate the relationship between the clauses.

WRONG: You promised to promote me by June 15, I expected promotion, in fact, six months ago.

RIGHT: You promised to promote me by June 15. I expected promotion, in fact, six months ago.

WRONG: The discs are shrunk on and keyed to the shaft, the inlet end of the shaft carries the overspeed trip body.

RIGHT: The discs are shrunk on and keyed to the shaft; the inlet end of the shaft carries the overspeed trip body.

WRONG: Most engineers like to keep up with the latest developments in their profession, they want to be progressive.

RIGHT: Most engineers like to keep up with the latest developments in their profession. They want to be progressive.

WRONG: The carbon rings are made in three segments to insure a good fit on the shaft, the ends are fitted so that a radial clearance of 0.002 to 0.005 inch on the diameter exists between the carbon and the shaft when cold.

RIGHT: The carbon rings are made in three segments to insure a good fit on the shaft, *and* the ends are fitted so that a radial clearance of 0.002 to 0.005 inch on the diameter exists between the carbon and the shaft when cold.

WRONG: The use of estimates by subordinates is generally supposed not to lead to good discipline, that objection lacks force when the manner of getting the estimates is the proper one.

RIGHT: The use of estimates by subordinates is generally supposed not to lead to good discipline, *but* that objection lacks force when the manner of getting the estimates is the proper one.

Often a writer makes a comma fault because he has failed to subordinate a minor idea to a major idea. Consider the sentences which follow:

WRONG: The president is in Chicago this week, he will visit you on Friday morning.

RIGHT: Since the president is in Chicago this week, he will visit you on Friday morning.

WRONG: We want you to be satisfied with Alpha Electric Corporation's products, we are offering you a free inspection every six months.

RIGHT: Because we want you to be satisfied with Alpha Electric Corporation's products, we are offering you a free inspection every six months.

WRONG: The shipment left our office on July 10, it was in perfect condition.

RIGHT: When the shipment left our office on July 10, it was in perfect condition.

In informal narrative or in style which is colloquial, it is common to have what are known as contact clauses. These occur in sentences in which the clauses are so closely related that a period would break up the thought unnecessarily. They read as one sentence, the voice not dropping when the end of the first clause is reached. Usually these are not accepted by editors of technical journals. They prefer two individual sentences, even though the clauses are closely related. Here are a few instances of contact clauses:

> The electrical engineer cannot afford to overlook the importance of the transfomer, it is vital in transmission work.
> Personnel men like students who have carried extracurricular activities, they help to assure success.

It must be emphasized that the amateur writer should not imitate this type of sentence. Substitute a period or a conjunction for the comma; when necessary, subordinate a minor idea to a major idea.

Dash. 1. Dashes are used to mark an abrupt change in thought in the sentence.

> E. W. Johnson, chemical engineer—how did he ever become an engineer, I thought?—was doing research on synthetic rubber.

2. Dashes are sometimes used between the two clauses of a compound sentence to indicate an abrupt separation between two ideas.

> The men on the floor ran as the ladle tipped—each man knew he was in danger.

3. Dashes are used to set off parenthetical statements which are not formal enough to be included in regular parentheses.

> The so-called typical engineer—a rugged, out-of-doors fellow, usually —knows what he wants and what he has to do to get it.

Ellipsis. When material is omitted from quoted matter, even if this material is only a single word, an ellipsis of three dots (. . .) is used. If the ellipsis comes at the end of a sentence, four dots are used. The extra one serves as the period which ends the sentence.

1. He explained in his article: "Telegraph messages . . . are sent over the same pair of wires as telephone messages."
2. His report noted, among other significant facts, that "The deadening effect of the application of the seniority rule can be found in the listlessness displayed by subexecutives and clerks in the offices of certain large railroad companies. . . ."
3. He maintained that ". . . we are affected by fear which is rapidly sweeping the nation."

Exclamation Mark. Exclamation marks are used after forceful interjections and after phrases, clauses, or sentences which express a high degree of emotion. They should be used sparingly, especially in business and factual writing.

1. After interjections: Alas! Ouch! Oh!
2. After phrases: To the power house! It's on fire! On your mark!

3. After clauses: Cut off the power! The man's dying! I'll shout, "Long live the Revolution!"

Hyphen. See also DIVISION OF WORDS; COMPOUND WORDS. Hyphens are useful to mark out the compound word when it may be confused with another word spelled in the same way, but which is not compound.

re-cover (to cover again)   recover (to get again, to win back)
re-creation (to create again)   recreation (diversion, play)

Hyphens serve between prefixes and proper names and titles.

non-Deion type breaker
Johnson, the ex-superintendent

The hyphen is often used when a series of adjectives limits a single noun.

A three-, six-, or twelve-phase inverter.

Consult your dictionary for proper hyphenation.

Parentheses. For material which adds additional information to a sentence but which does not stand in very close relationship to any part of it, parentheses are used.

The Chief Engineer (he is now in the Philippines) is expected back by the first of the month.

In a numbered series, parentheses are often used to enclose the numerals, as (1), (2), (3).

When the material within the parentheses is a complete sentence, the period indicating the end of this sentence comes within the parentheses, although it may be omitted entirely. Marks of punctuation which belong to the main sentence come outside the parentheses.

Parentheses should not be used to include postal zone numbers.

Periods. The commonest use for this mark of punctuation is to indicate the end of a statement. In rhetorical questions, where no direct answer is expected, the period is often used instead of the question mark. *Example:* I wonder whether any engineer has done as much for his profession as our speaker tonight.

See ABBREVIATIONS for the use of the period after abbreviations.
See FIGURES for the use of the period in sums of money.
See ELLIPSIS for the use of the period to indicate omissions.

Question Marks. 1. A question mark follows a direct question.

Why did you shut off the power?
Who authorized your report?

2. The question mark is not used after indirect questions.

He wanted to know what were the functions of the transformer.

3. If a question mark occurs within parentheses after a date or after any phrase, clause, or statement, it indicates that the material is questionable.

4. If the question mark is used with quotation marks, observe the following procedure:

    a. If the entire question is quoted material, place the question mark within the quotation mark.

       He asked, "What do you really think of my report?"

    b. If the entire question is not quoted material, but includes quoted material which ends at the same time as the question, place the question mark outside the quotation mark.

    Did you really say to the boss "I'm going to quit"?

Quotation Marks. Quotation marks are used to indicate all material quoted from the writings or sayings of others.

1. He told the student, "Your work is the best in the class."
2. I said to the engineer, "We want a detailed time study made of Department C."
3. I like the section labeled "Unknown Quantities" in your report *Factors Governing the Efficiency of Workers in the Machine Shop of the Acme Steel Co.*

When a direct statement which is quoted is interrupted in any way, put double quotation marks around each part of the quoted statement.

1. "This man," he said, "should really be made president."
2. "Do you believe," he questioned shrewdly, "that the workers are really producing to their capacity?"

When a quotation occurs within a quotation, enclose it in single quotation marks; when one occurs within this second quotation, put it in double marks.

1. E. B. Nelson remarked to Mr. Weatherby, "I don't like your remark that 'Most workers are lazy.' "
2. Mr. Weatherby replied, "You are too idealistic. Your statement, 'I have faith in the American working man' is like Tom Prentiss', 'Give me the American workman; he is a king; he is "the white hope" of industry.' You are both talking in idiotic generalities."

When a direct quotation consists of two or more paragraphs, use double quotation marks for the beginning of each paragraph and double marks at the end of the final paragraph. Do not use quotation marks at the end of intermediate paragraphs.

When using quotation marks with other marks of punctuation, there are two systems which may be followed: the *logical* or the *formal.* Care must be taken, however, not to confuse these and write sentences of which part is punctuated formally and part logically.

Certainly the simplest and the most widely used is the formal system. In this, the writer (1) always places commas and periods inside the quotation marks, (2) puts colons and semicolons outside the quotation marks, and (3) places dashes, exclamation marks, and question marks outside the quotation marks only when they relate to more than the quoted material. This book uses the formal system of punctuation.

The logical system, on the other hand, places periods and commas outside quotation marks when these periods or commas refer to the entire preceding material which includes more than merely the matter set apart in quotation.

The following sentences are punctuated according to the logical system.

1. He said he had read the article "Psychiatry in Industry".
2. He went on to tell us that "pharmacy is not only a science but an art".

Common usage favors the formal system of punctuation. It is much simpler to remember and to use. One has, however, to bear in mind that the periods and commas always go inside the quotation marks. In printing, the formal system eliminates the unsightly "white spaces" which would otherwise occur between the double spaces following the period or comma and the next printed letter.

The following sentences are examples of formal punctuation.

1. He said he had read the article "Psychiatry in Industry."
2. He went on to tell us that "pharmacy is not only a science but an art."
3. "I intend to write the report tomorrow," he replied. "I know I shall have plenty of time then."
4. He referred to President Withers as "the old man"; he did not know any better.
5. He asked, "When did you come to Pittsburgh?"
6. What do you mean by "decibel"?
7. The engineer who grabbed the hot wire shouted, "Help!"
8. God preserve us from "American Fascists"!

Semicolon. Semicolons have almost the value of periods, for they separate sentence elements to a greater degree than commas. Their uses follow:

1. When two or more clauses contain internal punctuation, separate the clauses by semicolons.

   a. The president, who was lazy, asked the secretary to write the note; the secretary, who happened to be busy with another job, begged one of the members to write it; finally, the member agreed.
   b. The motor which had just been installed and started, shorted; another motor caught fire.

2. Separate phrases by semicolons when they contain commas.

   a. Myer Cohen had published "International Relations and Engineering," in *Journal of Engineering Education,* November, 1961; Merrick Jackson had published "A Tie That Binds the Thousands," in *Steelways,* November 1962; and Harlan E. Youel had published an article, "The Communist Oil Industry," for the Planning & Economics Department of Gulf Oil Corporation.
   b. The route took us to Needles, California; from there to Los Angeles, Fresno, and San Francisco; and from 'Frisco to Seattle.

3. Separate clauses by semicolons when they are closely related in thought and have no conjunction to join them.

    a. The surveyor carried the transit; the chainman brought the rod, the line, plumb bobs, and other equipment.
    b. Engineering students enjoy mathematics; science students prefer chemistry.

4. Separate clauses by semicolons when the second clause is introduced by the formal conjunctive adverbs, such as *moreover, however, therefore, consequently, nevertheless.*

    a. The lineman had to repair the break; consequently, he set out as soon as he was given his instructions.
    b. Engineering students would like to have more liberal arts subjects; however, few of them have any time on their programs for such studies.

Question Marks. See PUNCTUATION.

Quotation Marks. See PUNCTUATION.

Real—Really

Really is an adverb and should be used in no other way. Sometimes *real* is confused with *really* in usage, as:

The motor operates *real* well. (The intended meaning of *real* in this example is *very*, but the use of *real* is incorrect.)

Correct forms:

He is *really* interested in personnel placement.
Real workmanship shows in this product.

Reason Is

When the engineer is writing, he should always follow such a statement as, "The reason is," by a substantive usually preceded by *that. The reason is because* is not a good form; it is redundant.

The *reason* I am late is *that* I had a flat tire.
The *reason* for changing the plans is *that* the old ones are inaccurate.

Reciprocal Pronouns. See PRONOUNS.

Refer Back

In this expression, *back* is needless. "Please *refer back* to our order No. 1892" should read "Please *refer* to our order No. 1892."

Reference to Pronouns. See PRONOUNS.

Reflexive Pronouns. See PRONOUNS.

Relative Clauses

Relative clauses are adjective clauses; that is, they modify a noun or a pronoun and are introduced by a relative pronoun, such as *which, who,* or *that.* They are usually placed immediately after the word they modify.

> The man *who took charge of the babbitting section* was formerly in B-7.

The italicized clause modifies *man.* It points him out and sets him apart from other men who may be under discussion.

At times the relative pronoun used to introduce relative clauses is omitted.

> The generator you had charge of is grounded.

Relative Pronouns. See PRONOUNS.

Remember of

Omit the "of." "I remember when you were champion shot putter," is correct.

Repetition. See also "Language Essentials," page 276.

Repetition in English prose may be a disadvantage or a useful device. If the repetition is awkward, unnecessary, and serves no good purpose, the writer should take pains to look up synonyms or vary his sentence structure in such a way as to avoid it.

> The *capacitor* was tested on the *capacitor test* floor, but it did not meet all the *tests* which we ordinarily apply to *capacitors* which we intend to put in service.

In this example the repetition of the words "capacitor" and "test" irritates the reader. The author could have revised his sentence and improved it.

> The capacitor did not meet all the test floor requirements we ordinarily ask of such apparatus when we intend to put it into service.

The most unfortunate type of repetition is the reappearance of a word in a different sense than it had in the previous part of the sentence.

> The meeting of our society was held last Wednesday and I enjoyed the society of a friend I hadn't seen for some time.

Good repetition is usually designed to draw attention to some object or concept which the writer wishes to emphasize.

Respectfully—Respectively. *Respectfully* may be properly used to close a formal letter; it indicates esteem or deference. *Respectively* is used to point out; to set up a one-to-one relationship.

Restrictive Modifier. See PUNCTUATION.

Reverend

Reverend, like *Professor,* should not be used without the first name or the initials of the holder of the title.

The Reverend E. S. Jones, not Reverend Jones

Do not abbreviate *Reverend* unless the initials are used with the name.

The Rev. T. E. Edwards

Rhetorical Questions

Rhetorical questions are those which require no answers by readers or audiences. The writer or the speaker often answers his own question.

> *And, in conclusion, what may we say of electronics research?* Just this: it is the one thing for which every large company has made an allotment in its budget.

Rise—Raise

Be sure to distinguish the difference in meaning between these two verbs. *Rise* is intransitive; it never takes an object. *Raise* is transitive and therefore takes an object.

I *rise* to go to work at five each morning.
I *rose* yesterday at 4:30 a.m.
I *have risen* every day at 4 a.m.
I *raise* the signal flag.
He *raised* the signal flag last week.
He *has raised* the signal flag every day for the past twenty years.

Round—Around

Round is the clipped form of *around;* it is not a preferable usage in formal writing.

Run-on Sentences

These are two sentences which have been run together into one. They may be separated by a comma, or by no punctuation at all. For a complete treatment, see PUNCTUATION, COMMA FAULT.

Same

Same may be either a pronoun or an adjective. Sometimes its pronoun use is not in the best taste, as "I am forwarding my application for membership in the ASME. Please acknowledge *same.*"

RIGHT: This is the same steel as that.
RIGHT: He gave the same [amount] to us.

The last use cited is not suitable for formal communication.

Scarcely—Hardly. See BUT—ONLY—HARDLY—SCARCELY.

Semi

Semi is a useful prefix for the engineer. It means "half, to some extent, partaking of the nature of." The prefix is not so precise as one might wish, but it is very useful when referring to matters which do not need more definite specifications. Generally, use a hyphen when *semi* precedes proper names, or words which begin with *i*, where the hyphen indicates the stop that must be made in speech. See the dictionary for exceptions.

> semi-inflated, semicircular, semi-Churchillian, semi-porcelain (an exception)

Semicolon. See PUNCTUATION.

Sentence. See "Language Essentials," pages 292–302 (Simple, Compound, Complex, and Compound-Complex Sentences).

Sentence Fragments. See "Language Essentials," pages 301–302.

Set—Sit

Sit implies volition on the part of some person or animal; *set* indicates that the object being handled has no will of its own.

Sit is intransitive; it does not take an object; *set* usually requires an object to complete its meaning.

The principal parts are *sit, sat, sat; set, set, set.*

Shall, Will—Should, Would

For the technical man's formal writing, he should remember that to express simple futurity, he should use:

I shall	We shall
You will	You will
He will	They will

Shall is used in the first person, both singular and plural, and *will* in the second and third. *Should* and *would* are used in the same way. Usage is divided on *shall-will,* but careful writers still observe the foregoing distinctions. Actually, *will* is used by many people for first, second, and third person.

Shifted Constructions

Shifted constructions are variations within the sentence itself of those portions which ought to have the same grammatical value. If two words are approximately equal in importance and the first is a noun, the second should also be a noun. Shifts occur principally in:

1. Subject—If the *turbine* gets steamed up, *you'll* get power for the shop.
   Revision: If *you* get the turbine steamed up, *you'll* get power for the shop.
2. Number—He asked the *test floor* to help him and *they* did.
   Revision: He asked the *men* on the test floor to help him and *they* did.
3. Person—After presenting his argument to the employees, *they* thought it a good idea and *it* was voted that they return to work.
   Revision: After presenting his argument to the employees, they thought it a good idea and voted to return to work.

These represent the more common errors in shifted constructions, although it is possible to shift almost any construction in such a way that it is not in parallel with the preceding equivalent word. (See PARALLEL CONSTRUCTIONS.) Shifts occur from nouns to adjectives, from nouns to adverbs, from clauses to participles, from clauses to nouns.

Slang

Since most of a technical man's communications tend to be formal, he has little use for slang in writing. He may often find it expressive, however, in ordinary conversation.

So

This conjunction is used to introduce clauses of result and purpose, but it should as a rule be followed by *that*. Avoid the use of *so* as an intensive (He was *so* tired from his night's work.)

Some

Some may be a pronoun, an adjective, or an adverb in function. As a pronoun it is often used to express an indefinite number.

Some of us were in the powerhouse.

A more common use is adjectival. In this capacity, *some* qualifies the noun it modifies.

Some people can never understand sine waves.

The adverbial function of *some* is confined to informal conversation and should not be used in writing.

The job was *some* harder than I expected. (If such a construction were translated into formal English, *some* would become *somewhat*.)

Sooner

Sooner has an adverbial quality in its representation of a time value. It is always followed by *than* in such common phrases as:

No *sooner* had he tripped the breaker *than* the crane collided with the end of the runway.

Sort of. See KIND OF.

Spelling

There are several helpful rules for spelling, but the best advice to be given a poor speller is that he work conscientiously to correct his fault and to overcome a few mistakes at a time. Usually he misspells because he cannot visualize the word correctly. The following rules are applicable in most cases, but it must be remembered that no spelling rule is completely effective.

1. A word accented on the last syllable and ending in one consonant preceded by one vowel doubles the last consonant when the set of letters to be added begins with a vowel.

regret, regretted, regretting
prefer, preferred, preferring
occur, occurred, occurring

2. The final consonant is not doubled when a suffix is added to those words which are not accented on the last syllable. Examples:

motor, motored
benefit, benefited

3. If the suffix to be added begins with a consonant, the final consonant of the stem word is not doubled. Examples:

red, redness
equip, equipment

4. If a suffix begins with a vowel and the stem word ends in *e*, drop the *e* before adding the suffix. If the suffix begins with a consonant, do not drop the *e* before adding the suffix.

prime, primary
rime, riming
sense, sensible

whole, wholesome
peace, peaceful
like, likely

5. A word ending in *y* usually changes the *y* to *i* when a suffix is added, unless the suffix itself begins with *i*. Examples:

weary, weariness
lonely, loneliness
but—fancy, fancying

6. *I* usually precedes *e* except when following *c*.

relieve
believe
but—deceive

These rules by no means cover all possible spelling variations. The following list of words may help the student who is prone to misspell. They are largely words used by technical people.

absence
absorb
absorption
access
accelerate
accommodate
accurate
acetylene
actinic
alcohol
aluminum
analysis
analyze
apparatus
arctic
article
association
attacked

babbitt
ballast
balloon
binary
breadth
bureau

canvas
canvass
category
caucus
cipher
circuit
circumference
committed
committee
complement
compliment
concede
conceive
condenser
controlled
converter
corollary
cycloid
cylinder

deleterious
deprecate
depreciate
desiccate
deteriorate
develop
diaphragm
differential
diminution
disintegrate
ductile

eccentric
eccentricities
efficacy
eighth
elaborate
electrolysis
electrolyte
elicit
eligible
embarrass
entropy
equipped
erratic
especially
exaggerate
excitation
exhaust
exhilarate

facilities
fallacy
familiar
feasible
February
fiery
filament
financier
formula
forty
four
funicular

gage (gauge)

garrulous
Geissler
gelatinous
glossary
glycerine
government
graphic
graphite
granular

harass
height
heinous
heterogeneous
hindrance
homogeneous
humorous
hydraulic
hypocrisy

illegible
illegitimate
illiterate
impediment
impracticable
inaccurate
incredible
independent
ingenious
insolvent
insulate
inverter
irrelevant
irresistible
itinerary

kerosene
kilovolt
kilowatt
knowledge

laboratory
languish
library
lubrication

luminescent

maintain
maintenance
malleable
manual
manufacture
metallic
miniature
miscellaneous
momentous
murmur

naphtha
negligible
neutral
neutron
ninetieth
noticeable
nuisance
numerical

obliterate
occurrence
ohmic
omission
omit
omitted
ordinance
ordnance
origin
oscillate
oscillograph
overrun
oxidation

pamphlet
paraffin
parallel
parenthesis
partially
particularly
perceive

perpendicular
perseverance
personification
personnel
photographer
photometer
physician
porcelain
possess
preference
prejudiced
preventive
privilege
propeller
pursuant

qualitative
quandary
quantitative
quantity

rarefaction
reaction
receipt
receive
receptacle
reception
recollect
recommendation
reference
referred
repellent
reservoir
resistance
rhythm
Roentgen

schedule
seismologist
seize
separate
shellac
sieve

simultaneous
sine
solder
spherical
spontaneous
stationary
stationery
strenuous
sulfur
superintendent
symmetrically
synchronous

technic (ique)
tendency
tensile
tension
theoretically
thermionic
thermometer
tragedy
transmission
tumefaction
tunnel
typical

uncertainty
unerring
unmistakable

vacuum
valuable
variable
vernier
vicious
vilify
villain
viscous
volatile

warring
weird
workable

Strata. See DATA.

Subject

The subject of a sentence is the word or group of words about which something is affirmed.

Subjunctive Mood. See MOOD; VERBS.

Subordinate Clauses. See ADJECTIVE CLAUSES; ADVERBIAL CLAUSES; CONDITIONAL CLAUSES; DEPENDENT CLAUSES.

Substantive

A substantive is the name of anything. It may be a noun, a pronoun, a gerund, an infinitive, or a noun clause; in other words, a word or group of words used as a noun.

Tabulations

The engineer is often required to present papers which include technical data. Such data are best shown by tables. Because of the physical appearance of tabulated material on the page, the eye of the reader is guided toward it. An example will indicate how tabulated material attracts attention:

Etching 24S-T Products—The etching solution used for revealing the structure of the heat-treated temper of 24S alloy (24S-T) was described by E. H. Dix, Jr., and F. Keller, and is made up as follows:

Hydrofluoric acid (conc.)	1.0 cc.
Hydrochloric acid (conc.)	1.5 cc.
Nitric acid (conc.)	2.5 cc.
Water	95.0 cc.

Tenses

Tenses are the time values expressed by verbs. Following is a table which shows the tenses of a representative verb. First person singular only is used.

Present:	I shout	Present Perfect:	I have shouted
Past:	I shouted	Past Perfect:	I had shouted
Future:	I shall shout	Future Perfect:	I shall have shouted

The meanings of the "simple" tenses on the left are clear; the action is occurring in the present, occurred yesterday, or will occur tomorrow. In what are called the "perfect" tenses, the time relationship is more involved. If present perfect is used (have shouted), the action has occurred in the past, but it may have finished just at the present time. If past perfect (had shouted) is used, the action has not only occurred in the past, but something else may have occurred between the completion of that action and the present time. (He had shouted before I dropped the load from the turbine.) In future perfect, an action is assumed to have occurred before some other action which is yet to take place. (I shall go [simple future] but I shall have gone before he comes.)

In the expression "I planned to go yesterday," notice that the infinitive follows the past tense. Avoid writing or saying "I planned to have gone yesterday." In past time I was still expecting *to go,* not *to have gone.*

Than

Than is usually used as a conjunction. Unlike *but,* which usually is used to connect clauses opposed to each other, or *and,* used to connect those of equal value, *than* is used as a connective between two elements of different values.

The rectifier is less liable to outages *than* the rotary converter.

That

That is one of the more versatile words of the language. It may act as a pronoun or a conjunction.

1. As a pronoun, *that* is used as either a demonstrative or a relative.

Demonstrative:

That is the way I like to see a job wired.
He said he was willing to work, but he wouldn't guarantee the results. I liked *that.*

Relative:

He knew only the things *that* I had taught him.
Alfred was acquainted with the plant *that* I knew in Minneapolis.

2. As a conjunction, *that* is often repeated between a number of dependent clauses to keep parallelism:

He knew *that* the turbine was not running, *that* the shop was down, and *that* someone would have to make the repairs.

Avoid overuse of *that.* If a clause can be begun without this introductory word, as "I knew he'd come," avoid its use. Try to avoid two *that's* in a single clause.

That Is

That words are always an introduction to some explanatory material to follow. They are often used to introduced material illustrating that which has preceded it. *That is* is usually followed by a comma and preceded by a semicolon.

The technical student needs to have mastery of several forms of composition; *that is,* he should know the business letter, the report, and the technical article, at least.

Then

Properly used, *then* implies the next event which happens after the one described in a preceding clause.

He warmed the vat of water with the steam line and *then* plunged the Fenwal switch into its receptacle.

Therefore

Therefore is a transition word, useful between paragraphs and sentences when no more efficient means of connection may be had. It is best to conceal it within a sentence rather than use it at the opening. It belongs to formal, rather than informal, writing.

There Is—There Are

There is and *there are* are common openings for sentences. Their number is determined by the predicate noun which follows. If the noun is singular, *there is* is the usage; if plural, *there are* is the correct form.

> *There are* three formulae for determining air drag on a wing.
> *There is* a unit process described in our textbook.

Those Kind. See KIND OF—SORT OF.

Till—Until

Till is the clipped form of *until* and has attained equal rank with it as an English word. The only difference in usage between them is that *until* is more often used to begin a sentence; *till* is more often used within the sentence.

Titles

Titles of books and magazines are underlined, italicized, or set in capital letters in typing. The titles of articles included within magazines are set in quotation marks.

> In *Mechanical Engineering,* Mr. Pender's article, "Rocket Power," will interest every student.

Do not capitalize conjunctions, prepositions, or articles within a title unless they begin it.

Today

Today is not usually hyphenated.

Too

The English language has three words with the same sound as *too*. They are *to, too, two*. *To* means direction toward, *too* means in addition to, and *two* is the number.

Toward—Towards

These words are interchangeable.

Transitive and Intransitive Verbs

A transitive verb requires an object. An intransitive verb may have a predicate nominative or predicate adjective, but never an object. Verbs in passive voice do not take objects. (See PASSIVE VOICE; VERBS.)

Unique

This word should not be compared. It has no comparative or superlative.

Verbals. See also INFINITIVES; GERUNDS; PARTICIPLES.

A verbal is a word or phrase derived from a verb but used as a noun, adjective, or adverb.

> *Singing* in the chorus is an extracurricular activity. (noun usage) (Gerund)
> The "*singing* mechanic" is ill today. (adjective usage) (Participle)
> He went *singing* on his way. (adverbial usage) (Participle)
> *To study* is painful. (noun usage) (Infinitive)

Verb Phrase. See PHRASES.

Verbs

These words indicate the action or being of the subject. They are capable of changes in mood (indicative, imperative, subjunctive), tense, voice, and number. English verbs, like those of Latin, have principal parts from which the various tenses may be formed. Following are the principal parts and a complete conjugation of a standard English verb. Both active and passive voices are given.

> *Principal parts:* hear, heard, heard

INDICATIVE MOOD

	Active Voice		Passive Voice	
Present Tense:	I hear	We hear	I am heard	We are heard
	You hear	You hear	You are heard	You are heard
	He hears	They hear	He is heard	They are heard
Past Tense:	I heard	We heard	I was heard	We were heard
	You heard	You heard	You were heard	You were heard
	He heard	They heard	He was heard	They were heard
Future Tense:	I shall hear	We shall hear	I shall be heard	We shall be heard
	You will hear	You will hear	You will be heard	You will be heard
	He will hear	They will hear	He will be heard	They will be heard
Present Perfect Tense:	I have heard	We have heard	I have been heard	We have been heard
	You have heard	You have heard	You have been heard	You have been heard
	He has heard	They have heard	He has been heard	They have been heard
Past Perfect Tense:	I had heard	We had heard	I had been heard	We had been heard
	You had heard	You had heard	You had been heard	You had been heard
	He had heard	They had heard	He had been heard	They had been heard

Active Voice

Future Perfect Tense:	I shall have heard	We shall have heard
	You will have heard	You will have heard
	He will have heard	They will have heard

Passive Voice

I shall have been heard	We shall have been heard
You will have been heard	You will have been heard
He will have been heard	They will have been heard

Subjunctive Mood

	Active Voice		Passive Voice	
Present	(if) I hear	(if) We hear	(if) I be heard	(if) We be heard
Tense:	(if) You hear	(if) You hear	(if) You be heard	(if) You be heard
	(if) He hear	(if) They hear	(if) He be heard	(if) They be heard
Past	(if) I heard	(if) We heard	(if) I were heard	(if) We were heard
Tense:	(if) You heard	(if) You heard	(if) You were heard	(if) You were heard
	(if) He heard	(if) They heard	(if) He were heard	(if) They were heard

(The remainder of the subjunctive forms are the same as those of the indicative mood.)

Imperative Mood

Present Tense:	Active Voice	Passive Voice
	(you) Hear	(you) Be heard

Very

Very is an intensive; that is, it adds to the strength of the word it modifies. The beginning writer may feel that it is a more useful word than it actually is, and may overuse it. Such a practice should be avoided.

Viewpoint

In the course of a paragraph or a paper, a writer who has not had a great deal of practice may change his viewpoint. He may have written in a formal, impersonal style ("*It* is believed that . . .") and then may have changed his viewpoint to a personal one ("*I* think that . . ."). This produces a lack of unity in his paper. Once a student has determined what he believes to be an adequate viewpoint, he should follow it throughout his manuscript.

Vocative. See Direct Address.

A vocative is any grammatical construction in which the writer addresses another person directly.

> Gentlemen, this is your president!
> John, please go to the tool room.

Voice. See Transitive and Intransitive Verbs.

English has two voices for expressing ideas. The more important of these is the *active voice* in which the subject is the actor and performs whatever action is indicated by the verb.

> The welder struck an arc on the motor casing.

Here the welder is the actor and performs the action shown by the verb. The sentence can be varied to illustrate *passive voice:*

> The arc was struck by the welder.

In this form, the subject is no longer the actor but instead the material upon which the act is performed.

Group 807 built the induction regulator. (*Active voice*)

The induction regulator was built by group 807. (*Passive voice*)

Most good writers make far greater use of active than of passive voice. It produces a better effect to use the former because such a use heightens reality.

The passive voice has, however, a number of uses in which it is more effective than the active voice. If one feels that the person or thing receiving the action is more important than the actor, the sentence should use passive voice.

Turbines are built here.

In this example, what is being built is more important than who builds it. The passive voice is consequently the one to use.

Want

People in several sections of America use the verb *want* without the infinitive. There is no objection to such a colloquial use, but it should not appear in writing. The sentence, "The engineer wants in," should be corrected, if it is written, to "The engineer wants to come in."

Way—Ways—Away

Way and *ways* are informal and should not be used in writing in place of *away*.

We

We is often used in editorials to refer to an individual writer. The engineer will have no use for the word in this sense; he should employ it only when speaking of himself and his colleagues.

Well—Good. See GOOD—WELL.

When—Where.

The beginning writer may err in using *when* as a connective. A common mistake is illustrated.

Rectification is *when* alternating current is changed to direct.

What the writer meant is, "Rectification is the changing of alternating to direct current." There is no time significance in the sentence; hence *when* should not be used. *Where* is often used incorrectly in much the same way. "Rectification is *where* you change alternating to direct current." In this sentence, there is no meaning of place; consequently *where* should not be used.

The phrase "is because" is just as incorrect as "is when" if the *because* introduces a noun clause. Avoid the following type of sentence:

WRONG: The reason I am not going is because I prefer to stay away.

RIGHT: The reason I am not going is that I prefer to stay away.

While

In its most common and accurate use, *while* is a conjunction with a time value. It is used often to introduce a clause which represents an action going on at the same time as that of the principal clause.

> *While* we were oiling the gears of the time-delay relay, the shop air line broke.

In formal writing, avoid using *though* for *while*.

Who—Whose—Whom

Who is the nominative form, *whose* the possessive, and *whom* the objective of the same pronoun. Whenever the case conditions of the sentence require a nominative (as in a subject) *who* should be used.

> *Who* is the new turbine oiler?
> Anyone *who* works in the shop should know that.

The possessive may be used in either a substantive or adjectival form. The use of a genitive (possessive) case as the subject of a sentence is unusual; it always implies the presence of something modified by *whose*.

> *Whose* is that?

The more common use is as a possessive adjective:

> *Whose* Crescent wrench is that?

Whom is the objective form of the pronoun and, as such, should be used whenever an object of a verb or a preposition is called for, or any other use requiring the objective case.

> The technician *whom* I met yesterday is learning glass-blowing.

Who and *whom* are often used interchangeably in speech situations without much, if any, impairment of meaning. In writing, however, it is well to use them in their proper grammatical positions.

Word Order

The standard English sentence usually proceeds from subject to predicate to object or predicate complement or predicate adjective. Often a writer wishes to vary this order for purposes of emphasis. The standard order follows:

> The generator turned quietly and powerfully.

A variation of this standard order may attract more attention to the qualities of quiet and power:

> The generator quietly, powerfully, continued to turn.

Sometimes the writer finds that a reversal of subject and object may be of advantage for emphasis.

Standard order:

I worked on that capacitor yesterday.

Reversed order (to bring attention to the capacitor):

That capacitor I worked on yesterday.

Yet

Yet sometimes functions as an adverb (I have *yet* to understand the theory) and occasionally as an adverbial conjunction (He knew that he should keep the voltage from rising, *yet* he let the ballast tube burn out).

You

In addition to its use as a personal pronoun, *you* is often an indefinite form. In addressing a customer through a descriptive bulletin, the phrase might be, "If the transformer has too much reactance, *you* observe considerable heating effect." In formal writing, it is advisable to replace the *you* by *one* and change the verb form, as in "If the transformer has too much reactance, *one* may observe considerable heating effect."

BIBLIOGRAPHY

Selected Bibliography

Letters

AURNER, R. R. *Effective Communications in Business with Management Emphasis.* Globe, Ariz.: Southwestern Publishing Co., 1958.

BOYD, W. P., and LESIKAR, R. V. *Productive Business Writing.* Englewood Cliffs, N. J.: Prentice-Hall, Inc., 1959.

BUCKLEY, E. A. *How to Increase Sales with Letters.* New York: McGraw-Hill Book Co., Inc., 1961.

BUCKLEY, E. A. *How to Write Better Business Letters.* New York: McGraw-Hill Book Co., Inc., 1957.

DRACH, H. E. *American Business Writing.* New York: American Book Co. 1959.

HATHAWAY, BAXTER. *Writing Mature Prose.* New York: The Ronald Press Co., 1951.

MARRA, W. J. *Streamlined Letters.* St. Louis, Mo.: National Retail Credit Association, 1955.

MAYBURY, S. B. *Principles of Business Letter Writing.* New York: The Ronald Press Co., 1959.

MURPHY, K. M. *Modern Business Letters.* Boston: Houghton-Mifflin Co., 1956.

PARKHURST, C. C. *Business Communication for Better Human Relations.* Englewood Cliffs, N. J.: Prentice-Hall, Inc., 1961.

ROSS, M. C. *NRB Manual of Successful Business Letter Writing.* Chicago: National Research Bureau, 1958.

SHEPPARD, M. *Plain Letters.* New York: Simon and Schuster, Inc., 1960.

SHURTER, R. L. *Effective Letters in Business.* New York: McGraw-Hill Book Co., Inc., 1954.

SHURTER, R. L. *Written Communication in Business.* New York: McGraw-Hill Book Co., Inc., 1957.

SMART, W. K., and McKELVEY, L. W. *Business Letters.* New York: Harper & Row, 1957.

STEPHENSON, J. *Principles and Practice of Commercial Correspondence.* New York: Pitman Pub. Corp., 1958.

STRONG, E. P., and WEAVER, R. G. *Writing for Business and Industry.* New York: Allyn & Bacon, Inc., 1962.

WANOUS, S. J., and ERICKSON, L. W. *The Secretary's Book* (Rev. ed). New York: The Ronald Press Co., 1956.

WILLIAMS, CECIL B., and BALL, JOHN. *Effective Business Writing* (2d ed.). New York: The Ronald Press Co., 1953.

Report Writing

BALL, J., and WILLIAMS, C. B. *Report Writing.* New York: The Ronald Press Co., 1955.

BLICKLE, M. D., and HOUP, K. W. *Reports for Science and Industry.* New York: Holt, Rinehart & Winston, 1958.

DOUGLASS, P. F. *Communications through Reports.* New York: Prentice-Hall, Inc., 1957.

HICKS, T. G. *Writing for Engineering and Science.* New York: McGraw-Hill Book Co., Inc., 1961.

KOBE, K. A. *Chemical Engineering Reports.* New York: Interscience Publishers, Inc., 1957.

PETERSON, M. S. *Scientific Thinking and Scientific Writing.* New York: Reinhold Publishing Corp., 1961.

RHODES, F. H. *Technical Report Writing* (Rev. ed.). New York: McGraw-Hill Book Co., Inc., 1961.

SIGBAND, N. B. *Effective Report Writing.* New York: Harper & Row, 1960.

SOUTHER, J. W. *Technical Report Writing.* New York: John Wiley & Sons, 1957.

TUTTLE, R. E., and BROWN, C. A. *Writing Useful Reports.* New York: Appleton-Century-Crofts, Inc., 1956.

ULMAN, J. N., and GOULD, J. P. *Technical Reporting.* New York: Holt, Rinehart & Winston, 1959.

VAN HAGAN, C. E. *Report Writers' Handbook.* Englewood Cliffs, N. J.: Prentice-Hall, Inc., 1961.

WEIL, B. H. (ed.) *Technical Reports.* New York: Reinhold Publishing Corp., 1954.

ZALL, P. M. *Elements of Technical Report Writing.* New York: Harper & Row, 1962.

Specifications and Contracts

ABBETT, R. W. *Engineering Contracts and Specifications.* New York: John Wiley & Sons, 1954.

DUNHAM, C. W., and YOUNG, R. D. *Contracts, Specifications, and Laws for Engineers.* New York: McGraw-Hill Book Co., Inc., 1958.

MEAD, D. W. *Contracts, Specifications, and Engineering Relations.* 3rd ed. New York: McGraw-Hill Book Co., Inc., 1956.

WERBIN, I. VERNON. *Legal Cases for Contractors, Architects, and Engineers.* New York: McGraw-Hill Book Co., Inc., 1955.

Speech

BARRICK, A. I. *Power of Effective Speech.* New York: Bookman Associates, Inc., 1959.

BORDEN, F. *Effective Speaking for All Occasions.* American Research Council, 1961.

BRYAN, M. *Dynamic Speaking.* New York: The Macmillan Co., 1962.

BRYANT, D. C., and WALLACE, K. R. *Fundamentals of Public Speaking.* New York: Appleton-Century-Crofts, Inc., 1960.

BUTLER, J. R. *Time to Speak Up.* New York: Harper & Bros., 1957.

CAPP, G. R. *How to Communicate Orally.* Englewood Cliffs, N. J.: Prentice-Hall, Inc., 1961.

CLYNE, J. F., and others. *Business Speaking.* New York: Oxford University Press, 1956.

DIETRICH, J. E., and BROOKS, KEITH. *Practical Speaking for the Technical Man.* Englewood Cliffs, N. J.: Prentice-Hall, Inc., 1958.

DYER, F. C. *Executive's Guide to Effective Speaking.* New York: Prentice-Hall, Inc., 1962.

IRWIN, J. V., and ROSENBERGER, M. *Modern Speech.* New York: Holt, Rinehart & Winston, 1961.

LOMAS, C. W., and RICHARDSON, RALPH. *Speech: Idea and Delivery.* Boston: Houghton-Mifflin Co., 1956.

MICKEN, R. A. *Speaking for Results.* Boston: Houghton-Mifflin Co., 1958.

SANDFORD, W. P., and YEAGER, W. H. *Principles of Effective Speech.* 6th ed. New York: The Ronald Press Co., 1963.

SANDFORD, W. P., and YEAGER, W. H. *Effective Business Speech.* New York: McGraw-Hill Book Co., Inc., 1960.

SARETT, L., FOSTER, W., and SARETT, A. J. *Basic Principles of Speech.* (Rev. ed.) Boston: Houghton-Mifflin Co., 1958.

SMITH, RAYMOND. *Principles of Public Speaking.* New York: The Ronald Press Co., 1958.

WEAVER, A. T., and NESS, O. G. *An Introduction to Public Speaking.* New York: The Odyssey Press, 1961.

WHITE, E. E. *Practical Speech Fundamentals.* New York: The Macmillan Co., 1960.

General Reading List

The technical man is often criticized because he is not so widely read as the majority of professional men. To a large extent, his specialized education is responsible for this. During his technical training, his time is taken up almost exclusively with scientific materials. After entering industry, however, he has as much free time as the average professional person. To be generally well read, he should use this time to read in fields other than his own. Consequently, the following short list of books may be of interest. No attempt has been made to arrange them in any order of excellence; opinions differ so widely on what constitutes a really good novel or biography that such a listing would be presumptuous.

Biography and Autobiography

Abbott, L. F.	*Twelve Great Modernists*
Adams, Henry	*The Education of Henry Adams*
Bennett, Arnold	*The Truth About an Author*
Bernstein, Herman	*Celebrities of Our Times*
Bliven, Bruce	*The Men Who Make the Future*
Bostwick, A. E.	*Pivotal Figures of Science*
Boswell, James	*Life of Samuel Johnson*
Casanova, Jacques	*Memoirs*
Cellini, Benvenuto	*Autobiography*
Churchill, W. L. S.	*Great Contemporaries*
Crowther, J. G.	*Men of Science*
Darwin, Francis	*The Life and Letters of Charles Darwin*
DeVoto, Bernard	*Mark Twain's America*
Freeman, Douglas Southall	*R. E. Lee, A Biography*
	Lee's Lieutenants
Harsanyi, Zsolt	*The Star-Gazer*
Henderson, Archibald	*Contemporary Immortals*
Herbert, Edward	*Autobiography of Edward, Lord Herbert of Cherbury*
Keller, Helen	*The Story of My Life*
Jaffe, Bernard	*Men of Science in America*
Jones, Ernest	*Life and Work of Sigmund Freud*

Malone, Dumas	*Jefferson and His Time*
Merezhkovsky, Dmitry	*Leonardo da Vinci*
Mizener, Arthur	*The Far Side of Paradise*
Moore, George	*Hail and Farewell*
Namer, Emile	*Galileo, Searcher of the Heavens*
Oliver, Peter	*Saints of Chaos*
Sandburg, Carl	*Abraham Lincoln:*
	The Prairie Years
	The War Years
Steffens, Lincoln	*The Autobiography of Lincoln Steffens*
Strachey, Lytton	*Portraits in Miniature*
Trollope, Anthony	*An Autobiography*
Twain, Mark	*Autobiography*

The Novel

ENGLISH

Austen, Jane	*Pride and Prejudice*
Beerbohm, Max	*Zuleika Dobson*
Bennett, Arnold	*The Old Wives' Tale*
Brontë, Charlotte	*Jane Eyre*
Brontë, Emily	*Wuthering Heights*
Butler, Samuel	*The Way of All Flesh*
Collins, William Wilkie	*The Moonstone*
Conrad, Joseph	*Victory*
Dickens, Charles	*Pickwick Papers*
	David Copperfield
	Martin Chuzzlewit
	Great Expectations
Dodgson, Charles L.	
(Lewis Carroll)	*Alice in Wonderland*
Fielding, Henry	*Tom Jones*
Forester, C. S.	*Captain Hornblower*
Forster, E. M.	*A Passage to India*
Galsworthy, John	*The Forsyte Saga*
Greene, Graham	*The Power and the Glory*
Hardy, Thomas	*The Return of the Native*
	The Mayor of Casterbridge
	Tess of the d'Urbervilles
	Jude the Obscure
Huxley, Aldous	*Brave New World*
Joyce, James	*Portrait of the Artist as a Young Man*
Lawrence, D. H.	*Sons and Lovers*
Meredith, George	*The Egoist*
Orwell, George	*1984*
Sterne, Laurence	*Tristram Shandy*
Thackeray, William Makepeace	*Vanity Fair*
Waugh, Evelyn	*Decline and Fall*
Woolf, Virginia	*To the Lighthouse*

AMERICAN

Anderson, Sherwood	*Winesburg, Ohio*
Buck, Pearl	*The Good Earth*
Cabell, James B.	*Jurgen*
Cather, Willa	*Death Comes for the Archbishop*
	A Lost Lady
Clemens, Samuel L.	*The Adventures of Huckleberry Finn*
Clark, Walter Van Tilburg	*The Ox Bow Incident*
Crane, Stephen	*The Red Badge of Courage*
Dos Passos, John	*U. S. A.*
Dreiser, Theodore	*An American Tragedy*
Faulkner, William	*Light in August*
Fitzgerald, F. Scott	*The Great Gatsby*
Hall, James Norman	*Men Against the Sea*
Hemingway, Ernest	*A Farewell to Arms*
	The Sun Also Rises
Howells, William Dean	*The Rise of Silas Lapham*
James, Henry	*The American*
	The Portrait of a Lady
Lewis, Sinclair	*Babbitt*
Marquand, John P.	*The Late George Apley*
Morley, Christopher	*Thunder on the Left*
Melville, Herman	*Moby Dick*
Norris, Frank	*The Octopus*
Porter, Katherine Anne	*Pale Horse, Pale Rider*
Rawlings, Marjorie K.	*The Yearling*
Saroyan, William	*The Human Comedy*
Steinbeck, John	*The Grapes of Wrath*
Warren, Robert Penn	*All the King's Men*
Wharton, Edith	*Ethan Frome*
Wolfe, Thomas	*Look Homeward, Angel*

Detective, Horror, and Science Fiction

Bentley, E. C.	*Trent's Last Case*
Bradbury, Ray	*The Illustrated Man*
Burke, Thomas	*Limehouse Nights*
Chesterton, G. K.	*The Father Brown Stories*
Cummings, Roy	*The Girl in the Golden Atom*
Dickson, Carter	*The Plague Court Murders*
Doyle, Arthur Conan	*The Adventures of Sherlock Holmes*
Freeman, R. Austin	*The Unconscious Witness*
Hammett, Dashiell	*The Thin Man*
Heard, G. F.	*The Great Fog*
Lovecraft, H. P.	*Collected Stories*
Rhode, John	*Poison for One*
Sayers, Dorothy	*The Nine Tailors*

Stout, Rex	*The Red Box*
Taylor, Phoebe Atwood	*The Crimson Patch*
Wells, H. G.	*The Time Machine*
	The War of the Worlds
	Food of the Gods

Plays: English and American

Anderson, Maxwell	*The Wingless Victory*
	Winterset
Barrie, J. M.	*Dear Brutus*
Barry, Philip	*The Animal Kingdom*
Connelly, Marc	*The Green Pastures*
Coward, Noel	*Design for Living*
Eliot, T. S.	*Murder in the Cathedral*
Galsworthy, John	*Justice*
Green, Paul	*Johnny Johnson*
Goldsmith, Oliver	*She Stoops to Conquer*
Hellman, Lillian	*The Little Foxes*
Howard, Sidney	*The Silver Cord*
Jonson, Ben	*Volpone*
Kaufman, G. S., and Hart, M.	*You Can't Take It With You*
Lindsay, H., and Crouse, R.	*State of the Union*
Macleish, Archibald	*J. B. 1958*
Marlowe, Christopher	*Dr. Faustus*
Miller, Arthur	*Death of a Salesman*
O'Casey, Sean	*Juno and the Paycock*
Odets, Clifford	*Golden Boy*
O'Neill, Eugene	*The Hairy Ape*
Shakespeare, William	*Henry IV* (I and II)
	Twelfth Night
	Hamlet
	King Lear
	Othello
Rice, Elmer	*Street Scene*
Saroyan, William	*The Time of Your Life*
Sherwood, Robert E.	*Abe Lincoln in Illinois*
Shaw, George Bernard	*Man and Superman*
Sheridan, Richard B.	*School for Scandal*
Synge, John M.	*Playboy of the Western World*
Ustinov, Peter	*Love of Four Colonels*
Wilde, Oscar	*The Importance of Being Earnest*
Wilder, Thorton	*The Skin of Our Teeth*
	Our Town
Williams, Tennessee	*The Glass Menagerie*

Short Stories

Benet, Stephen Vincent	*The Devil and Daniel Webster*
Brush, Katherine	*Night Club*
Dreiser, Theodore	*Free and Other Stories*
Faulkner, William	*A Rose for Emily*
Foley, Martha	*Best Short Stories of the Year*
Lane, Rose Wilder	*Innocence*
Lardner, Ring	*Hair-Cut*
Mansfield, Katherine	*The Garden Party*
Mitchell, Joseph	*McSorley's Wonderful Saloon*
Saroyan, William	*My Name is Aram*
Steele, Wilbur Daniel	*The Man Who Saw through Heaven*
Twain, Mark	*The Man Who Corrupted Hadleyburg*

Essays and Letters

Beerbohm, Max	*And Even Now*
Chapman, John Jay	*John Jay Chapman and His Letters*
Chase, Richard	*The Democratic Vista*
Darwin, Charles	*The Voyage of the Beagle*
Emerson, Ralph Waldo	*Essays*
Huxley, Aldous	*Collected Essays*
James, Henry	*Selected Letters of Henry James*
Lamb, Charles	*The Essays of Elia*
Orwell, George	*Shooting an Elephant*
Russell, Bertrand	*Unpopular Essays*
Smith, Logan Pearsall	*Trivia*
Thoreau, Henry David	*Walden*
White, E. B.	*One Man's Meat*

Poetry

Aiken, Conrad	*Collected Poems*
Auden, W. H.	*Selected Poetry*
Crane, Hart	*Complete Poems*
Dickinson, Emily	*Poems*
Donne, John	*Poems*
Eliot, T. S.	*Complete Poems and Plays, 1900–1950*
Frost, Robert	*Complete Poems*
Hardy, Thomas	*Collected Poems*
Jeffers, Robinson	*Selected Poetry*
Macleish, Archibald	*Collected Poems*
Poe, Edgar Allan	*Poems*
Robinson, Edward Arlington	*Collected Poems*
Sandburg, Carl	*Collected Poems*
Shapiro, Karl	*Poems, 1940–1953*

Stevens, Wallace	*Collected Poems*
Thomas, Dylan	*Collected Poems*
Whitman, Walt	*Leaves of Grass*
Williams, William Carlos	*Collected Earlier Poems*
Yeats, William Butler	*Collected Poems*

Index